MAN AND AFRICA

The central motif, designed by Frank Kovacs, of the Haile Selassie gold medals prepared in London by Messrs Spink for the Haile Selassie I Prize Trust.

MAN and
AFRICA

A Ciba Foundation Symposium
jointly with
The Haile Selassie I Prize Trust
under the patronage of
His Imperial Majesty Haile Selassie I
Emperor of Ethiopia

Edited by

GORDON WOLSTENHOLME

and

MAEVE O'CONNOR

With 24 illustrations

LITTLE, BROWN AND
COMPANY

1965   BOSTON

EDITORS' NOTES

The views expressed in this book are those of individuals, and should not be taken as those of the institutions and organizations with which members are connected, except where this is made clear.

•   •   •

A political map of Africa, which can be pulled out for easy reference, is to be found at p. 384 of this book, among the biographical notes on members of the symposium.

v

The Ciba Foundation

for the Promotion of International Co-operation in Medical and Chemical Research
41 PORTLAND PLACE, LONDON, W.I

CONTENTS

CONTENTS

PREFACE

G. E. W. WOLSTENHOLME

EARLY in 1963 I had the honour of being invited by His Imperial Majesty Haile Selassie, Emperor of Ethiopia, to organize a Trust in avowed imitation of the great Nobel Foundation, to be financed wholly through the munificence of His Imperial Majesty himself, the purpose of which was to be the award of national and international prizes ". . . to encourage the activities and proficiencies of Our People particularly in the advancement of health, prosperity, and the exercise of the fine and applied arts, and also to strengthen spiritually and culturally the bonds between Our People and the people of the African continent and of the whole world . . .".

The drafting of the greater part of the Charter, its enlargement to include both a special award (the Empress Menen) to be given on the initiative of the Trustees and also a wider range of activities intended to promote as well as recognize national work of outstanding merit, the establishment of officers, staff, committees, temporary offices and administrative procedures, the formulation and institution of the award schemes in the first year and the preparation of gold medals and diplomas, proved to be an immensely rewarding and interesting task. Since work in London had to continue as usual, indeed at an abnormally high level, I made many journeys between England and Ethiopia, and in all this the Trustees and Council of the Ciba Foundation provided warm encouragement and support.

For someone such as myself, formerly as ignorant of Ethiopia as most outsiders, and now privileged to enter into friendship with many of its people, and to join in many aspects of its life, both the country and its inhabitants were a revelation. The highlands are as beautiful as any country I have seen in world-wide wanderings; the people lively, graceful, gentle and courteous. It was a surprise to find a land so rich and fertile, especially in comparison with some of its malnourished neighbours, yet even this land barely at the beginning of development. The Emperor and his people, firmly rooted in a long history of independence, seemed capable of enjoying the trust of the newly independent African states and the old colonial powers, of Christians and Mohammedans, Jews and Arabs, Africans and Asians, coloured and white races, communists and capitalists, monarchs and republicans. Such impressions fortified the belief which I already held, that Africa could still, despite "Congolism", set an example to the whole world in composite planning and co-operative effort, and at the same time provide a much-needed element of stability in the confused struggles of ideologists and still more in the inevitable global convulsions to be expected from mortality control and the resulting explosion of nearly all populations. The years 1963 and 1964, during which the Haile Selassie I Prize Trust was founded and carried out its first full year of activity, coincided with the birth of a real measure of African Unity, to a great extent through the inspiring leadership of the Emperor of Ethiopia. The temptation to try to aid, if only in a catalytic sense, the early tender growth of unity was irresistible.

Partly, therefore, to emphasize the potentialities of the whole African continent, and partly to gather a number of internationally known guests to add distinction to the first Presentation Ceremony for the Haile Selassie Awards, I obtained permission from His Imperial Majesty to arrange one of the Ciba Foundation's small international conferences in Addis Ababa, close to the time of the Presentation Ceremony in October 1964. Under the title "Man and Africa" it was hoped to consider the physical and political geography, climate, resources, communications, productivity and development of the African continent, and the number, rate of growth, composition, bodily and mental health and education of its peoples.

His Imperial Majesty, who is, if one may say so with respect, far ahead of the vast majority of his own and other people in recognizing the essential needs of mankind for peace, tolerance and fair rewards, readily granted his gracious patronage to this small but well-intentioned contribution towards such needs. We were also most fortunate to enjoy the farsighted and wise support of the President of the University, Lidj Kassa Wolde Mariam, who accepted the Honorary Presidency of the symposium, and to whom we were mainly indebted, in the event, for an unforgettably magnificent excursion to the Nile Falls, Bahar Dar and Gondar.

The Chairman of the Haile Selassie I Prize Trust, His Excellency Tsehafe Taezaz Aklilu Habte Wolde, and his fellow Trustees cordially welcomed the holding of the conference under the joint auspices of the Prize Trust and the Ciba Foundation, and generously made available to us the pleasant conference room in the Prize Trust's attractive permanent premises.

It is a great pleasure to acknowledge here the energetic co-operation of the Prize Trust's Director, Dr. Abebe Ambatchew, and of all its staff, notably Woizero Teru-worq Haile and Ato Wondimagegnehu Assefa, in providing full facilities for the meeting and warm hospitality to its members.

Ato Abebe Kebede, Director of the Haile Selassie I Foundation, who despite all his own important responsibilities for hospital and welfare services had never spared himself in helping me in every detail of the organization of the Prize Trust, and whose friendship was the rock on which all could be built, placed us further in his debt by arranging that the Foundation would under-write part of the group's hotel expenses.

With pleasure also I record our thanks to Ato Afewerk Teklé for delightful hospitality to all the members and their ladies, and more personally for his inspired part in the design of the Haile Selassie gold medals and for his unfailing, vital support in establishing all the affairs of the Prize Trust at a level which could fairly command international respect, bring due honour to Ethiopia, and render some appropriate return to His Imperial Majesty for his superb generosity.

Once again, this time with a gratitude directly proportional to the great distance of Addis Ababa from London, we are indebted to Professor F. G. Young for his masterly chairmanship of one of our conferences. It was a happy chance that he could bring a message from the University of Cambridge to His Imperial Majesty just forty years after the University had conferred upon His Majesty his first honorary degree. On behalf of the Ciba Foundation Professor Young also presented His Imperial Majesty with a bronze plaque, taken from the original mould prepared in London by Messrs. Spink & Son for the double profile of the Emperor and the late Empress which appears in the centre of the Haile Selassie Prize Trust gold medals. Replicas of this plaque were also presented to the Honorary President, Lidj Kassa, and to His Majesty's grandson, His Highness Commander Iskinder Desta, who had done much to encourage and promote many of the varied aspects of my responsibilities in Ethiopia.

The symposium could not have been achieved without the co-operation of the United Nations Economic Commission for Africa. Unfortunately Mr. Robert K. A. Gardiner, Executive Secretary of the Commission, was engaged in an important economic conference in West Africa at the time of our meeting, together with some of his chief colleagues, but through his interest and kindness many experts from Africa Hall contributed most valuably, as individuals, to our programme.

It was a great disappointment that a number of members found themselves at the last moment unable to get to Addis Ababa for the conference, doubly unfortunate that these were mostly Africans, and ironical that it was their great responsibilities for African development that kept them away. We particularly regretted the absence, in addition to Mr. Gardiner, of His Excellency Tom Mboya, Professor R. P. Baffour, Professor D. S. H. W. Nicol, Professor Mohammed Abdalla Nour, Professor K. Diké and Professor A. M. Hegazy. We sorely missed the presence also of the great J. B. S. Haldane, and his death in India shortly afterwards acutely emphasized this misfortune. If there was an unexpected predominance of non-Africans, it is nevertheless hoped that their heartfelt concern for Africa and their expert knowledge of its problems will make this written record of the proceedings wholly acceptable to all Africans who are themselves concerned for the welfare of their immediate countrymen and their neighbours.

In helping to prepare these papers and discussions for publication Maeve O'Connor has exercised all her talents. I wish also to record my thanks to Mrs. Nancy Spufford for the devoted care with which she dealt with the quite exceptional administrative problems in the organization of this symposium and with questions of design and diplomacy in the production of the gold medals and diplomas for the Prize Trust; to Mrs. Margarete Silverman for her assistance during the meeting and invaluable help in providing information on which the Prize Trust's international awards could be launched; and to Mr. John Rivers of J. & A. Churchill Ltd, who on this occasion, for the love of it, has done far more to help make the book acceptable than is normally the duty of a publisher.

This is the 100th volume to be produced by the Ciba Foundation, and I make no apologies, except to her, that for once I acknowledge in a preface my own incalculable debt to my wife, Dr. Dushanka Wolstenholme. I doubt if it would have been possible to have overcome some of the difficulties in setting up the Prize Trust without her advice and encouragement; how infinitely more this is true of all the work of the Ciba Foundation over sixteen years, only I can know, and I am deeply and humbly thankful.

SPEECH BY THE PRIME MINISTER, HIS EXCELLENCY TSEHAFE TAEZAZ AKLILU HABTE WOLD

On behalf of his Imperial Majesty I extend a warm welcome to all of you distinguished visitors, who have come here to exchange views and knowledge at this symposium on "Man and Africa".

Many scholarly gatherings have been held in the past to examine and realize the aspirations and objectives of man in one or more parts of Africa, and it is already evident that this symposium may well prove significant to the whole continent of Africa. We hope that the efforts incorporated in your assembly and in the organization of "Man and Africa" will be rewarded with a fruitful exchange of views and will be successful in enlightening yourselves and those who later read your discussions.

We express our indebtedness to the Ciba Foundation, which has assumed the main burden, and to its Director, Dr. Wolstenholme, without whom this gathering would not have materialized.

It is with great pleasure and my very best wishes for its success that I declare the symposium on "Man and Africa" officially open.

REPLY TO THE PRIME MINISTER BY THE CHAIRMAN, PROFESSOR F. G. YOUNG, F.R.S.

Your Excellency,

As Chairman of the conference, I have the privilege and honour of thanking you, on behalf of the members of it, for bringing us the message which His Imperial Majesty, the Emperor, has been graciously pleased to send. In addition we are highly appreciative of the support for the conference which is marked by the presence of Your Excellency among us here today.

We were sad to learn of the illness of His Imperial Highness, the Crown Prince, which has prevented his being present, and we should be grateful if you would convey to His Imperial Highness our wishes for his speedy recovery from his indisposition.

We are gratefully aware of the deep interest which His Imperial Majesty has shown in the arrangements which have led up to our assembly here for this conference under his patronage. We shall wish to have our appreciative thanks recorded as a part of the proceedings of this conference.

Thank you, Sir, for coming here to give your support to our deliberations,

SPEECH OF WELCOME BY THE HONORARY PRESIDENT, HIS EXCELLENCY LIDJ KASSA WOLDE MARIAM

On behalf of the Haile Selassie I Prize Trust, of which I am a Trustee, I wish to welcome you and at the same time to express my gratitude for the honour bestowed upon me as Honorary President of this symposium; it is an honour which I feel I do not deserve, an honour which I pledge to discharge to the best of my ability.

This august body is assembled here to discuss "Man and Africa" —man and Africa in their manifold aspects. It is altogether fitting and by no means accidental that this symposium is under the joint auspices of the Ciba Foundation and the Haile Selassie I Prize Trust —the former a well-established foundation and the latter a very young one. It is fitting because you are here to discuss, to analyse and to explore old and new problems—the old problems of man and the old problems of Africa, problems which have been the evil consequence of neglect. You are also here to discuss the new problems of man, problems which are the price of progress.

The eyes of the world look to Africa, old or new, with considerable sympathy, but from this symposium can emerge an illuminating cross-cultural investigation of the social, educational, material and political progress of this continent.

May your deliberations prosper, in knowledge, understanding and friendship.

REPLY TO THE HONORARY PRESIDENT BY THE CHAIRMAN

I should like on behalf of us all to express appreciation of the inspiring words of welcome spoken by His Excellency Lidj Kassa, not only in his rôle as Honorary President but as a Trustee of the Haile Selassie I Prize Trust and also as President of the Haile Selassie University. We are most grateful for his presence here today.

CHAIRMAN'S OPENING ADDRESS

PROFESSOR F. G. YOUNG, F.R.S.

Your Excellencies, Ladies and Gentlemen:

It is significant of present trends of thought throughout the world that an international meeting, under the joint auspices of two charitable Trusts in widely separated countries, is assembled here in Ethiopia to survey the problems and potentialities of Africa as a whole.

It is a venturesome task that we have agreed to undertake; but our presence here today makes clear our belief that it should be undertaken at the present time. The record of our discussions can make, I believe, a useful contribution to the study of the progress of man.

We are fortunate to have here today to lead our discussions many who are outstanding authorities on particular aspects of the affairs of the African continent, but I doubt whether any one of these authorities would claim to have detailed knowledge of all the matters that must be considered during the four days of our conference. Moreover, some of us, and in this category I include myself, can claim no special or technical knowledge of the individual subjects before us, though we all share a lively interest and concern in Africa and its affairs. I earnestly hope that in the discussion which will follow each of the papers nobody will hesitate to ask a question because he fears that the answer is known to everybody present except himself, and that it deals with a matter too obvious to merit consideration. I am sure that such an assumption will always be wrong; moreover, it is often the simple question that promotes the greatest discussion. Let us take nothing for granted and let us be unafraid to display individually any ignorance that may exist about any of the many aspects of the wide subject that we have undertaken to discuss.

Before we start I should like to take the opportunity of expressing our appreciation of the labours of the Directors of the two Trusts under whose auspices this conference has come into being. To Dr. Abebe Ambatchew, the Director of the Haile Selassie I Prize Trust, I can say how delighted we are to be taking part in the first conference with which his Trust is associated, and that we are most grateful indeed to him for all the work he has most effectively put into the preparations for this conference. It is no mean feat that, in conjunction with Dr. Wolstenholme, arrangements have been made to choose and bring together a group of people such as are assembled here today, to ensure that they arrive and depart more or less simultaneously, and to house them in such comfort as we enjoy. We are grateful to you, Dr. Abebe, for the part you have played in these complicated arrangements. I am sure that all the members of the conference will wish me to express our thanks through you to the members of your staff for the highly successful preparations that they have made under your direction and supervision.

Dr. Wolstenholme has had much experience in arranging international conferences for the Ciba Foundation, but the range of subjects at this conference is, I know, a new experience for him. The Ciba Foundation is a charitable Trust which exists "for the Promotion of International Co-operation in Medical and Chemical Research", but fortunately its Trust Deed is drawn in wide terms. Some years ago, at my suggestion, Dr. Wolstenholme agreed to arrange a conference on the origin of the Etruscans; together we first looked up the Trust Deed to ascertain whether this subject was covered by its terms and we found that it was. When the subject of the present symposium came up for consideration, naturally the Trust Deed was again consulted, and the Executive Council of the Ciba Foundation, of which I have the honour to be a member, had no difficulty in deciding that consideration of such a subject was in order, and in endorsing the proposal of the Director. We are grateful to you and to your staff, Dr. Wolstenholme, for the experience that you have so effectively brought to bear on the arrangements for this exceptional conference.

Mankind has evolved from lower forms of life by the operation of forces which involved little or no volition; but as man has evolved, so the higher centres of his brain, the seat of conscious thought, have played a more and more significant part in his appreciation of the world around him, and in determining his reaction to it. In saying this I, for one, do not accept the view that the conscious mind is an epiphenomenon of no significance in the determination of man's activity. In taking thought about his future evolution, man must first understand the facts of his present situation. The stage reached in the collection of factual material about himself and his surroundings substantially differs in different parts of the world. Knowledge about the growth of population of countries, their geography, their resources in terms of water, minerals, agriculture, and biological materials in general; their transport, communications and means of communication of knowledge; their nutrition, health and education—all these are naturally of the greatest importance in an attempted assessment of what the future may hold in store, and these subjects naturally form an important part of the contributions to the symposium which opens today.

A most important point here is that we are considering not countries in isolation or in groups but a vast continent as a whole. This in my view is clearly the right thing to do in the context of the modern world. The growing realization among the inhabitants of the world that their thoughts could not remain directed to problems behind national frontiers was, I suppose, given practical witness by the foundation of the League of Nations after the First World War. The Second World War and its aftermath greatly accelerated the growth of awareness that as far as possible the affairs of the world should be considered as a whole; and as a step towards this much thought has been turned towards the association of larger units than had been considered before—

larger units than individual countries. The countries of Europe and of the Americas have come together in many different ways during recent years, and the Commonwealth of Nations to which Britain belongs is another example of the growing consciousness of an international community of interest. Likewise the countries of Africa have naturally begun to consider their community of interest and it is a wish to make some contribution to the fostering of this interest that lies, in part, behind our gathering here now.

In speaking of evolution one clearly must not ignore the fact that evolution can occur only at some cost. Necessarily in the process something that exists must give way to something that is for greater good, and the disturbance of an existing equilibrium can result in temporary difficulties. In chemistry—if I may refer to the subject here—Le Chatelier's theorem tells us that when a system is in stable equilibrium and the equilibrium is disturbed, the components tend to rearrange themselves to minimize the effects of the disturbance. This theorem surely applies to more than the physical sciences, but as yet we can say little quantitatively about its application in the affairs of the world we live in.

An interesting and important paper on the problems of educational evolution has been published by Professor Arthur Lewis.* This is a revised and extended version of a paper presented to the U.N.E.S.C.O. Conference on the Educational Needs of Africa held here in Addis Ababa in May 1961. Professor Lewis points out that the extension of education in an underdeveloped country is bound to involve economic difficulties and temporary frustrations which cannot be avoided but whose effects may be minimized if they are foreseen and intelligently allowed for. For example, Professor Lewis points out that an economy can ultimately absorb any number of educated people, and that: "It is erroneous, when making a survey of the need for skilled

---

* 1964. Education and Economic Development. In *International Social Science Journal*, **14**, 685.

manpower, to confine one's calculations to the numbers that could be absorbed at current prices. One ought to produce more educated people than can be absorbed at current prices, because the alteration in those prices which this brings about is a very necessary part of the process of economic development. On the other hand, this adjustment is painful and fraught with political dangers. Like all social processes, it requires time for relative smoothness.''

This quotation from Professor Lewis's paper is, I think, of particular significance, and no doubt Dr. Sutton, Mr. Mancini, and other contributors will give us many thoughts which are relevant to this particular point of view. At this stage, I only wish to emphasize the fact that the advantages to be gained by mankind's evolution can often be won only at a cost which should not be ignored beforehand.

In our conference we shall be transcending both the accepted boundaries of specialized knowledge and the boundaries of countries as they exist. Further, let us include, if it seems to be appropriate, knowledge of every sort and from all continents if it be relevant to any part of the subject of our conference: ''Man and Africa''. And above all, as I said earlier, let us not hesitate to display our ignorance of any aspect of this vast and indeed almost overwhelming subject.

I

THE GEOGRAPHICAL IMPLICATIONS OF MAN AND HIS FUTURE IN AFRICA

An Introductory Comment

G. C. LAST

THE PHYSICAL BACKGROUND

AFRICA is the second largest continent on the globe and claims one-quarter of the world's land surface (Fig. 1). It almost certainly represents the core of the primitive continent, Gondwanaland, from which the other continental masses in the southern hemisphere have split and drifted.

Africa has its foundations in a rigid block of ancient rocks which have been subjected to gentle warping over most of the

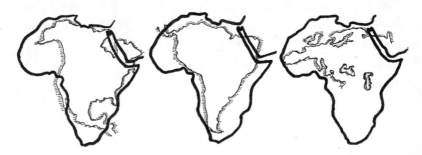

Fig. 1. The comparative size of Africa.

continent to form a series of basins and swells which today mark the extensive broad and shallow river basins and the watersheds which separate these basins (Fig. 2). Much of the warping has been along the margins of the continent so that these basins often

6

have a narrow outlet formed at the point where the river has broken through the up-warping. This also means that few African rivers are navigable from the coast to any great distance

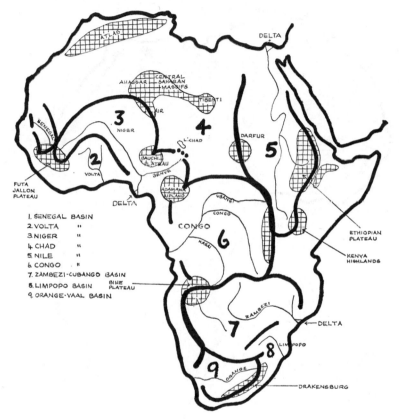

Fig. 2. River basins of Africa.

inland although the middle courses occupying the central floor of the basin are often important highways. The Congo River is an excellent illustration of all these characteristics.

At the northern and southern extremities of the continent, sedimentary rocks have been folded to produce the only distinct mountain ranges in Africa. Along the eastern side of the continent the Archaean basement has cracked, in movements probably associated with the migration of the continents from Gondwana-land, to form the impressive Rift Valley System. The area now

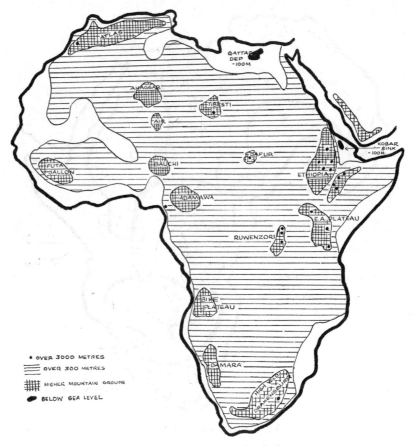

Fig. 3. Africa: general relief.

occupied by Ethiopia seems to have been the site of the most prolonged and violent volcanic activity associated with the faulting, and the resultant Tertiary lava plateaux flanking the Rift Valley in this region form the most extensive area of very high land in Africa (Fig. 3).

The highest relief features on the continent are associated with these four geological events, the warping, the limited areas of fold movements, the Rift Valley structures and volcanic activity in various parts of Africa but particularly associated with the Great Rift System.

For the rest, Africa is characterized by wide areas of high plateaux which present an unbroken and level surface to the eye.

Africa's lakes nearly all owe their origin to the Rift Valley System or to down-warping in different parts of the continent. The former type have the typical long, narrow shape, of which Lake Tanganyika is the best example. The latter—for example, Lake Victoria in a down-warp on the plateau between the two branches of the Rift System, and Lake Chad occupying the centre of the Chad down-warp—are more rounded in shape. A third category of lakes is associated with the fact that the high edges of the African plateaux often prevent the flow of rivers to the sea and the floors of the resultant basins of inland drainage in several parts of the continent are occupied by marshy lakes.

The continent is unique in its position, being balanced almost equally around the equator. Africa's central position in relation to other land masses is also interesting. All other continents lie within a ten thousand kilometre radius from a central point in Africa, a position which can be claimed by no other land mass[1].

This may well be of great strategic, political and economic significance in the future, and the changing pattern of relationships on the globe could make of Africa a new heartland for humanity.

With two-thirds of the continent lying within the tropics and only the northern coastline of Morocco, Algeria and Tunisia situated more than 35° from the equator, Africa can with justification be described as the hottest of the continents. If all temperatures were reduced to sea level no part of Africa would experience temperatures lower than 50°F in any one month[2].

The tendency to high temperatures is strengthened by two other factors. The greatest east-west extent of the continent is situated half-way between the equator and the northern tropic.

Here in tropical latitudes there is a broad expanse of land, remote from the sea, and over this Saharan land surface very high temperatures are experienced. In general, there is little maritime effect on temperature conditions in Africa since there are few areas of coastal lowland extensive enough to allow oceanic influences to penetrate the interior of the continent. Most of

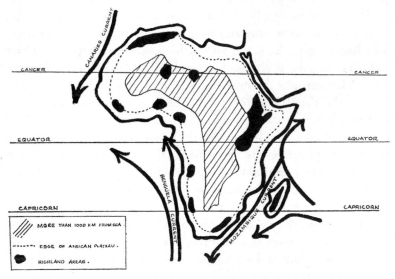

Fig. 4. Factors influencing climate in Africa.

Africa is plateau, more than 500 metres above sea level, and with a higher rim close to the coast. The basin-shaped areas (particularly the Kalahari region of the Cubango-Upper Zambezi basin) tend to become the areas of high temperature, and are very little influenced by the ocean (Fig. 4).

At the same time, in other regions of Africa, we have lower temperatures than would normally be experienced in these latitudes. Where there are extensive areas of very high land, temperatures, even on the equator, are temperate rather than tropical. The best example of the control of altitude over temperature is the extensive Ethiopian Plateau. The same effects are felt in the East African Highlands and on the High Veld of South Africa. In East Africa, three areas (Kilimanjaro, Mount Kenya and the Ruwenzori Mountains) are high enough to

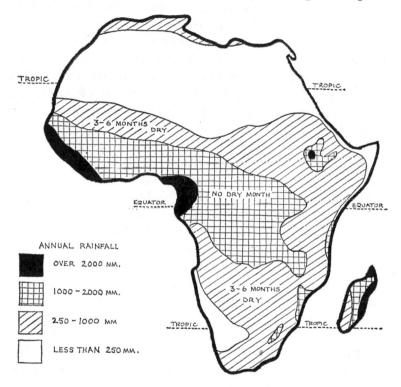

FIG. 5. Rainfall in Africa: annual and seasonal distribution.

experience permanent snow and all these mountain groups have developed glaciers. All are located within a very short distance of the equator.

Parts of the High Atlas are also high enough for permanent snow.

At first glance the rainfall map (Fig. 5) will show that not only does Africa have large areas which receive only a limited amount of rainfall, but that over most of the continent, rainfall is seasonal and so there are extensive areas with up to six dry months in the year. Only a comparatively restricted belt stretching eastwards from the Gulf of Guinea towards the highlands of East Africa has rain in each month. There is no other continent where the water situation creates such large problems for man. In many parts of the continent, rainfall is unsatisfactory either because it is deficient in quantity, or because it is restricted to a short season (usually the hottest season when the effectiveness of rainfall is reduced by evaporation). In the northern half of Africa, the special location of the wide expanse of the Sahara in relation to the Trade Wind System produces the largest area of hot desert on the globe. More than a quarter of the continent suffers from water shortage and rather under one-third suffers from hot, wet, over-watered conditions. In all, it can be said that 60 per cent of Africa's land surface presents water problems to the farmer.

Vegetation in Africa has undergone considerable disturbance by man. Only relatively small patches of primeval forest remain as a result of forest exploitation and shifting agriculture, and most of the moist tropical forest zone is secondary vegetation. It has been argued also that the savannahs of Africa are largely man-made and would revert to woodland if left undisturbed. Certainly, most of the savannahs are burnt off annually so that only the fire-resistant species of the larger vegetation remain. Finally, in the vast Saharan region it is not yet clear how much of the desiccation is the result of man's activities, and how much is due to climate change.

POLITICAL GEOGRAPHY

There are some 125 political units on the globe and of these at the moment Africa claims more than 50 (see map, p. 384), the creation and emergence of which merit some consideration. Almost without exception, these political units reflect the pattern of colonial occupation imposed upon Africa. The whole process of political transformation, which has taken place within living memory, has been remarkable.

The first stage of this movement gained impetus after the Berlin Conference of 1884–85, and by the beginning of the First World War the brightly coloured colonial map of Africa had been created. But even more remarkable was the process of change after the Second World War. Prior to 1955, the only states on the continent which were independent and under African rule were Ethiopia, Egypt, Liberia, Libya and Morocco. Only eight years later, the heads of 32 independent states attended the Summit Conference in Addis Ababa. These states followed no general pattern. They ranged in size and complexity from Nigeria with its population of 42 million to Gambia with just over a quarter of a million, and from Algeria, Congo (Leopoldville) and Sudan, each with areas of over two million square kilometres, to Rwanda, with 26,000 square kilometres.

Apart from the speed with which independence was achieved, one extremely interesting feature of this new era is the rapidity with which Africa has institutionalized its sense of continental unity. The common historical experiences of African peoples under colonial rule which culminated in the demand for independence were certainly partly responsible for this early expression of continental unity, but part of the explanation lies in the fact that Africa has gone through its period of revolutionary change at a time when the development of air transport has made continental contacts relatively easy. It is now possible for the Organization of African Unity to summon national delegates to emergency conferences in a matter of days. Continental feelings can be sounded and African decisions can be taken through personal contact with comparatively little inconvenience. In the short space of time since 1962, independent Africa has assembled six times to discuss questions of continental significance. Perhaps the fact that Africa can meet and has met successfully in the early stages of this new era will enable the general concept of unity to be realized and maintained in its many practical aspects and permit Africa to avoid the narrower expressions of nationalism which have plagued humanity in other areas. It is at any rate a major triumph for man in Africa that his 32 heads of state were sufficiently inspired by the imperative of continental action to remain awake and in session at half-past one in the morning to sign the Charter of African Unity (25 May, 1963).

For some years before the Addis Ababa Summit Conference there had been concern over the practical difficulties which would arise with independent statehood. With independence came all the possible causes of friction, division and disintegration in political Africa. Differences of tribe, language, culture, colonial tradition, political ideology, levels of economic development and internal social structure—all these have hampered both internal unity and easy political association between African states. And yet it seems that the creation of the Organization of African Unity represents a strong underlying desire among African states to find and channel a sense of continental unity and identity. It may be that this overall awareness of being African is the only effective factor which can meet the underlying threat of disunity.

Other sources of friction in Africa are the result of external economic relationships imposed upon African countries or surviving from colonial times. Many individual countries see no alternative to their current links with such organizations as the European Economic Community, but at the same time African governments through the Organization of African Unity and the Economic Commission for Africa are seeking to establish more suitable continental economic organizations, of which the African Development Bank is the first example.

THE STATE OF ECONOMIC AFRICA

Although it is the second largest continent on the globe, Africa, with 25 per cent of the land surface and 8 per cent of the world's population, contributes only 2 per cent of the total value of world output, an amount equal to about half the annual output from the United Kingdom. The income per head is only one-tenth of that of industrialized countries. Within the continent the production of wealth is unequally distributed, with far more than the average coming from the northern and southern extremities. The economies of African countries are still based on a pattern of subsistence agriculture, with 40 per cent of the total wealth of the continent coming from agriculture compared with around 10 per cent in the developed areas of the world. The average area of land per head under cultivation is three times that of Western Europe. There are twice as many livestock per head of population and the area of grazing land per animal is many times that found in Western Europe. These relationships are partly the result of the low population density of Africa but they are also due to the methods of agriculture: Colin Clark estimated[3a] that African peasant agriculture produces only perhaps 0·5 per cent of the output of highly mechanized agriculture and therefore African man today needs more land merely to exist [ab,c].

In the production of energy and in industrial development, Africa lags even further behind. Her energy potential lies largely in the development of hydroelectric power but present developed energy is only 0·1 per cent of the potential. The continent could produce on its own the equivalent of all the power already produced in the world. The largest single source is the Congo River which could produce energy equal to the total produced today in the United States[4]. Industry, outside the North African coast and the Republic of South Africa (which country is responsible for 40 per cent of all African industrial output), is still largely limited to processing industries for commodity exports and small-scale consumer goods industries[5].

In certain specific areas Africa makes important contributions to the world economy. In agricultural products she supplies more than 50 per cent of the world's cocoa, palm oil, palm kernel oil, groundnuts, olive oil and sisal, and in minerals more than 50 per cent of the world's gold, cobalt and chrome, with a third of the world's copper and phosphate, to mention only the most important.

Africa has occupied an important position on the world's economic stage for some time but the standard of life of her own people has remained abysmally low. If the 1950's were the culminating point in the demand for freedom of action within the continent, it seems that the 1960's will mark the demand for a new economic relationship with the rest of the world. This, in fact, was one of the major considerations at the 1964 Trade and Development Conference in Geneva.

The major effect of previous economic contacts between Africa and the European powers was to insist upon the transformation of Africa's subsistence and consumption economy into an export economy—but at the expense of the original food-growing economy. Thus, in one of the areas of Africa where this process was most developed we find the following situation:

"Before its intensive occupation by the French, the fertile coastwise uplands of Algeria had been profitable producers of food for home consumption, notably cereals and mutton. But French settlers had no interest in growing food for the local market and turned, almost from the first, to the production of wine for export. The area under vines rose from a mere 4,000 acres in 1830 to no fewer than 750,000 acres in 1953.

"Algerians began feeling a new hunger. For while the production of cereals had remained at about the same level since the 1880's, the population (thanks largely to modern medicine) had almost tripled in the same period. It has been calculated that the average Algerian had five quintals of grain a year in 1871, four in 1900, but only 2½ in 1940. The situation on the eve of the great insurrection of 1954 was that fewer than one thousand European landowners possessed about one-seventh of all cultivable land outside the barren southern regions, while more than half a million peasant families had no land at all."[6]

To a larger or smaller extent the same thing has happened all over the continent.

POPULATION

No certain figures exist for many areas on the continent but the present population estimate of around 270 million represents only about 8 per cent of the world's total. This is only slightly more than the population of Russia or one-third of the population of China or one-half of the population of India. This means that Africa on the whole is extremely sparsely populated—only Australia has a lower population density. Moreover, the population is extremely unevenly distributed and is characterized by small isolated patches of high population and even over-population.

Three centuries of slave-trading activity resulting in the total export or destruction of probably 50 million people have certainly had serious effects on the size of the present population. But environment has also provided three major limitations to the growth of population. Man in Africa has water problems, soil problems and disease problems. High average temperatures mean an absence of seasonal control of disease-bearing organisms. These have been called "The Rulers of Africa" by Professor Stamp[7]. Professor Kimble defines African health conditions as follows:

"Lacking a balanced diet and adequate protection against cold and damp, and living in ignorance of the elementary principles of sanitation and out of reach of hospitals, doctors and drugstores, the average tribal African lives in thralldom to sickness. For him sickness is the norm; it starts at birth, or even before, and continues until death. And he is a very lucky African who is not sick of more than one thing. . . ."[8]

The climates of the continent also produce over-watered and under-watered regions so that in some areas exhausted and eroded soils limit population, while in other drier regions the use of the land is limited to nomadic pastoralism and population densities are therefore low.

From the economic point of view the size of individual countries in terms of population may also prove a handicap to development. On the average an African country has a population of six million inhabitants compared with 11 million in South America and 43 million in Asia.

The spread of medical services in Africa, which now has only one doctor for 20,000 head of population[9], will certainly contribute to a reduction in the death rate and an increase in the expectation of life, and the future population of Africa is a question of considerable importance both to the continent and also to the rest of the world. By A.D. 2000 Africa's population may have doubled if the expected rate of increase is fulfilled. In A.D. 2000 the proportion of Africans to the rest of the world will be about the same but the rest of the world (which now has an average population density nearly three times that of Africa) will then have at least 3,000 million extra mouths to feed. Africa in A.D. 2000 will still have more usable land per head of population than the rest of the world and should be more developed at a time when the rest of the world will be overcrowded. In these circumstances, the question, "Will the development of African resources be able to keep pace with the growth of her population?" seems to be over-shadowed by the larger question, "How can the resources of Africa contribute to the growing imbalance of world population and food production?"

THE DEVELOPMENT OF AFRICAN RESOURCES

Africa in the 1960's is divided into a number of political units whose boundaries are largely the creation of external influences.

President Nyerere has said: "The boundaries which divide African states are so nonsensical that without our sense of unity they would be a cause of friction. We have no alternative but to start from the position which we inherited after the colonial partition of Africa."[10]

The colonial powers took only some 25 years to partition the second largest continent on the globe. This was achieved in a manner designed to satisfy the demands of speed and topographic clarity rather than with any view to the long-range problems of development. The pattern created will plague Africa for some time to come. More than one-third of Africa's boundaries are geometrical and play havoc with natural geographical regions. The supreme example of absurdity in territorial claim-staking is the existence of Gambia where the river has been sealed effectively from its natural hinterland[11].

The use of rivers as international boundaries is of particular significance to Africa. Africa has more than her share of large river basins. Of the 15 river basins on the globe which are more than one million square kilometres in extent, six are in Africa. But in most cases these have been sub-divided by political boundaries. There are in Africa 48 international river basins of which 19 are shared by more than two states or territories. In 23 international river basins the river forms a political boundary. Ethiopia shares all but one of her major rivers with neighbouring countries and even the exception, the Awash, has its toes in French Somaliland. The Nile basin is shared between eight countries.

Many of these rivers "offer massive opportunities for hydro-electric development or for multi-purpose schemes comprising also irrigation, water supply and flood control."[12] In fact, the economic future of Africa lies to a large extent in the intelligent development of river basins, in multi-purpose schemes which will make the maximum use of available water for power and for irrigation and which will pay due regard to the adequate conservation of all natural resources within the river basin. There are, however, few countries in Africa which can embark on such a programme independently of their neighbours. But this may prove an economic and political blessing to Africa and may provide the starting point for major projects by countries with common river boundaries or which share large river basins, and this may encourage broader economic developments.

If we are to view integrated river basin development as an important step towards African economic progress, we should bear in mind that the harnessing of power and the construction of irrigation canals does not, by itself, solve all problems. The implications behind such developments are enormous. With the dams, canals and power stations must come farmers with new methods, and new seeds, backed by transport, credit and marketing facilities. Parallel with these there must be growth in the industrial sector. All this involves a great social and economic transformation and the education systems do not yet exist in Africa which will produce the kind of people able to accept such technical and social innovation. Opening new areas for economic development often means settling new communities which will be permanent and which will fit themselves to the social, economic and technical requirements of the new environment, become masters of these and develop a sense of purpose. If our experience of existing irrigation projects and resettlement projects in Africa tells us anything it is that we do not yet understand the human requirements behind such schemes.

Africa must also overcome a legacy of economic separatism. Colonial territories, once created, were subjected to separate economic development. With the exception of the large French colonial blocks in West and Equatorial Africa, they became isolated units each producing raw materials and foodstuffs (often a single crop) for the export market. The infrastructure which was created followed the requirements of this type of economy. Ports were established which attracted and concentrated all ancillary industry; railways and roads were built inland from the ports to the sources of export commodities. Apart from certain areas like the former Central African Federation where moves were being made towards the integration of facilities, "there are not yet ten international rail links in the whole of tropical Africa."[13] Today the major trends in the development of African transport facilities are towards providing links between neighbouring countries, developing the pattern of transport within individual countries, and finally, establishing the most effective routes for transcontinental traffic. We are, however, still faced with a proliferation of national economic plans which are seeking economic advance through the establishment of home industries to satisfy the local consumer market, which very often is not large enough to support the industry at its most economic scale of development. There is now an extremely small volume of international trade between countries on the continent and although the establishment of transport links will stimulate inter-territorial trade the volume will be restricted until some element of interstate planning supersedes purely national economic planning.

In 1963 the Economic Commission for Africa concluded that: "The overall economic picture . . . is far from satisfactory." "Insufficient integration of national economies, the lack of diversification of production, low productivity and, consequently, low income levels and inadequate savings, together with mal-nutrition, poor health conditions and unsatisfactory educational levels still remain the basic characteristics of Africa."[14]

On the other hand, the major work of the Economic Commission for Africa has been the collection and processing of the data necessary for long-term economic planning, and the Organization of African Unity has been constructing the political foundation of Africa's future.

GEOGRAPHY IN AFRICA

These few comments serve merely to underline what is generally known about Africa: that economically, the colonial experience "took Africa apart", to use Basil Davidson's phrase[15], and that the urgent need is to put it together again economically and socially; that African resources are undeveloped and, although the potential is great in all respects, a full cataloguing of these resources is as yet in its infancy; that full potential cannot be realized unless there is far-sighted and active collaboration between countries to develop the resources of the continent as a whole.

It is clear that geography must play a vital rôle in these developments—a rôle which involves two levels of activity. One of the greatest handicaps facing man in Africa today is the lack of precise information concerning the ecology of natural resources on the continent. As Professor Hance has put it, ''In Africa, the force of the physical environment is tremendously important. The physical problems seem to be greater and more intransigent than in the middle latitudes. The need here is for research and still more research.''[16] Perhaps the recent U.N.E.S.C.O. conference in Lagos on the organization of research and training in Africa in relation to the study, conservation and utilization of natural resources will result in co-operative action between countries and also between the various fields of study. No one country and no one science can produce effective results in isolation. On the research level, geography has a vital part to play in providing man with the facts of his environment in Africa[17].

But the problems to be faced in this area are small compared with the more general rôle which geography must play in the education of succeeding generations. The great difficulty in a society which must move rapidly forward in order to survive is to think far enough into the future to define the conditions *now* which will permit the future survival of the younger generation still in the classroom. We must tell them in 1964 what they must do in 1984 and this is difficult when change is rapid. In geography we are now beginning to pay lip service to the more obvious and immediate requirements of African students. But, although we in Africa accept in principle that geographical studies must begin at home, that they must be related to the salient features and problems of the students' own environment, we are still a long way from the realization of this elementary step. There are good reasons. Textbooks must be rewritten, and teachers must appreciate an African-orientated view of their subject before they can pass this on to their students. But this is only the first step in the process. As Hudson Hoagland has said, ''The fate of man has become the prize in a gruelling race between education and disaster.''[18] Man has come from bewilderment through knowledge to truculence and the brink of self-destruction. To survive, he must add understanding of himself to knowledge of his environment. The change required of geography on the continent of Africa is that it should cease to concern itself exclusively with mere description and a synthesis of the facts of the environment. It must also discuss the control and development possibilities of the environment. It must combine effectively with the physical sciences and with historical studies to produce a fully integrated curriculum. And this must give students an overall picture of man's development and a view of man's chances for survival. There will always remain the general and traditional functions of the subject in developing powers of observation and enquiry, imagination and memory, and the ability to record, assemble and relate facts. But more important is to meet the challenge of contributing to a proper understanding of man as a changing element in a dynamic environment. This may in turn help to control the self-destructive impulse in man who, by and large, still subscribes to the ancient belief that "The welfare, prosperity and power of the group into which I happened to be born is more important than the welfare, prosperity, power or even the lives of the members of any or all other groups."[19]

Acknowledgments

The figures are reproduced by kind permission of the Curriculum and Research Department, Ministry of Education and Fine Arts, Addis Ababa.

DISCUSSION

Brown: Mr. Last, you have reviewed the geography of Africa in its physical and political aspects. Is it a fact that the boundaries of most countries in the world, as they have evolved, have been determined very largely by physical factors, whereas in Africa colonial development disregarded natural frontiers? And if there is in fact a significant difference between Africa and other continents in this respect, do you think that the resulting difficulties will in the end be more of a hindrance or a help in the development of the continent?

Last: I think it is true that in the older continents the boundaries between countries are the result of a great deal of pushing backwards and forwards until a natural line has been established which has some relation with the landscape. But Africa is not the only continent, surely, which has these artificial boundaries; Australia is geometrically divided into its states; a vast section of the United States is also subdivided in the same way.

Your second question is something which fascinates me. Maybe the boundary problems which divide natural areas in Africa are so obvious that they will themselves generate discussion and collaboration between states (for example, in the development of river basins) and provide an immediate starting point for international co-operation.

Mesfin: What do you think would have happened without colonialism in Africa? From our present knowledge of boundary disputes in Africa and the statement that colonialism divided Africa into the fifty or so political units existing today, do you think that without colonialism there would have been more political units or less?

Last: This is not a question one can answer easily. Contemporary experience in Africa has given us examples of both unification and disintegration. Considering all the underlying forces of possible disintegration (which are not peculiar to Africa, incidentally), there could easily have been a great deal more subdivision. The most obvious example of disintegration is the Congo, which today is divided into more administrative units than existed under the Belgians.

Goody: Yet even now the Congo is divided into fewer administrative units than existed before the Belgians came. In Africa in, say, 1850, one might very easily identify four or five hundred distinct political units. There are many fewer today.

Mesfin: Take, for instance, Ethiopia during the Italian occupation—Italian East Africa included Eritrea, Somalia and

Ethiopia. Take the Anglo-Egyptian Sudan and Egypt, or the most glaring example—French Equatorial Africa and French West Africa, both large units now broken up into several countries. As I see it, colonialism really brought about larger political units, not smaller political units.

Mustafa: I think that must be right, because the states or regions into which the countries have been divided have either been tribal or depended upon accessibility, i.e. on how easy it would be for a specific unit to live and to communicate together. As Mr. Last said, a glaring example of this is the Congo, and even in the Sudan there would have been some 20 political units, depending upon the number of tribes or groups of tribes which have things in common.

Before the Anglo-Egyptian invasion of the Sudan, there was another invader from outside and both Egypt and the Sudan were under Turkish administration. Had it not been for that, maybe Upper Egypt would have been one political unit, Lower Egypt another separate political unit, Northern Sudan, Southern Sudan, Eastern Sudan, Western Sudan, and so on. So I agree that the colonialists tended to bring together numbers of tribes or groups which would otherwise have been independent.

Last: The colonial powers represented a certain stage of economic development, for which a certain territorial arrangement was required. The economic status of Africa before its partition would not demand such territorial arrangements.

Howard-Goldsmith: To answer Ato Mesfin's question one would need to look into a crystal ball. I would like to consider the opposite view; if there had not been any colonial occupation, some of the stronger countries would have naturally started to conquer their neighbours. There were some great empires in the past—for example, the Mossi empire around what is now called Upper Volta and which was once for a time the principal West African empire.

If there had been no outside interference, Africa might have been carved up into fewer than the fifty units there are today. The stronger countries would have conquered and taken over the surrounding territories, as I believe happened also in Europe and in other parts of the world which were allowed to develop without much outside interference.

Monod: Yes, but none of the big West African empires were powerful for a long time; there was a succession of empires, starting, growing and then collapsing to make way for the next one. I don't know of any empire which lasted for centuries.

Dekker: We can compare Africa with Europe if we take a period of a few centuries. The map of Europe is certainly different from what it was 200 years ago, and who can tell what it will look like in another 200 years? There you have your 400 years, which is the period we are speaking about, particularly in West Africa.

Young: Uganda is interesting in this connexion. The Kingdom of Buganda was an active central authority in a large area of what we now call Uganda before the British came on the scene, and it seems to me that the unity that has now been fostered in Uganda might have developed even had there been no colonial period. It may be an example of where federation (if we may call it that) might have occurred and even gone further if there had been no colonial intervention.

Sutton: I think the facts are rather against that. When a truce was imposed in Uganda by the colonial power a real struggle was going on among the kingdoms there and it seems very doubtful that this would have issued in a wider unity, federal or otherwise. But, in turn, the difficulties in East Africa at the moment certainly illustrate some of the problems of effectively breaking down the territorial divisions left by the era of colonialism. We have a heritage of a common market and common institutions in East Africa, and the most urgent desire of some of the major leaders is to bring about a genuine political federation. It has been very difficult to go ahead with this and I think the general opinion at the moment is that it is not likely to proceed very quickly even in perhaps the most favourable circumstances one is likely to find anywhere in Africa.

Last: This is largely because of one of the factors militating against unity that I mentioned—the disparity in the levels of economic development between the three possible members of the East African Federation. It is difficult to imagine there being any immediate economic advantage to Uganda in being associated with Tanzania.

Sutton: If you consider the greater size of the common market, there are real advantages for all in this situation. The whole East African Federation nearly faltered three months ago, not because of Uganda but because of Tanzania's fears that it would be impossible to industrialize the country without breaking away from Kenya, which as the principal industrial centre tends to attract more of the new industries in the common market area. It was a very considerable feat for these East African countries to have succeeded in making the Kampala Agreements last April, which preserve the common market and make it possible for each of the countries to see itself developing its own industries.

Ewing: It seems to me that we are now on the right track. To ask whether there should be more or less unification is to put the emphasis on the wrong question, that of the number of individual political states. The important thing is to develop extensive co-operation among existing nations on the commercial plane. This can be done without joining together politically.

What the African is actually thinking of now is of going ahead step by step with the genuine development programmes necessary, which would certainly require close co-operation. To start at the other end and worry about political unity would be to obscure what the real problem is and would not necessarily lead to fewer political boundaries.

Goody: If one looks at the whole world, the examples one can find of common markets and extensive economic co-operation between states that have no political unity are very few and far between. It would be an error to think simply in terms of economic co-operation without also considering the concentration of political power, because without the latter countries can always withdraw or contract out.

It is rather sad that despite the talk of African unity, one often cannot buy the products of the country next door. Even short-range operations of this kind are rendered difficult largely because of political considerations rather than because of economic difficulties.

Brown: The colonial occupations undoubtedly divided up the African continent so artificially that today the need for revision of national boundaries is clear enough. It will be interesting to see whether this situation will facilitate regional arrangements or merely be a source of constant friction.

Mesfin: It seems that, broadly, three forces are at work in Africa today: tribal forces based on tribal or linguistic affiliations; forces which accept the legacies of colonial rule and attempt to build nations within their frontiers; and forces of pan-Africanism. It is, of course, clear that conflicts occur between these three forces, as demonstrated by the territorial disputes between Algeria and Morocco, Ethiopia and Somalia, and other African states. Which of these forces will prevail is very difficult to say at this moment.

Young: The tendency of nations to fall apart is illustrated by the fact that there are still nationalist movements in Europe— the Walloons and the Flemish in Belgium, for example, or even the Scots and the English in Great Britain!

Michaelis: I was fascinated the other day to see that one of the old ideas mentioned by Jules Verne in 1905 in his book ''Invasion de la Mer'', has been taken up again. The United Arab Republic is said to be thinking of digging a canal between the Mediterranean and Qattara Depression for two reasons: first of all, to generate hydroelectricity from the difference in height between the two water levels, and secondly to create an inland sea, the evaporation from which might influence the surrounding climate.

Are there any other similar depressions round the coast of Africa where schemes like this might produce hydroelectricity and a change of climate?

Last: There is such a depression in Ethiopia—the Kobar Sink in the northern Afar Depression. This lies more than 100 metres below sea level at no great distance from the coast and I imagine it would offer advantages similar to the Qattara Depression scheme. There are considerable mineral deposits in the region, notably potash, which is now being exploited, and a local hydro-electric source would be of advantage to a potential chemical industry.

Monod: There is another series of depressions in southern Tunisia and south-eastern Algeria—the Shott Depressions. About fifty years ago there was a big project (the Roudaire Project) but it was neglected and nothing has been done.

2

CLIMATE AND WATER RESOURCES IN AFRICA

GERARD DEKKER

"For when they learned that all Greece is watered by rain and not, as Egypt is, by the flooding of rivers, they remarked that the day would come when the Greeks would be sadly disappointed and starve—in other words, if God sees fit to send no rain but afflicts us with a drought, we shall all die from famine because we have no source of water other than the rain which God chooses to grant us."

HERODOTUS

(*Translation*: Aubrey de Selincourt)

AFRICA extends from a little north of 35° N to almost 35° S. Except for the northernmost belt and the southern Cape, it has a climate of the type called tropical, the weather pattern being determined by conditions within the easterlies. The combination of high temperatures and a rainfall which is in most parts strictly seasonal means that large areas of the continent are basically dry for long periods each year, even though certain areas suffer regularly from floods during the wet season.

Seasonal variations, together with a certain inter-annual irregularity shown by the occurrence of periods of floods and droughts, make rainfall a very important factor when the development of land and water resources is considered. Temperature, wind and precipitation all have a great impact on the conditions under which man attempts to improve his wellbeing, but while precipitation can be influenced by man only on a very limited scale, its results can be subjected to human interference on a far larger scale than can temperature and wind. My subject will therefore be precipitation and the resulting surface and ground-water, in particular its variability and the implications of this variability for the development of available water resources.

In the neighbourhood of latitudes of 30° N and 30° S there exists around the world a quasi-permanent belt of high pressure cells. In these cells air is descendant and divergent and weather is generally dry. Around the equator, a trough of low pressure is found where air is ascendant and convergent and rainfall occurs. The presence of these two belts of high pressure, separated by the trough of low pressure around the equator, explains the regular easterlies which occur at lower latitudes. It is the displacement of the areas of high and low pressure over Africa and in the neighbourhood of the continent which largely causes the seasonal variations in precipitation in tropical Africa.

Rainfall over most of Africa is, then, strictly seasonal, but it is very variable (see Fig. 1), and in order that the available precipitation should be better assessed, its magnitude should be studied as a part of the water balance. The amount of incoming radiation being large and temperatures high, potential evaporation from an open water surface is high over most of the continent when compared with the rainfall, as can be seen from the following figures:

Location	Annual potential evaporation (mm.)
Sahara	2,500–3,000
West Africa at 16° N	2,000
West Coast	1,200–1,500
Karamoya, East Africa	1,800
Aberdare Mountains, East Africa (altitude 2,400 m.)	1,250
South-west Africa	2,800

Compare these figures with the following data from the middle and higher latitudes: Madrid, Rome and Athens 930 mm.; Amsterdam 650 mm.; Norway 300 mm.

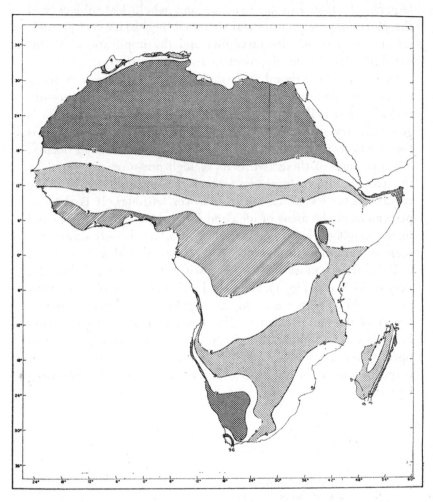

Fig. 1. Number of months with average precipitation less than 50 mm. (Data from Climatological Atlas of Africa [1961]. Lagos and Nairobi: C.C.T.A./ C.S.A.)

The high potential evaporation makes the actual evaporation and the transpiration from the vegetation, if water is available, also high. The combined effect of evaporation and transpiration is called evapo-transpiration.

Meigs[1] has calculated that 42 per cent of the African continent is arid or extremely arid, and 22 per cent semi-arid, leaving only 36 per cent as sub-arid and humid (see Fig. 2). Twenty-six African countries include within their territories areas which are classified as dry or semi-dry.

When population figures and rainfall data are compared it is seen (Table I) that 20 per cent of the population lives in arid or very arid regions where average annual rainfall is below 250 mm., where it is generally considered that crop-growing is not possible without the use of irrigation. Twenty-two per cent live in regions where precipitation is between 250 and 500 mm., 42 per cent where it is between 500 and 1,500 mm., and consequently only 16 per cent live on land which receives on the average more than 1,500 mm. per annum.

The high potential evapo-transpiration, combined with conditions imposed by a pronounced dry season and the fact that most rainfall occurs in storms which are separated by sometimes relatively long spells of dry weather, causes only a comparatively small part of the rainfall to enter the rivers as surface run-off. The nature of the soil and sub-soil in many places is such that the flow entering the river from ground-water storage is small. All these factors result in a small ratio between annual precipitation and river flow. Table II shows some data for a number of African rivers. It should be mentioned that owing to particular conditions, the figure for the Ogoué is exceptionally high for Africa. The figure given for the Meuse in France is a representative one for a non-glacier-fed river in Western Europe.

For a particular river basin this ratio between the annual precipitation and the run-off generally increases with the annual precipitation, since evapo-transpiration tends to remain the same. The ratio however is also influenced by the distribution of storms

2

in a particular year. In what follows much will be said about the annual variation of precipitation and of run-off. It should be kept in mind that in many cases the inter-annual variation of flow

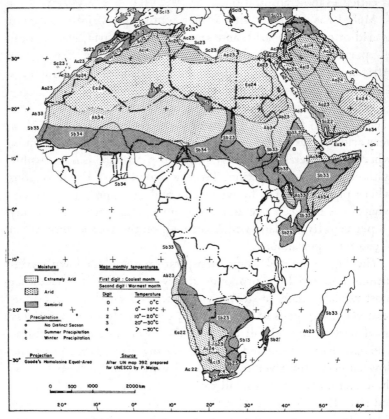

Fig. 2. Distribution of arid homoclimates in Africa (after United Nations map 392, prepared for U.N.E.S.C.O. by Meigs).

from a river basin is somewhat larger than that of the rainfall over that basin.

The inter-annual variability of rainfall at any particular place increases generally with the decrease of average annual precipitation, and decreases with the altitude. Biel defines variability as the mean deviation*, that is to say the sums of all deviations from the mean averaged without respect to sign, and he has published a world map[3] indicating regions with equal annual variability. The arid regions, semi-arid regions and even areas normally

Table I

CLIMATIC AND HYDROGRAPHIC DATA FOR AFRICA

	Area (sq. km.)	% of total area
Moist climate	10,900,000	36
Semi-arid	6,650,000	22
Arid	7,900,000	26 ⎫
Extremely arid	4,800,000	16 ⎬ 42%†
Total surface	30,250,000	100

Annual rainfall (mm.)	Estimated % of population
250	20
250–500	22
500–1,500	42
1,500	16
	100

(Total population: 272,000,000)

	sq. km.
Area covered by the international river basins (only the areas contributing to the river flow are taken into account)	13,300,000 (44% of total area)
Area covered by lakes	195,000
Area covered by swamps	260,000

† After Meigs[1].

classified as sub-humid show a variability of over 20 per cent (Fig. 3), which indicates that serious droughts must occur. Only a very limited area around the equator has a dependable rainfall with a variability of less than 15 per cent. Large areas, including the Sahara and south-western Africa, have a variability of over

---

* For symmetrical or moderately skew distributions, the mean deviation is about four-fifths of the standard deviation[2].

40 per cent, which means that rainfall is really only erratic. Generally speaking, it appears that the variability of rainfall on the African continent is larger than on the other continents except perhaps Australia. Only in Uganda and around Lake Victoria is the variability below 10 per cent. The figures mentioned here are for annual rainfall. For monthly rainfall the variability is even greater. For instance, even in the Congo basin where precipitation is fairly well distributed through the year, monthly rainfalls of 500 per cent or 0 per cent of the average for

Table II

RATIO BETWEEN RUN-OFF AND ANNUAL PRECIPITATION

River	Average ratio
Senegal at Bakel	0·11
Niger at Kourroussa	0·27
Benue at Riao	0·22
Vaal at Standerton	0·09†
Congo at Leopoldville	0·25
Chari at Fort Archambault	0·05
Many smaller rivers in East Africa	0·10
Ogoué at Lambaréné	0·45
Meuse (France)	0·47

† Varied between 0·02 and 0·29

that month are observed, even during years for which the total annual rainfall is close to the average.

As mentioned above, most rainfall in Africa is derived from disturbances associated with waves in the easterlies. The rain-producing clouds are of the cumulus type, unlike the temperate zones where the rain-bringing cloud is stratus. Thus, in most parts of Africa, the amount of annual rainfall is determined by the number of storms and the variability of this number explains the large variability in rainfall. As the storms often cover large areas, carried as they are by the higher-altitude easterlies, droughts and floods usually cover large areas. This can conveniently be shown by using annual flow data of large river basins. Even a large variation of precipitation over a small area would not much

affect the total flow from the basin. Table III gives some information on the observed maximum and minimum annual flow of a
number of large African river basins.

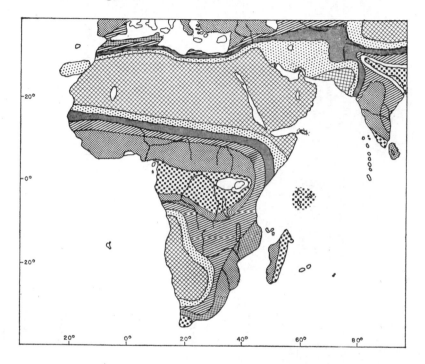

The figures denote percentage departures from normal

Under 10   10-15   15-20   20-25   25-30   30-40   Over 40%

Fig. 3. Annual rainfall variability in Africa.

Although there is an important inter-annual variation in
rainfall, there is also a certain tendency for wet years, and
for dry years, to appear in groups, which tendency could be
explained by a certain persistence of the anomalies in the pattern
of the circulation of the air. The existence of this tendency is

37

Table III

ANNUAL FLOW OF SOME LARGE AFRICAN RIVERS

River	At	Catchment area (sq. km.)	Period	Average annual discharge ($10^9 m^3$)	Maximum annual discharge ($10^9 m^3$)	Year	Minimum annual discharge ($10^9 m^3$)	Year	Ratio max./min.
Nile	Aswan		1871–1908	103					
			1909–1945	83					
			1871–1945	93	137	1879	45·5	1913	3·0
Niger	Koulikoro	122,000	1907–1960	49	74·8	1925	26	1913	2·9
Benue	Yola	108,000	1934–1957	23·4	35·1	1938	14·2	1937	2·5
Senegal	Bakel	202,000	1913–1961	24·3	41	1942	9·8	1944	4·2
Orange	Prieska	340,000	1913–1938	10·6	29·4		1·9		15·5
Kafua	Kafua	154,000	1905/6–1949/50	5	14·6	1947/48	1·8	1948/49	8·1
Zambezi	Kariba	514,000	24 years	40	93·5		18·4		5·1

See References, Nos. 4, 5, 6 and 7.

observed when the few available records of river flow which go back far enough for this purpose are studied. The average annual discharge of the Nile for the period 1871 to 1908 was 103×10^9 cubic metres (m.^{3}). For the period 1909 to 1945 it was 83×10^9 m.^{3}, or about 20 per cent less[4]. (The maximum annual discharge during these two periods was 137×10^9 m.^{3} in 1877; the minimum $45\cdot5 \times 10^9$ m.^{3} in 1914.) The familiar story of the seven fat years and the seven lean years still holds true today.

Another example has been noticed by Hofmeyr and Schulze[8] in Capetown, where the annual rainfall became significantly lower between 1901 and 1930. The regression line computed by these authors goes through 720 mm. in 1901 and through 500 mm. in 1930. On the other hand, the period 1938 to 1960 became gradually wetter.

The lower part of Table IV gives more data on observed fluctuations of precipitation and of river flow occurring over short periods. In order to put these fluctuations in a better perspective, the large climatic fluctuations having a geological time scale are given in the upper part of the table. The last relatively humid period in North Africa and the Sahara was from 5000 to 2500 B.C. Butzer[10] has convincingly demonstrated that during the Roman and Byzantine periods, North Africa did not enjoy better climatic conditions than today. The deterioration of the water resources of this area and the devastation of what was once cultivable land are therefore not due to changes of climate but to human actions.

The absence of recent major climatic changes, however, does not prevent the short-term fluctuations from being very real. Although as yet unpredictable, short periods—lasting up to perhaps 10 to 15 years—of years with floods producing precipitation, and groups of years during which droughts will be frequent, should be expected. The study of annual river flow and of lake levels shows this clearly. Fig. 4 shows the annual flow of the Senegal, Niger, Benue and Nile rivers. Groups of years of large annual discharge and of years of relatively small annual flow are

Table IV

SOME CLIMATIC VARIATIONS OVER AFRICA

Period B.C.	East Africa	Northern Africa	Central Sahara	West Africa
1,000,000	Moist Pluvial (Kageran) Interpluvial Pluvial (Kamasian) Major interpluvial Pluvial (Kageran) Interpluvial Pluvials (Gablian I, II)	Pluvial (?) Pluvial (?) Pluvial with two maxima(?)	Dry	
10,000				
9,000			Moderate temperatures, humid	
8,000	Dry			
7,000		Extremely dry		
6,000		Dry	Hot and dry but rains in mountain areas	
5,000	Wetter (Makalian)			
4,000		Moist, warmer	Sahelian climate	
3,000	Dry	Dry		
2,000				
1,000		Slightly moister	Desert climate	
500	Wetter (Nakurian)			Wetter than today (Nok)

A.D.				
1200–1500			Moister than today	
1700	Snow remained for months on mountains in Ethiopia			
1800–1830	Nile low			
1845–1855	Nile abundant			
1870–1898	Nile abundant	Wet period in Algeria		Sudan belt very wet
1884–1896	Nile abundant			
1900			Ahaggar (Hoggar). Before 1900 winter and spring rains dominant. After 1900 summer rains dominant	
1902–1915				Sudan belt dry
1915–1939				Sudan belt moderately wet
1939–1944				Sudan belt dry
1950				Sudan belt wet

From References, Nos. 9, 10, 11 and others.

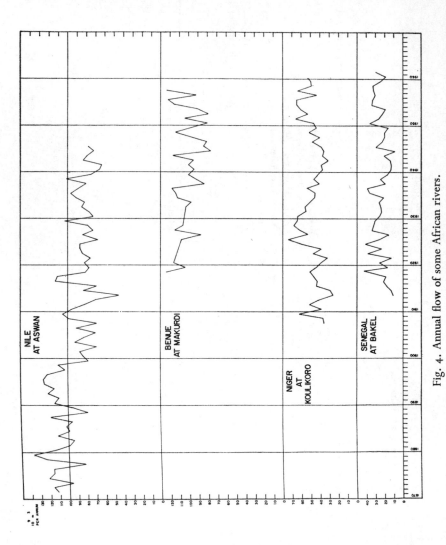

Fig. 4. Annual flow of some African rivers.

recognizable, although the variation is of course irregular. Another example can be taken from South Africa, where the mean flow of a number of rivers in four successive years has been compared with the mean annual run-off of these rivers. In many cases a ratio of 0·5 or lower was found and in one case a value as low as 0·14 was observed.

The records of lake levels in Fig. 5 are also an indication of the existence of dry and wet periods. It is by now well realized that the levels of some lakes, for instance those of Lake Tanganyika and of Lake Nyasa, are not determined only by the annual inflow of river water and rainfall, but also by the outflow through their outlet, the capacity of which is subject to variation due to silting, scouring and the growth of weeds. Thus, high lake levels do not necessarily indicate an increase of precipitation and the analysis of lake levels should be done with care. However, the rapid rise of the levels of the three lakes during the last few years is not due to a reduction of the capacity of their outlets* but to the high rainfall obtaining during these years. The fact that these lake levels started rising more or less simultaneously incidentally also shows the extent of the area over which the rainfall has been subject to fluctuation.

We find then, in Africa, two problems, the understanding and practical solution of which are crucial for further development of its water resources: (1) the seasonal variation of precipitation, and (2) the inter-annual variability of precipitation with a tendency for wet years and dry years to appear in clusters.

To ensure a sufficient supply for the dry season and for the lean years, saving and storage of water during the rain-giving season and during the fat years is the obvious measure. Nature has already provided for this storage in the form of lakes and swamps and ground-water. In Africa, south of the Sahara and north of the Kalahari, many large lakes and swamps exist. The total surface

---

* The outlet of Lake Victoria used to be formed by a series of rapids in which recently the Owen Falls Dam has been constructed in such a manner as not to affect the natural capacity of this outlet.

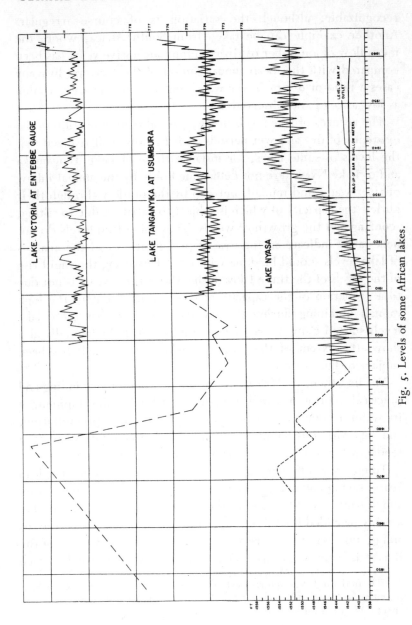

Fig. 5. Levels of some African lakes.

covered by the great lakes is estimated to be around 200,000 sq. km., and that covered by perennial swamps 250,000 sq. km.

The effect of many of these surfaces of water is to decrease the magnitude of the flood-peak downstream, to increase the dry-season discharge and, in some cases, to maintain during relatively dry years a larger flow of water than would be the case if they did not exist. In certain cases, these natural reservoirs cause the flood waters to arrive after the rainy season and thus at a favourable time in the downstream part of the basin. The retarding effect of the swamp and lake area of the Niger interior delta in Mali on the Niger flood also causes the period of navigability on the Niger in Nigeria to extend far into the dry season.

The price—expressed in the volume of water lost in the lakes and swamps by evaporation and transpiration—to be paid for this favourable effect is, however, high. From Table V it can be seen that according to present estimates the losses by evaporation and/or transpiration exceed the rainfall on the lake and swamp surfaces, except for Victoria where the average rainfall is slightly greater than the evaporation.

This price for storage should be compared with its alternative: the water flowing to the sea without being used. Thus it is that the huge losses by evaporation expected for the reservoir of Sadd El Aali, namely, 10×10^9 m.^{3} per annum, are considered to be acceptable when compared with the present flow to the sea.

The construction of dams and storage reservoirs permits man to increase the dry-season river flow for the purposes of water-power, irrigation, navigation, etc. Besides the Sadd El Aali, various other large dams are at present under construction or being considered. Most reservoirs are intended for inter-seasonal regularization. Depending on the size of the reservoir, this often means that if rainfall during the wet season has been below average, the water available during the dry season will also be below average; in other words, the quantity of water which will become available for use during the dry season depends on the magnitude of the precipitation during the previous wet season.

Table V

AVERAGE ANNUAL YIELD FROM SOME AFRICAN LAKES AND SWAMPS

Name	Catchment area (sq. km.)	Surface water (sq. km.)	Surface swamps (sq. km.)	Average annual inflow (10^6 m.^{3})	Average annual outflow (10^6 m.^{3})	Average yield + (10^6 m.^{3})	Average yield — (10^6 m.^{3})
Victoria	195,000	67,500		16,600	21,200	4,600	4,300
Kyoga		1,800	4,500	24,000	19,700		200
Edward and George		2,140		2,200	2,000		300
Albert		5,300		2,500	2,200		
Sudd region				28,000	14,000		14,000
Tana	13,500	3,000		6,500	3,500		3,000
Interior delta Niger	330,000	25,000 (max.)		70,000	35,000		35,000
Chad		From 15,000 to 25,000		40,000	Negligible		40,000
Tanganyika	238,700	32,000		17,300	6,400		10,900
Okavanga delta	400,000		7,500	7,500	Negligible		7,500

From References, Nos. 4, 7 and others.

The determination of the capacity required for inter-annual regularization of river flow is a difficult problem. Because of the cyclic behaviour of periods of dry and wet years, the existing record of annual flow cannot always be considered to be a random sample. No forecast can be made of the order in which the floods of various magnitudes will follow each other in the future. Periods for which good records exist in Africa are short, with the exception of the Nile.

The storage capacity required to ensure an annual outflow from a reservoir equal to a certain percentage of the average flow increases with this percentage but also with the number of years over which the outflow is to be maintained[4, 12]. In the available range of reservoir capacities, a size will often be reached at which the marginal increase in annual losses by evaporation will be higher than the marginal increase in annual outflow. Thus, there appears to be a physical limit to inter-annual regularization, a limit which is below the annual average flow. The question of economic limits on the size of a reservoir will not be considered here. There is, however, still another restrictive factor: the number of potential dam sites for important storage reservoirs in Africa is limited, due to the great geological age of the land forms. This renders the preservation of other means of regularization of the availability of water, i.e. the existing swamps and lakes and the ground-water reserves, most important.

GROUND-WATER

Especially in the dry regions, important replenishments of sub-surface water reservoirs occur after heavy storms such as those which recur every ten years or so. On the other hand, in some semi-arid regions a period of dry years can so seriously affect the ground-water level that even tree crops suffer. Even in some of the more humid regions where surface water ceases to run during the dry season, ground-water is often the only water available for man and beast for a part of the year.

In various parts of Africa, the exploitation of ground-water is already too intensive and the amount of water pumped up exceeds the replenishment. The decline of the water table in Tripolitania, Libya, has been as much as 8 metres in 25 years[13] and there is no reason to suppose that the rate of decline will decrease, unless pumping is reduced. In the Republic of South Africa, where twice as much water is used from underground as from the surface conservancy schemes, the water table has fallen dangerously and yields are diminishing.

The question of replenishment of the ground-water reserves is of course crucial, and it is only quite recently that attention has been paid to this. Important factors are the infiltration rate and the magnitude of evapo-transpiration. In western Africa generally no infiltration from rainfall occurs north of the isohyet* of 400 mm., unless the water is concentrated in streams and a certain depth of water of the stream has been reached[14]. In the Kordofan, the run-off has to concentrate to a thickness of 1·5–2 metres before infiltration through the sand is possible. In the Kalahari region no marked surface drainage system is observable, with the effect that there is no concentration of run-off. A depth of 2 metres of the fine-grained aeolian sand can easily store 50 cm. of water, and the sand layer is generally much thicker. This water is removed by evaporation from the soil and transpiration by the vegetation and, up to the present, no important ground-water reserves have been discovered. Wildlife in this region thrives on the vegetation and the moisture it contains. It is of interest to note that the human inhabitants of the region obtain water from the sand by sucking it out with a kind of long straw. It is only more to the western side of this area, where impervious calcite layers occur, that sufficient concentration of run-off takes place for the creation of exploitable ground-water reservoirs[15].

In northern and western Africa extensive water-bearing formations exist in the intercalary continental, the Albian of the Algerian Sahara and the Nubian sandstones of the Libyan desert.

* Line on map joining places with equal rainfall.

48

It is of course questionable whether exploitation of these ground-waters in the Central Sahara would be of any economic interest or justify the costs of further exploration, but at the fringes of the desert, real possibilities exist and the search for water should be actively pursued.

Much water of good quality has been found in the Nubian sandstone series in the United Arab Republic, which will make the exploitation of the good soils in a number of the depressions possible (e.g. the New Valley Project). On the other hand, it appears that the water trapped in similar formations in Libya is very highly mineralized.

It has been estimated that the water reserves in the intercalary continental in the northern Sahara in Algeria are being replenished at a rate of about 25 m.^{3}/sec.[16] This implies that exploitation of this water at a higher rate would lead to "mining", i.e. ultimately to depletion, although reserves are considerable. Where large reserves exist, however, fear of depletion should not be allowed to interfere in decisions regarding the use of ground-water, as long as it is known what is happening. Either the available water reserves are used for economic benefit, or such reserves are kept intact and no economic benefit will be obtained. Progress in techniques and economy of de-mineralization processes will ultimately become available which will allow the use of the existing immense quantities of mineralized ground-water. After the depletion of these, sea-water could be used.

In West Africa, ground-water resources are limited to pockets of weathered rock. The quality of this water is generally good but the lack of permeability of these water-bearing formations makes it difficult to obtain sufficient water for the large cities from these sources. The ground-water in these pockets often shows large seasonal variations in level. Also, in the Cambrian, no extensive aquifers* exist. It is only from the sedimentary formation that ground-water can be abstracted in large quantities. The important reserves contained in these formations are often formed by fossil water, replenishment is very slow or completely absent, and

---

* Water-bearing strata.

49

water quality varies. Only in the sedimentary rock along the coast do some well-replenished water-bearing layers exist from which a number of the large cities obtain their water supplies.

In eastern Africa no large water-bearing formations like those in northern Africa exist. Water is often found in fault lines and fractures of the granites and, as in West Africa, in pockets of weathered rock. But the high fluorine content of the water from many boreholes and wells makes it unfit for human consumption and presents a serious problem.

In the dry and semi-dry areas, use is sometimes made of the water stored in the sandy river beds. This water is replenished during the few times per year the river is in spate. Successful trials have been made with sand-storage reservoirs. In these reservoirs, which are made by constructing a dam across the river, the deposit of sand is promoted, the effect being that water is stored in the sand. Evaporation is thereby reduced and the efficiency of a sand reservoir surpasses that of an open reservoir in the same climatic conditions.

In southern Africa ground-water is found in many places, but not in the Kalahari or south-west Africa. However, the quality is often bad. Both in Karroo formations and in the basement complex the total dissolved solids in the ground-water exceed 1,000 parts per million (p.p.m.) over large areas. In the southern part of Mozambique it has been necessary to take, as the upper limits of acceptable sodium chloride content, 2,000 p.p.m. for drinking water for human consumption and even 5,000 p.p.m. for cattle.

CONCLUSIONS

We see thus that unlimited availability of water in Africa is, even outside the arid and semi-arid areas, hardly something that can be taken for granted.

An economy which is still preponderantly based on agricultural production is intimately related to the availability of "timely" water and, with the further development of irrigation, the introduction of cash crops, hydroelectric schemes, urban water supply and sanitation, and water-using industries, it will in future become more dependent on the provision of water. Unless great care is taken with the planning of the use of the available resources, and unless strong government control of the conservation of those resources is exercised, the vulnerability of the economy to periods of floods and droughts would increase with further development.

In order to limit this vulnerability as much as possible and to ensure that sufficient water is available at the right time, certain principles should be taken as guides for action.

Development of water and land resources should be based on a proper inventory and a thorough analysis of the hydro-meteorological and hydrological phenomena. Intensified hydrological field-work is necessary to remedy the serious lack of data in many countries. Modern methods of hydrological observations and analysis, such as those developed in East Africa, have proved to lead to quicker results than can be obtained with the more classical methods. The rainfall analysis as published by Griffith[17] for East Africa should be made for the whole of Africa. Isohyets with reliability indications should be prepared. Further comparative precipitation studies, making use of the few long-term rainfall records available, could help to assess the minimum quantity of water that can be expected to be available in the various river basins, large and small.

Our knowledge of tropical meteorology is still very limited. Intensified studies in this field are a prerequisite for medium and long-term forecasting of such phenomena as the onset of the rainy season and its intensity, even if only qualitatively. The fact that droughts and floods usually cover large areas makes it likely that these phenomena would become predictable if more were known of the displacement of air currents. Such prediction could be of great practical interest, both for direct agricultural application and for the operation of the large dams now being constructed or planned. Meteorological and hydrological conditions extend beyond political borders. It is therefore essential that research in this field should be planned internationally according to regions in which meteorological and hydrological conditions are similar. I hope that the International Hydrological Decade which starts in 1965 will result in increased attention by African governments to these problems. This attention means, however, money and skilled manpower, both scarce resources.

The planning of land use—from a physical point of view— should not be based solely on its classification according to agricultural properties. The rôle of the various parts of a river basin in the water balance should be carefully analysed before land is allocated to a particular use. Land management in the upper parts of a basin should aim at an efficient transformation of seasonal rainfall into usable water resources. The goal should be a high yield of water available for optimum economic use, well distributed through the year. In the lower parts of the valley, high-value crops can often be produced, and industries may require, now or in the future, large quantities of water. Thus, a decision on the exploitation of highlands should take fully into account the long-range effect on the water balance and the economic use that could be made of water further downstream. This does not necessarily prevent the economic use of the available high land. There are fortunately examples in Africa of the application of this principle whereby the high land is still exploited profitably. But this principle affects the kind of use to be made, which use will often not be the traditional one.

The problems of conservation of land and water resources cannot be separated. Calculations based on precipitation and its distribution in time, and on the relief of Africa, show that as a continent Africa is likely to be subject to stronger erosion than any other continent, except South America. I do not wish to sound like an alarmist—there is, I believe, as yet no reason to be so—but the aspect of erosion should be seriously taken into account when the use of resources is being planned. Human actions, and not a change of climate, have been the cause of the present poor conditions of land and water resources in northern Africa. Accelerated erosion through bad land and water management is at present taking place in other parts of Africa, even in the sub-humid and humid areas, such as the Ethiopian highlands, Rwanda, Burundi, Guinea and Nigeria. It is not yet too late to call a halt to this process.

Development of water resources could do much to reduce the risks of drought in those areas where at present the success of dry farming is marginal. The application of additional irrigation, if envisaged on a proper scale, may overcome failure during periods of low rainfall caused by the late onset of the rainy season. It is of course undeniable that during droughts the quantity of water available for irrigation also will be smaller than during wet years. This again indicates the necessity of limiting the development of water resources to a level with a low degree of risk.

If there is a choice, water resources should be primarily developed where they are plentiful, rather than where water is scarce. It is apparent from what has been said earlier that in a particular country such a choice does not always exist. In Africa as a whole, however, there are large water resources, the development of which has scarcely begun. The quantity of water which flowed into the Bight of Benin from the river Niger during the year with the lowest record would be sufficient to grow sufficient rice for more than half the population of Nigeria. With a few exceptions, not even a start has been made on the development of the often abundant water resources of West Africa. The waters of the Congo are used on only a very limited scale. In East Africa many rivers show good possibilities for development but their resources are as yet untapped. Much water evaporates from the Sudd region, Lake Chad and the Okavango swamps without benefit to man. Fisheries on the large African lakes are far from being developed to their limit. Of the great hydroelectric potential of Africa, only 0·6 per cent is being exploited. Only the Nile basin and some basins of northern Africa have a great part of their available resources used, but there is still much room for the intensification of their development. It is true that many of the regions which have rich water and other resources are virtually uninhabited because of the health hazards and the annual or perennial flooding. However, the dense population in low, formerly flooded land areas in other parts of the world shows the great possibilities if these hazards could be overcome. Modern means are now available to improve the present conditions and to make these areas habitable and productive.

Increased use of water resources where rainfall is low may increase the risk of economic losses through droughts. In the semi-dry areas of Africa, animal husbandry is often the main, and frequently the only possible, economic activity. In many areas the production of meat is at present restricted by the limited number of water points, besides of course by the unwillingness of cattle owners to sell. This unwillingness is not always without reason: experience with periods of drought has taught owners to keep as large a herd as possible in order to make sure that at least some animals will survive. A larger number of well-distributed water points will increase the area on which cattle can be kept, but cannot much increase the total number of cattle kept, unless certain other far-reaching measures are taken. During periods of drought, it is often not so much the availability of water as the availability of grass and fodder that becomes the determining factor for the survival of cattle. Droughts will occur in the future and unless the land is undergrazed during normal and wet years, serious reduction of the herd should be expected from time to time. This aspect should be taken into account when evaluation is made of the construction of water points and other investments required for the further development of a cattle industry.

The great amount of evaporation from open water surfaces calls for special attention. A high ratio between storage capacity and reservoir surface will reduce losses, and this means that reservoirs should be deep, and they should be situated in that part of the river basin where evaporation is minimal. This is often in the headwater area where the climate is cooler and the number of rainy days, and consequently the number with high humidity, is greater than further down the valley. The rainfall on the reservoir surface will partly offset the evaporation. This principle means in some cases that it might be advantageous for a country to have its storage reservoirs outside its borders in the headwater area of the river, i.e. in a neighbouring country. This calls for deep and mutual trust between neighbours.

Physical planning of the development of water resources should take into account the river basin as a hydrographic unit. This is a sheer physical necessity, as conservation of water and land resources in one part of the basin often affects the possible use of these resources further downstream. This necessity has important consequences for Africa, which has 48 river basins which extend over more than one country. Many of them include parts of three countries or more. Together they cover a surface of 13,300,000 sq. km., or 44 per cent of the total area of the African continent. International co-operation thus becomes a prerequisite for the planning of the development of these basins. Fortunately, this is increasingly being appreciated by many governments. Recently treaties relating to the international co-ordination of river basin development have been concluded by the interested governments in respect of the Senegal, the Niger and the Chad basin, and river basin commissions have been set up. A foundation has thus been created for a rational and economic development of these river basins.

SUMMARY

With the exception of the north coast and the southernmost part, the total surface of the continent of Africa lies within the influence of the low-latitude easterlies. Over most parts of Africa, the amount of annual precipitation is closely related to the number of disturbances associated with the waves in the easterlies and this explains the observed large annual variation of rainfall. The rainfall regime of various parts of Africa is discussed.

There is a certain tendency for years with abundant rain and years with less than average rainfall to occur in groups. Examples are given. This phenomenon, together with the seasonal character of rainfall, makes the regularization of the availability of water most important. The rôle played in this respect by the natural lakes and swamps and by ground-water is discussed. There are physical limits to the possibilities of inter-annual regularization by the construction of dams and reservoirs.

Greater use of water could increase the vulnerability of the economy to periods of droughts. Water should in the first place be developed where it is plentiful, because short-term climatic fluctuations in these areas will have relatively less effect than in those regions where water is scarce. The availability of water affects land use and *vice versa*. Land-use planning should therefore also take into account the natural or potential rôle of the land in the hydrological cycle. Because of the effect that land and water development in one part of a river basin has on the potential development of these resources in other parts, planning of the use of these resources should be basin-wide. The large number of rivers in Africa which cross international borders shows how essential international co-operation is in this field.

DISCUSSION

Young: I have heard it said that for the prevention of erosion it is more important to hold back water in the upper parts of river basins than to build big dams further down. Is that an accepted view?

Dekker: If possible, the upper parts of a basin should be used for storage, but not all the water can be stored there, and I think both parts should be used. Two factors have to be considered: if average rainfall is low the run-off during the wet season should be decreased as much as possible, and the infiltration of the rain made as high as possible, so that some ground-water is available during the dry season. If this is done, erosion will be fought at the same time. Of course, if all storage is in surface reservoirs further downstream, then the use that could have been made of the water in the upper part of the basin is not being taken into account. On the other hand, I feel that the possibility of storage by conservation only is very limited.

Last: Another factor is the land use in the upper basin. Would you agree with the general principle that in the upper parts of the river basin projects which make minimum demands on water should be developed, so that the water use is spread over the whole basin? For example, the development of plantations and irrigation schemes in the upper part of the basin enormously increases evaporation and reduces the flow downstream. Is it not possible, for example, that the development of irrigation schemes in the middle Awash river valley in Ethiopia may in the long run create difficulties for the full development of the lower part of the basin?

Dekker: I think that the main criterion should be the economic return on using water in the upper part of the river basin, compared with its use in the lower part of the basin.

Mancini: Do you mean that you might not use the water in the upper part of the basin at all? What do you mean by economic criteria?

Dekker: If you use the rainfall in the upper part of the basin, for example in plantations, you will reduce the available quantity of water in the lower part of the valley. Wherever it is used, a certain investment of money is required. Mr. Last asked if I believed the management of land in the upper part of the valley should be such that sufficient water is available in the lower part of the valley. My reply is that in the final analysis, the water should be used in such a way as to make it give an economic return as high as possible.

Mancini: Are there certain plantations that need less water so that a bigger amount can go down, in addition to your economic return on the timber?

Dekker: One has a certain field of choice; but if you want a crop in the lower part of the valley, you need plenty of water, and if you also want to grow something in the upper part of the valley, you may find that the supply fails both.

Acock: Can the lessons learned in other continents be applied to Africa in regard to the prevention of erosion? I think you referred to erosion as being higher in Africa than in other regions. What makes it higher?

Dekker: Potentially erosion is higher in Africa than in other continents, as calculated by Fournier[18] some years ago. The erodibility of all the other continents is much higher than in Europe. The United States has a slightly higher level of erodibility than Latin America; erodibility is certainly higher in Asia. The report does not say that so much erosion is actually going on in the continent. It indicates that we have to be careful.

Africa is one of the hottest continents—it is very wide across the equator, which partly explains why it is so hot. Evaporation is probably higher here than anywhere else. It is an unfortunate fact which has to be taken into account. When evapo-transpiration is higher, more water is needed to reach the same crop production as, for example, in Europe, where a mean rainfall of 1,000 mm. is plenty.

Young: Is there any significant difference with different crops in the transpiration loss through leaves? How does maize compare with a tree such as eucalyptus?

Dekker: Eucalyptus has a higher transpiration than maize. Not only is the total leaf surface larger, but its growing season is longer than that of maize.

Last: We have for a number of years informed students that reafforestation and afforestation are a major step to be taken in the conservation of natural resources. Yet now there seems to be more than a suggestion that trees are not always the best answer to the problem. In fact by planting trees one may reduce the amount of water available. Also it is clear that afforestation has to be done carefully because natural resources may be affected in other ways; a clear example is to be found here in Ethiopia where very closely planted eucalyptus has in many areas resulted in an increase in erosion, simply because nothing grows underneath these trees, and sheet erosion takes place on a large scale. It is important that we should get a correct outlook for the future on the true significance of afforestation.

Secondly, Mr. Dekker says that where we have a choice, we should develop water resources where they are plentiful, rather than where they are scarce; and yet, earlier in his paper, he gave us some figures on the distribution of population in relation to arid and semi-arid areas. In general it seems that a very high proportion of the population of Africa lives in the areas where water is scarce. If economic advance and a rise in living standards are required, then there may be some conflict between this and Mr. Dekker's general principle of developing only where there is plenty of water, if this is going to leave a very high proportion of the population untouched.

Dekker: I think the idea of saying that all forestry is good was based on the necessity of preventing erosion. If there is no vegetation cover at all, the rainfall will wash off soil with the result that there is no infiltration any more, no ground-water will flow in the dry season, and all the rainfall which comes down runs off immediately. To prevent this, one has to prevent erosion, and reafforestation is a way to prevent erosion; but vegetation is the basic idea and one can make a choice—bamboo, normal tropical product, tree plantation, short grass cover, or long grass cover. The main point is protection against erosion. Forestry is not necessarily the right answer. In the given climatic and zoological conditions one looks for the cover which is most efficient.

Regarding the distribution of population, I observed that one should develop water where it is, and although there may not be very much rainfall in some places, such as Egypt, this certainly does not necessarily mean there is no water.

There are other places in Africa without very much rainfall but with plenty of water—the Chad, Niger and Senegal rivers.

In East Africa where there is good soil and plenty of water, there is not always sufficient population. But in a country such as Mali, where funds are limited, my suggestion is that it would be preferable to start developing where there is good soil and water, and if necessary bring the population there, instead of developing a place where there are plenty of people but which lacks plentiful water and good soil.

Mesfin: Are not trees important factors for soil formation in the long run, and the most important economic possibility where there is very little soil?

Gille: On the plateau of Ethiopia, the climatic climax is constituted by forests. For instance, the climatic climax of the semi-humid upper highland forest, to which the surroundings of Addis Ababa are related, is represented by the juniperus forest. *Juniperus procera* is an evergreen tree, about 30 to 40 metres high, which grows very slowly. Most of them were destroyed during the past century. Some relics, about two or three metres in diameter and 400 years old can, however, still be seen near Addis Ababa in the Menagasha National Park. The destruction led to heavy erosion of the soil of the region. Some 30 to 40 years ago eucalyptus trees, which grow rapidly, were introduced to replace the juniperus forest. As Mr. Last has described, it is impossible for shrubs to grow under the eucalyptus and the soil is not, therefore, completely covered. One must be very careful when introducing new species in a different environment. Results can be beneficial, but they can also be detrimental.

Lambo: Mr. Dekker said that there were 48 international river basins in Africa and observed that international co-operation was extremely important for their development. Is there any international charter or resolution with regard to the development of such rivers, for example the Nile?

Dekker: There are treaties on the Nile between Sudan and U.A.R.; there are international conventions on the Niger river and on the Chad basin, which are different from the Nile treaties. The Nile treaties between Sudan and U.A.R. relate to the distribution of the available water. The treaties recently concluded on the Senegal and Lake Chad basins refer to co-ordination and co-operation between the governments concerned to start developing the valleys. I think it is mainly a question of treaty law—there is no internationally recognized principle which is generally accepted.

Lambo: In terms of development, could anybody get hold of —or claim—the source of any particular river, and have the undisputed use of its water?

Dekker: In international negotiations on this subject, the existing use at the time of negotiation is very often of great importance.

Mustafa: A certain part of international law deals with international rivers, and the rules laid down would apply where there is no treaty to the contrary. The states along a river can change these rules or modify them by treaty, but if they do not do so, then these rules are automatically applied.

Michaelis: Underground water resources were discovered some time ago in the Sahara. Are they capable of development on a large scale? Are they likely to provide water supplies on a continental scale?

Dekker: It appears that there is a considerable amount of water; unfortunately there are no people in the heart of the Sahara, though the water will be useful for oil companies and so on. It is only in the northern part, in Algeria, Egypt and Morocco, that a number of people are living.

Michaelis: In prehistoric times there were human settlements in what is now the Sahara Desert, and there should be the chance to use the underground water again to reconstruct such settlements.

Dekker: People need water but they also need good soils, and a market for their products. I think that very good soils and a lot of water are available in other parts of Africa where at present people only keep cattle.

Monod: This question of the ground-water in the Sahara is very interesting, but mention must be made of the problem of whether ground-water is only storage water, that is, not renewable water, or whether it is still replenished from outside regions.

I should like to draw attention to two relevant publications, the "Climatological Atlas for Africa"[19] and the I.U.C.N. meeting on the ecology of man in a tropical environment[20], in which great emphasis is put on water problems. Dr. L. S. B. Leakey says, for instance (p. 28): "Underground water in much of tropical Africa, such as Kenya and Tanganyika, is often non-potable for various reasons, but there is plenty of it. Surely conservationists could call upon sufficient colleagues in other sciences to find not merely ways, but economic ways, of turning water which is not fit for animal and human consumption into water that is fit for that purpose. Surely we can find ways, not merely expensive ways but economic ways, of turning the water of our oceans, of our salt oceans, to water that is usable along the whole coastal belts, so that we do not have to take vast amounts of fresh water from inland to feed the population at the coast".

Dekker: I think Dr. Leakey was talking about the fluoride content of the water in East Africa, which very often spoils it, and makes it unfit for human consumption.

Monod: I should like to hear you speak further of the variations in the climate. In fact there has been no sign of real climatic changes (as distinct from mere fluctuations) for at least 2,000 years; to see a real sign of climatic variation one has to go back to the post-pluvial optimum which is in the Neolithic Age, i.e. something like four to six thousand years ago.

And a minor point about the minimum rainfall on the west coast—the Accra, Togo, Dahomey savannah gap: I know the orientation of the coast, more or less parallel to the monsoon winds, has been taken into account, but there is another explanation which could be related to the rather low temperatures of the sea, which are due to the upwellings extremely noticeable on these coasts.

My final word is about the maximum rainfall at the base of the Cameroon mountains, at a small place called Debuntsha which has had more than 10 metres' annual rainfall—in fact it is a world record except for the Tcherapundjee record. Even a small village on the south coast of Fernando Póo island has 10 metres' rainfall in the year.

Dekker: Yes, I am sorry I couldn't go through all the questions of climatic variations in my paper, but I did include a table of the most important variations during the geological past, together with some more recent short-term fluctuations, as far as we know them.

Howard-Goldsmith: Mr. Last in his opening paper gave us the impression that there is an enormous hydroelectric potential in Africa and he especially referred to the Congo river as being the greatest untapped reserve, whereas you have now pointed out geological conditions which do not lend themselves to dam construction. On the one hand, we have this huge hydroelectric potential; on the other hand, we can't use it. If conditions are really unfavourable, then why call it a potential? Would you clarify that point?

Dekker: Africa is potentially very rich in hydroelectric power, but this idea is based on theoretical computations which take into account an average run-off. This principle is not valid in many parts of Africa, where the number of potential dam sites is limited. It is perhaps permissible in the Congo because, of all the rivers in Africa, the Congo has one of the most regular flows: at a certain time of the year rain is coming off the northern part of the basin, at another time of the year off the southern part, and in the middle zone of the Congo there is a very regular flow. So in the Congo, although there are still not many possibilities for the construction of storage dams, the water available and the regular flow will give a high output.

Wolstenholme: Do seasons of inadequacy of the Indian monsoons coincide in any way with periods of drought on the African continent? In other words, do famine periods in India coincide with difficult periods for agricultural productivity in Africa, or might it possibly be the reverse?

Dekker: I have no opinion on this.

3

PROBLEMS OF POPULATION SIZE, GROWTH AND DISTRIBUTION IN AFRICA

JEAN BOURGEOIS-PICHAT

U NTIL world war II, few attempts had been made to enumerate population in Africa. At that time sample surveys were almost non-existent and data were obtained through censuses. Only four countries had a relatively long tradition of census-taking, namely Algeria, Egypt, Tunisia and the Union of South Africa. Of course, small territories like the island of Mauritius had had censuses since 1851 but the populations of these territories were of negligible size in comparison with the population of the whole continent. Table I gives a summary of census-taking history in Africa before world war II, together with the corresponding size of the population in 1962. It shows that before world war II 31 per cent of the estimated population of Africa had been enumerated. Of course, the accuracy of the results varied from country to country.

ENUMERATION OF POPULATION SINCE WORLD WAR II

After world war II, the situation improved rapidly and today, through censuses, sample surveys and partial counts, data have been obtained for 91 per cent of the estimated total. Fig. 1, which refers to the year 1962, gives the state of our present knowledge of African populations. On this map, censuses and sample surveys have been divided into two broad categories: recent and old. A census or a sample survey has been considered as recent if it was taken not earlier than 1959. Ethiopia, Mauritania, and Somalia were the only countries for which

3

65

conjectural estimates had to be made. Table II gives the African population in 1962, distributed according to the six categories of Fig. 1 Comparison with Table I shows clearly the improvement which has occurred since world war II. Of course, the situation

Table I

CENSUSES OF POPULATION IN AFRICA BEFORE WORLD WAR II

Countries	Year of First census	Last census	Number of censuses	Population in 1962 (thousands)
Algeria	1896	1936	10	11,300
Angola	1940		1	4,936
Basutoland	1904	1936	4	713
Bechuanaland	1911	1936	3	335
Cameroon (British Adminis-tration)	1921	1931	2	1,340*
Egypt	1882	1937	6	27,285
Gambia	1901	1931	4	306
Libya	1931	1936	2	1,244
Mauritius	1851	1931	10	682
Mozambique	1928	1940	2	6,750
Portuguese Guinea	1940		1	549
Somaliland (Italian)	1931		1	1,960*
Spanish Guinea	1920	1932	2	253
Swaziland	1904	1936	4	275
Tunisia	1911	1936	5	4,290
Union of South Africa	1904	1936	4	16,640
Total				78,858
TOTAL AFRICA				269,424

* Estimate.
Sources: *Demographic Yearbook* (*United Nations*, 1955, 1963).[1, 2]

is changing continually but Table II gives a fairly good idea of what has been done and of what remains to be done.

It is interesting to compare the population of Africa as a whole with that of other large territories of the world. The populations of Africa, North America, and the U.S.S.R. are of the same order of magnitude, being respectively 269, 277 and 221 million. The European population of 434 million is 60 per cent more than the

African population, while Asia is six times larger at 1,764 million; South America and Oceania are smaller: 153 and 17 million. These data, which refer to 1962, are summarized in Table III.

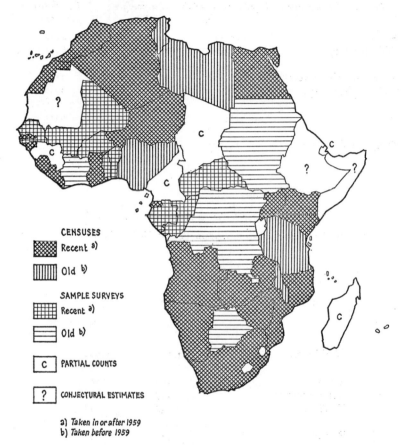

CENSUSES
Recent ª)
Old b)

SAMPLE SURVEYS
Recent ª)
Old b)

C   PARTIAL COUNTS

?   CONJECTURAL ESTIMATES

a) *Taken in or after 1959*
b) *Taken before 1959*

Fig. 1. Population in Africa in 1962 according to the processes of enumeration.

DENSITY OF POPULATION IN AFRICA

The 269 million people living in Africa are unequally distributed through the continent. First, there are concentrations along the coasts on the north of the continent along the

67

Table II

POPULATION IN AFRICA IN 1962 ACCORDING TO THE PROCESSES OF ENUMERATION

Processes of enumeration	Population (1962) (thousands)	Percentages	Cumulative percentages
Recent censuses†	118,415	44·0	44·0
Old censuses‡	57,441	21·3	65·3
Recent sample surveys†	16,808	6·2	71·5
Old sample surveys‡	36,357	13·5	85·0
Partial counts	16,373	6·1	91·1
Conjectural estimates	24,030	8·9	100·0
TOTAL	269,424	100·0	

† Taken in or after 1959.
‡ Taken before 1959.
Sources: *Demographic Yearbook* (*United Nations*, 1963).[2]

Population and vital statistics report. (United Nations Publication).[3]

Table III

WORLD POPULATION IN 1962 BY TERRITORIES

	Millions	Distribution per
World total	3,135	1,000
Africa	269	86
North America	277	88
U.S.S.R.	221	71
Europe	434	138
Asia	1,764	563
South America	153	49
Oceania	17	5

Sources: *Demographic Yearbook* (*United Nations*, 1963).[2]

Mediterranean, on the west along the Atlantic ocean and on the east mainly below the equator, along the Indian ocean, including the east coast of Madagascar. Apart from these coastal concentrations, there are four other zones of high density:

(a) Three areas in Nigeria.

(b) A zone of very high density in Burundi and Rwanda, followed eastwards in Uganda and North Kenya by a zone of relatively high density.

(c) A concentration of population in a region of the Republic of South Africa centred around the capital (Pretoria).

(d) Finally, concentrations of extraordinarily high density along the Nile river, mainly in the delta.

All these regions of high density represent only 5 per cent of the total area and 31·6 per cent of the total population.

At the opposite extreme, there are huge territories representing almost empty lands. Some are deserts unfit for human settlement but some would be suitable for the development of large populations. In between, there are sparsely populated lands. Fig. 2 illustrates this sketchy description and Table IV gives some figures on the population density of the various zones.

In the zone marked by checked lines in Fig. 2, the density is comparable to that in many zones in Europe and North America. Territories included in this zone seem therefore ready for economic development, at least from the point of view of number of people needed to organize a market economy. The dotted zone, and even more so the white zone, suffer from having populations too small for rapid economic development, except for certain areas around big cities.

URBANIZATION IN AFRICA

Urbanization is another aspect of population distribution. Cities of 200,000 inhabitants or more in 1962 have been marked on Fig. 2. Most of them are in the high density zones, and they represent 14·1 per cent of the total population of these zones. If these cities are left out of account the remaining area still has a relatively high density (48·7 inhabitants per square kilometre) which is comparable to the density of rural areas in Europe.

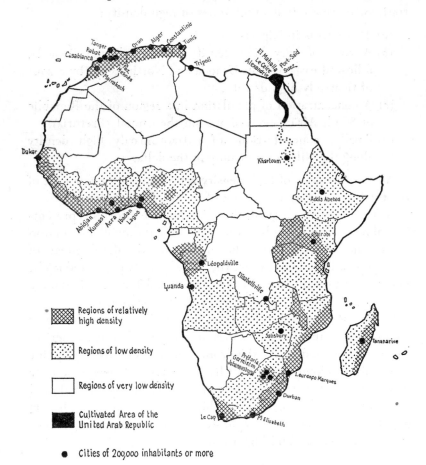

Fig. 2. Population density in Africa in 1962 (see also Table IV).

The few big cities which exist in the low density zones represent the exception referred to above when the suitability of these two types of zone for economic development was mentioned.

The Nile valley and the delta deserve a special comment. Densities here are the highest in the world, even if big cities are left out of account.

To summarize, there were in 1962 19·8 million people in Africa living in cities of 200,000 inhabitants or more. This represents only 7·4 per cent of the total, and the African population does not appear highly urbanized in comparison with the

Table IV

POPULATION DENSITY IN AFRICA IN 1962 (SEE ALSO FIG. 2)

Regions	Areas (square km.)	Population (millions)	Inhabitants per square km.
Regions of relatively high density	1,500,000	85 (12·0)†	56·7 (48·7)‡
Regions of low density	10,865,000	115 (1·3)†	10·6
Regions of very low density	17,900,000	42 (0·4)†	2·4
Cultivated area of the United Arab Republic	35,000	27 (6·1)†	771·0
TOTAL	30,300,000	269 (19·8)†	8·9

† Population in cities of 200,000 inhabitants or more.
‡ Density when cities of 200,000 inhabitants or more are excluded.

other continents. But this is a provisional situation. Migration from rural to urban areas is a feature of the demographic situation in the African continent today.

It follows from this low level of urbanization that most of the working population in Africa are engaged in agricultural activities. Unfortunately, few data are available on the economic activities of people in Africa. Nevertheless, Table V shows clearly that Africa is still at the beginning of the process of industrialization.

CHANGES IN POPULATION SIZE

However interesting it may be to have a view of the African population at a given time, it is essential to know what forces are at work which may cause the situation to change.

Table V

PERCENTAGE DISTRIBUTION OF THE MALE ECONOMICALLY ACTIVE POPULATION BY SECTORS IN SOME TYPICAL CONDITIONS AND IN SOME AFRICAN COUNTRIES

Sectors*	Less† developed countries	Countries‡ at an intermediate level of development	Highly§ developed countries	Algeria (Moslems) 1954	Ghana 1960	Morocco (indigenous) 1952	Tunisia 1956	United Arab Republic 1960
Primary	70	38	20	84	67	67	70	59
Secondary	13	28	44	7	15	10	11	12
Tertiary	17	34	35	9	18	23	19	29
All activities	100	100	100	100	100	100	100	100

* Types of occupation—Primary: Mining, agriculture and related activity.
Secondary: Manufacturing, construction, electricity and gas.
Tertiary: Commerce, transport and communications and services.
† 29 countries in Africa, Asia and Latin America.
‡ 8 countries (1 in Asia and 7 in Latin America).
§ 11 countries (2 in North America, 7 in Europe, 2 in Oceania).
Sources: Data provided by the Population Branch of the United Nations.

For many years it was considered that most of the African population, at least the population south of the Sahara, did not increase very much, and the estimates were kept constant for long periods of time. This is no longer the case and the general consensus now is that all African countries are increasing their numbers at a rate comparable to that in other developing countries, which means at an accelerating rate.

We will first consider the natural components of population variations, namely natality and mortality.

CRUDE BIRTH RATES IN AFRICA

Fig. 3 gives the crude birth rates, estimated around 1960, in almost all African countries. Before I comment on this map, I should point out that data on fertility, mortality and migration in Africa are very far from being complete. Efforts so far have been mainly concerned with improving the population count. This means that for measuring population variations one has to rely on estimates obtained through sample surveys or through indirect methods using all the resources of demographic analysis. Maps such as Fig. 2 have therefore to be interpreted with caution.

Nevertheless it appears from Fig. 3 that crude birth rates are high everywhere in Africa, but particularly in the north of the sub-Saharan region where values are close to the maximum ever recorded for the human species. A zone with a relatively low birth rate appears below the equator. But all these findings have to be confirmed by more detailed analysis and new data.

Crude birth rates such as those shown in Fig. 3 suggest that in Africa birth control is not being practised, whatever social restrictions may be operative. Of course the crude birth rate is the end result of a complex interaction of factors involving biology, sociology, psychology and so on. It is essential to go a little further into this field of complex inter-relationships if one wants to gauge what the future trends in the size of the African population might be.

STERILITY OF AFRICAN COUPLES

To give birth to a child a woman must first be fertile. At the beginning of the childbearing period, around 15 years, most of the women are fertile. At the end of the childbearing period,

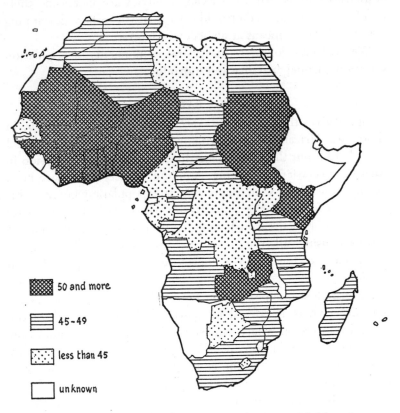

Fig. 3. Estimates of crude birth rate in 1962 (per 1,000 inhabitants).

around 45, they are all sterile. From 15 to 45, sterility is therefore increasing. It is possible to study the progression of sterility with age in a population by using data on women 45 years and over classified according to the number of children ever born. These statistics tell us, for example, that out of 100 women having had a third child, only perhaps 85 have had a fourth child. This means that 15 per cent of couples became essentially sterile during the mean interval between the third and the fourth child. This is true of course only in populations which do not practise birth control, which is the case here. As the mean age of mothers at the birth of a child of a given parity is always more or less the same, and also the mean interval between births, it is possible to transform the probabilities of becoming sterile between two successive births into probabilities of becoming sterile at a given age during, let us say, one year. One then obtains a table comparable to a mortality table which gives at a given age the probability of dying during the next year.

When such calculations are made for all the countries of the world for which data are available, it is possible to define several characteristic patterns of progression of sterility with the age of the women. The variations appear to be quite large. Table VI gives an idea of these variations.

In the last line of the second part of this table, one finds for the various patterns of sterility *the expectation of fertile life* for a woman at the beginning of the childbearing period. It is calculated in exactly the same manner as the expectation of life given in mortality tables. The lowest sterility ever observed in the world was that of French Canadians during the eighteenth century. The expectation of fertile life for a girl 15 years old was 29 years. The highest sterility corresponds to data collected in the Portuguese territories in Africa, where the expectation of fertile life for a 15-year-old girl is only 13·4 years. An intermediary pattern corresponds to data collected in a sample survey in Guinea, where the expectation of fertile life is 17 years. Next comes North Africa with 21·6, and then Europe before the birth control era, with 25·1 years.

To summarize, according to the few data available for Africa, it seems that African countries south of the Sahara, and particularly below the equator, are characterized by a very rapid progression of sterility with the age of the woman. In North African

Table VI

SOME DATA ON STERILITY OF HUMAN SPECIES

(A) Probabilities (per cent) of becoming sterile between successive births for some typical regions and some African countries

Order of birth	Typical patterns†					Observed data†					
	French Canadian (18th century)	Europe before birth control	North Africa	Africa south of Sahara and above the equator	Africa below the equator	Egypt 1948	Senegal 1960	Guinea 1953	Mozambique 1950	Angola 1957	Portuguese Guinea 1950
0	1·0	2·5	2·0	5·6	10·5	8·0	5·6	5·2	13·9	11·9	8·0
1	1·2	3·0	3·2	8·0	14·1	4·6	6·8	6·9	10·3	9·6	11·4
2	1·5	3·5	5·1	10·6	18·3	6·6	8·9	7·5	14·4	13·3	21·0
3	2·0	4·3	7·5	15·4	23·0	8·6	12·1	11·5	18·0	16·4	30·7
4	2·7	5·5	10·8	20·1	29·0	11·6	15·3	14·5	23·2	22·0	36·9
5	4·0	7·0	16·0	26·5	36·0	16·5	20·8	19·6	29·8	27·4	45·9
6	5·7	9·3	21·0	34·0	45·0			23·8			
7	8·9	12·3	28·0	42·0	50·5			32·3			
8	13·0	17·0	36·0	52·0	60·0	36·0	23·5	38·3	42·0	43·0	54·0

(B) Sterility tables: Percentages of fertile couples by age groups of women for five patterns of sterility

Age groups (in years)	French Canadian (18th century)	Europe before birth control	North Africa	Black Africa south of Sahara and above the equator	Black Africa below the equator
15–19	99·3	98·1	99·3	97·6	94·0
20–24	97·5	93·5	96·1	88·5	77·4
25–29	94·9	87·5	88·3	72·8	54·3
30–34	91·4	79·1	72·9	49·2	29·7
35–39	82·7	66·8	48·3	23·9	10·4
40–44	65·5	48·6	22·3	6·7	2·0
45–49	37·2	24·4	4·8	0·7	0·3
50–54	6·4	3·9	0·2	0·0	0·0
55–59	5·9	0·0	0·0	0·0	0·0
Expectation of fertile life at 15 years (in years)	29·0	25·1	21·6	17·0	13·4

† The typical patterns have been obtained by adjustment of observed data published in various issues of the Demographic Yearbook of the United Nations. The observed data given in this table are only part of the data used for the adjustment.

77

countries, sterility is not so high, but is however higher than in Europe.

ABILITY OF FERTILE COUPLES TO PROCREATE

The second component of the level of fertility is the ability of fertile women to procreate. This ability depends on many factors, such as the length of the temporary sterile period following each birth, the conception delay and the proportion of conceptions ending in miscarriage.

The temporary sterile period depends partly on breast feeding but also on sexual taboos. The conception delay depends on the frequency of sexual relations and the duration of the life of the ovum in the genital tract of the woman. Miscarriage depends on the health of the woman and also on the way of life. The ability of fertile women to procreate is therefore the result of a complex interaction of various biological and social factors. It does not seem that Africa differs in that respect from other countries not practising birth control.

In the second column of Table VIII fertility rates for fertile women not practising birth control are given. They can be considered as characterizing the developing countries. By multiplying these rates by the proportion of fertile women corresponding to the various patterns of sterility, one obtains the fertility rate of women engaged in reproductive activity, i.e. women who are called "married" in the vocabulary of census-taking. Table VIII gives an example of such a calculation in using the sterility pattern characterizing black Africa, south of the Sahara and above the equator. To obtain the fertility rate of all women whether or not they are engaged in reproductive activity, a third component has to be taken into account: marriage.

MARRIAGE IN AFRICA

Marriage is found in every society. Its meaning may not be the same everywhere but it seems that it is possible to admit that, in any census of the population, women who declare they are married are really engaged in reproductive activity.

Table VII

NUPTIALITY PATTERN IN AFRICA: PERCENTAGES OF MARRIED WOMEN BY AGE GROUPS

(A) North Africa

Age groups (years)	Algeria (Moslems) 1948	Egypt 1937	Egypt 1947	United Arab Republic 1960	Tunisia 1946	Tunisia 1956	Morocco 1960	Proposed pattern for North Africa
15–19	31·4	23·6	24·2	31·3	27·0	29·3	49·1	30
20–24	71·7	83·1	73·2	73·2	66·7	73·2	85·9	75
25–29	83·3		87·2	88·7	81·0	88·1	91·0	88
30–34	85·4	88·0	87·6	89·7	84·8	89·6	90·1	88
35–39	83·1		86·7	88·8	83·5	87·1	86·0	86
40–44	75·9	74·0	74·3	79·2	79·6	82·0	76·9	78
45–49	65·7		72·7	75·8	73·3	71·3	67·5	70
50–54	50·6	50·7†	54·9	54·9	62·8	62·0	51·8	50

(B) Black Africa

Age groups (years)	Portuguese Guinea 1950	Senegal 1960–61	Togo 1958–60	Congo (Leopoldville) 1955–57	Guinea 1955	Proposed pattern for Black Africa
15–19	43·9	60·1	52·0	45·2	80·7	60
20–24	87·5	84·3	92·6	85·2	96·4	92
25–29	94·3	93·3	95·8	91·2	96·4	95
30–34	95·1	93·8	94·5	90·8	95·9	95
35–39	94·7	94·1	91·8	85·8	94·2	95
40–44	92·3	86·9	84·3		90·8	87
45–49	86·7	83·1	76·6	67·5	82·8	83
50–54	75·3	70·6	65·7		71·8	70

† For the age group 50–55.

The entry into and the departure from reproductive activity are the result of many factors: *social factors* ruling the formation and the breakdown of the unions, the customs concerning remarriage of widows, and also *biological factors* affecting mortality. It follows that the pattern of development of the conjugal life of women varies from one country to another. In exactly the same way as we have determined sterility patterns characterizing certain populations, it is possible to define nuptiality patterns. Table VII shows how it can be done by using census data available for two areas, North Africa and Africa south of the Sahara. Table VII shows clearly two different patterns for the two areas. Marriages are more frequent among Africans south of the Sahara than in North Africa.

CONCLUSIONS REGARDING FERTILITY IN AFRICA

Finally, fertility rates for all women are obtained by multiplying the fertility rates of married women by the percentage of married women given in Table VII.

Table VIII gives the details of the calculation for the following combinations:

I Pattern of sterility: Black Africa between the Sahara and the equator.
Pattern of nuptiality: Africa south of the Sahara.

Other calculations not shown here in detail have been made for two other combinations:

II Pattern of sterility: Black Africa south of the equator.
Pattern of nuptiality: Africa south of the Sahara.
III Pattern of sterility: North Africa.
Pattern of nuptiality: North Africa.

The first combination corresponding to Table VIII gives a crude birth rate of 50 per thousand, which is quite in agreement with the rate shown in Fig. 3 for black Africa south of the Sahara and above the equator. The second combination gives a crude birth rate of 40 per thousand, which is in close agreement with the

Table VIII

COMPONENTS OF FERTILITY IN BLACK AFRICA SOUTH OF THE SAHARA AND ABOVE EQUATOR

Age groups (years)	Fertility rates of fertile women (per 1,000)	Sterility† pattern Black Africa south of Sahara and above equator	Fertility‡ rates of married women (per 1,000)	Nuptiality§ pattern for Black Africa	Fertility‖ rate of all women (per 1,000)
15–19	489·6	0·976	477·9	0·60	286·8
20–24	491·1	0·885	434·6	0·92	399·9
25–29	484·4	0·728	352·7	0·95	335·2
30–34	471·6	0·492	232·1	0·95	220·5
35–39	458·5	0·239	109·6	0·95	104·1
40–44	444·2	0·067	29·8	0·87	25·9
45–49	424·4	0·007	3·0	0·83	2·5

Sum of the rates   1,374·9
Multiplied by 5   6,874·5
Divided by 2·05   3,353
Gross reproduction rate   3·353
Approximate crude birth rate (per 1,000)   50

† Data taken from Table VI.
‡ Product of the two preceding columns.
§ Data taken from Table VII.
‖ Product of the two preceding columns.

rate given in Fig. 3 for black Africa below the equator. The third combination gives a crude birth rate of 50 per thousand which is close to the rate given in Fig. 3 for North Africa.

We now understand a little better the differences appearing in Fig. 3 but we are in no better position to make any forecasts: the evolution which is taking place in Africa may have all kinds of effects on the various factors mentioned. Urbanization, for example, may modify the nuptiality pattern of black Africa by reducing the proportion of married women and thus reducing the crude birth rate. But urbanization because of its tendency to suppress breast feeding may also shorten the temporary sterile period following each birth and thus increase the crude birth rate. The cause of the high sterility rate in Africa is also a problem. Is it due to poor health conditions? In that case, improvement of these conditions will increase the proportion of fertile women and hence the crude birth rate.

Anything seems possible and that is probably why demographers generally adopt the assumption that fertility will remain constant, at least in the near future. I have no better choice to offer you. My only purpose has been to show that this is a complex problem to be solved only by further research.

MORTALITY IN AFRICA

Let us turn now to the other component of population variations: mortality. Here we know the trend: mortality is decreasing or at least will decrease in the future. Unfortunately we do not know the present level very well. Decreasing mortality is one of the major events which has occurred so far in the evolution of the human species. For thousands of years the development of mankind was hampered by the heavy toll to be paid to death. An expectation of life at birth of between 25 and 30 years, which corresponds to a crude death rate of 35 to 40 per thousand, was considered normal. Mortality began to decrease approximately two hundred years ago in industrialized countries and in two centuries the expectation of life at birth has increased in these countries from 30 to almost 75 years. In fact, for a long time this decrease in mortality was the result of industrialization and this explains why the developing countries did not participate significantly in the movement until recently. The discovery of new means of action against diseases, relatively cheap and very efficient, opened the way to a decrease in mortality not necessarily linked with economic development, which is now spread all over the world. African countries are participating in the movement but lack of information prevents the extent of the change from being measured.

Fig. 4 gives a summary of our present knowledge of the crude death rate in Africa. The data refer to various years centred around 1960 and sources are varied. Circled data refer to death rates obtained through sample surveys, which generally are not representative of the whole of a territory. Other data refer to recorded deaths, which are known to be seriously under-enumerated. In some cases, both types of information are available and a comparison of registered and estimated death rates gives an idea of the under-registration. It is not uncommon to find that only half of the deaths are registered, and in Portuguese territories maybe only 15 per cent are registered.

It seems however possible to draw some conclusions from these data. In Africa south of the Sahara, mortality appears to be high by comparison with the results obtained so far in other developing countries. A crude death rate of 25 per thousand could be taken as representing the level of mortality in that region in about 1960. The corresponding expectation of life at birth would be between 35 and 40 years. But the situation was certainly improving rapidly and a gain of one year of expectation of life at birth every two calendar years does not seem unrealistic.

In North Africa, Egypt and the Sudan, the situation appears more favourable. A crude death rate of 20 per thousand, which corresponds to 45 years of expectation of life at birth, seems plausible, and here again an increase of one year of expectation of life every two calendar years seems possible.

MIGRATORY MOVEMENTS

And what about the third component of population variations —migration? We have to confess that we know very little about it. We know that migrations take place throughout the African

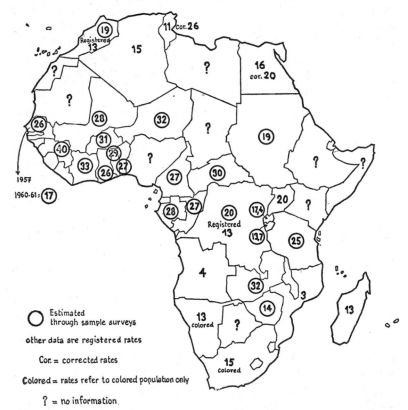

Fig. 4. Crude death rates around 1960 (estimated and registered rates per 1,000 inhabitants).

continent, but I will not dare to give even an estimate of these migratory streams. Migratory movements to and from Africa are not very important, except in some cases such as Algeria, and for Africa as a whole population variations are the result of the natural components, fertility and mortality.

RATE OF GROWTH OF POPULATION

What can be said, therefore, on the rate of growth of the African population? In black Africa between the Sahara and the equator a crude birth rate of 50 per thousand and a crude death rate of 25 per thousand give a rate of growth of 2·5 per cent. In North Africa, the crude birth rate being a little lower than 50 per thousand, a crude death rate of 20 per thousand gives a rate of growth approaching 3 per cent. Below the equator, owing to a much lower crude birth rate, the rate of growth might be a little more than 2 per cent. But these data refer to the year 1960 and because of the decline in mortality, the rate of growth is probably now approaching 3 per cent everywhere in Africa. Such a rate of increase has obvious implications for economic and social development. To conclude, let us review some of them rapidly.

ECONOMIC IMPLICATIONS

Table IX gives the age composition of three populations corresponding to three sets of demographic conditions which can be considered as characterizing three stages of development:

Population A, with high fertility and moderately low mortality, represents Africa today, or at least Africa in the immediate future.

Population B, with high fertility and high mortality, is Africa of the past.

Population C, with low fertility and low mortality, corresponds to the industrialized countries.

There are small differences between the age composition of populations A and B. This shows that the decline in mortality does not very much affect the age composition of the population. This decline produces a slight increase in the proportion of people at both ends of the age pyramid, i.e. young and old people, and therefore a decline in the proportion of people in the active period of life.

85

Table IX

AGE COMPOSITION OF THREE POPULATIONS CORRESPONDING TO THREE TYPICAL SETS OF DEMOGRAPHIC CONDITIONS

	Demographic conditions		
	A	B	C
Gross reproduction rates (%)	3·0	3·0	1·5
Expectation of life at birth (years)	50	30	70
Crude birth rates ⎫	45	48	22
Crude death rates ⎬ per thousand	16	34	9 .
Rates of increase ⎭	29	14	13

	Age distribution *					
Age groups (years):						
0–4	177		165		105	
5–9	145		132		97	
10–14	123	445	117	414	91	
15–19	105		104		85	378
20–24	88		92		79	
25–29	74		79		74	
30–34	62		68		69	
35–39	52		58		64	
40–44	43		48		59	
45–49	35		40		54	
50–54	28		32		49	
55–59	23		24		44	
60–64	17	527	18	563	39	531
65–69	12		12		32	
70–74	8		7		25	
75–79	5		3		18	
80–84	2		1		10	
85 and over	1	28	<0·5	23	6	91
All ages	1,000	1,000	1,000	1,000	1,000	1,000

A, B and C: see text.

* Age distribution (per thousand) of populations in which the demographic conditions described at the top of the table are kept constant.

The decline in mortality, however, has an important bearing on the rate of growth of the population. Population A increases twice as much as population B.

The decline in fertility produces an effect on both the age structure and the rate of growth. Population C is much older than population A or B at both ends of the pyramid, i.e. has in proportion fewer young people and more old people. Even if one extends the limit of the inactive young to 19 years the burden of the young people is lighter in population C than in population A. The problem of the aged people, almost negligible in populations A and B, becomes important in population C. Finally the rate of growth of population C is approximately the same as the rate of growth of population B. The effect of the decline in mortality is compensated almost exactly by the effect of the decline in fertility.

An estimate of the various components of the school problems in the three populations, as given in Table X, will assist us to understand how these modifications of age structure and rates of growth affect each other.

The case of a city of 40,000 inhabitants is considered in the three populations, and the school population is defined as formed by the children 5 to 14 years old. In populations A and B the size of the school population is of the same order of magnitude, around 10,000 pupils, whereas in population C there are only 7,500 pupils. This is due to the fact that populations A and B have more or less the same age composition, and this is much younger than population C.

Problems of welcoming the new pupils and orienting those who leave the school are not very different in populations A and B, and even in population C. Differences arise over the problem of finding places for the new pupils. In population B, i.e. in Africa of yesterday, the difference between numbers of the entering and departing pupils was 232. But it happened that 93 pupils died during the year so that new premises had to be built for only 139 pupils. In population A, i.e. in Africa of today, the difference between the entering and departing pupils was much higher, 349 instead of 232, and there were only 37 deaths. Finally it is necessary to build new premises for 312 pupils instead of 139. The burden is multiplied by 2·25.

Table X

THE SCHOOL PROBLEMS IN THREE POPULATIONS OF 40,000 INHABITANTS CORRESPONDING TO THREE SETS OF TYPICAL DEMOGRAPHIC CONDITIONS

Component of school problems	A	B	C	C¹
Total population	40,000	40,000	40,000	40,000
Children 5–14 years (pupils)	10,720	9,960	7,520	
Children 5–19 years (pupils)				10,920
New pupils at the beginning of the year	1,239	1,114	802	802
Pupils having left school at the end of the preceding year	890	882	700	653
Difference between the two preceding lines	349	232	102	149
Pupils dead during the preceding year	37	93	5	8
Increase in school population	+312	+139	+97	+141
Number of teachers (1 for 20 pupils)	536	498	376	546
Rate of recruitment (% of people reaching 20 years)	3·2	2·7	1·8	2·6
People reaching 20 years	752	780	648	648
New teachers	24	21	11	17
Teachers leaving for retirement	4	3	5	7
Teachers dead during the preceding year	5	11	1	3
Increase in number of teachers	+15	+7	+5	+7

A, B and C correspond to the demographic conditions of Table IX (and see text). C¹ see text.

Let us turn now to the problems related to the teachers. Allowing one teacher for 20 pupils it is easy to calculate the total number of teachers needed in the three populations. Assuming that the teachers are recruited among people reaching 20 years of age and that the age of retirement is 65 years, it is easy to calculate the rate of recruitment required by the age structure of the population. This rate increases in passing from population B to population A, but not tremendously (20 per cent). It is enough to recruit three more teachers each year (24 instead of 21). In population C, the burden of recruitment of teachers is much lower, approximately half of the burden in populations A and B.

As soon as the rates of recruitment required by the age composition are reached, all the problems are solved. The fact that less teachers are dying in population A than in population B is enough to provide the additional teachers needed for the additional pupils. Finally in population B as compared to population A, i.e. Africa of the past and Africa of today, the burden of building new schools is increased by 125 per cent and the burden of recruitment is increased by 20 per cent.

From population A to population C, i.e. from Africa of today to an Africa decreasing its fertility and continuing to lower its mortality, the burden of building new schools would be divided by 3 and the burden of recruiting teachers would be divided by 1·8. This means, however, that the school population is still defined in population C as the population aged 5 to 14 years. It would be more realistic to consider that, in a population corresponding to the demographic conditions of population C, the school population would include the children 5 to 19 years old. This case corresponds to the column marked C¹ in Table X, where the situation would be more or less the same as in population B. In other words, an *Africa of today* which decreased its fertility and continued to decrease its mortality, and at the same time increased the time spent at school, would find more or less the same problems as *Africa of the past*. One big difference, however, would exist: the number of deaths among pupils and teachers would be much lower in population C than in population B.

All these calculations are based on the assumption that what is called the school population is *really* at school. This is not, unfortunately, the case in most African countries, and the task of providing school facilities for all children of school age generally represents a burden much higher than the additional burden brought about by changing demographic conditions.

In some African countries it is necessary to multiply the existing facilities four or even five times. An increase of 3·1 per cent instead of 1·4 per cent in these facilities as a result of changing demographic conditions might appear trivial. It ought to be stressed, however, that this increase is an annual increase which will continue indefinitely, whereas the filling of the gap will occur only once. The two problems are different and solving one does not ease the solution of the other.

The school problem has been chosen here as an example. Many other socioeconomic problems could be studied in the same manner. They will be discussed during this symposium, and it was right, I think, to begin with a broad review of the demographic forces at work in Africa today. These forces and others influence all the problems to be discussed here and it is my hope that I have thrown some light on the way they are acting.

DISCUSSION

Monod: Monsieur Bourgeois-Pichat has drawn our attention to the complexity of the factors influencing fertility. In a recent and most interesting paper[4] Professor Gallais from the University of Strasbourg explains how the various patterns of social structure, for example patrilinear and matrilinear systems, and also what he calls the local attitude of society, can influence fertility. Two examples of such attitudes are what he calls the ''natalist attitude'' and the ''formalist attitude''.

Also I should like to draw your attention to a recent book, ''The Population Crisis and the Use of World Resources''[5], which is entirely devoted to this question of fertility. Africa is not specially treated in this book, but it is mentioned frequently.

Lambo: The demographic changes taking place in Africa have tremendous implications for future economic development, and also for health resources and health planning. Does the future picture as presented constitute a demographic imbalance in Africa? In Europe and North America the proportion of old people to young adults is very high. In Africa, in contrast, the relatively large population of young people under 15 years of age has been interpreted as "unfavourable" to economic development. In the light of what has happened in advanced countries, we can regard this as a transitional period during which the changes will be adverse and will create psychosocial problems.

Bourgeois-Pichat: It is true that the proportion of young people is higher in Africa than in Europe. But when a population passes from a state of very high fertility to a state of low fertility, usually at the same time there is an increase in education and so on, and the limit of the young inactive population is raised, let us say, to about the age of 19 or 20. So there is a certain compensation from the economic point of view between the two phenomena. This is why in Table IX (Population C) in my paper I included among the young people those aged 15 to 19. The compensation is only partial and the burden of the young people is still higher in Africa today than it is in Europe. In Europe today there are 38 per cent of inactive young people under 20, while in Africa there are 44 per cent of inactive young people aged 0 to 14 years. So the main feature of populations with high fertility is really the burden of young people.

With reference to the old people, when mortality declines there is a small increase in the proportion of old people and a smaller increase in the proportion of young men, and thus a small decrease in the proportion of people of working age, but the variations are small and not very important. The main important changes occur when fertility decreases. In terms of the old people, I think what you said, Professor Lambo, is only partly true.

Lambo: If it is only partly true, there is a great need to carry out sample surveys or population studies to determine our health needs in the light of socioeconomic change. Conditions such as psychosocial reactions, juvenile delinquency, prostitution, etc., which are consequent upon the new social life of African populations, are at one end of the scale and, at the other end of the scale, the appearance of old people, which is a new phenomenon in Africa and which may demand new health measures, has to be evaluated. Here we can learn a lesson from Europe and begin to make provisions in our social services for the elderly people. This changing age structure is a factor in the appearance of "new" diseases in Africa for which little or no provision has been made.

Patel: There are of course many difficulties in manipulating the complex phenomena of fertility, sterility, mortality, and nuptiality. Would you care to comment on the probable growth rate of population in Africa for the next two decades and for the following two decades?

Bourgeois-Pichat: I think we can consider an annual growth of 3 per cent as a conservative estimate. For economists who are planning development, it is better to take a 3 per cent rate of growth rather than anything less. A new publication[6] of the United Nations on population forecasts for all countries in the world gives a rate of growth of 3 per cent for Africa as the most probable estimate of population growth for the next decade. After ten years, I do not know what will happen—we will have to wait and see. The rate of growth is certainly a more important consideration than changes in the age structure.

Patel: If after ten years population in Africa increased faster than expected, but at the same time the level of education rose more rapidly than is now anticipated, do you think that the transition to low fertility might come about significantly earlier in Africa, say soon after 1980? In that case, the present population growth rate would rapidly rise from 2·0–2·5 per cent to 3 per cent in the earlier phase (1960 to 1980), and drop afterwards. By the end of the century it might well be down to 1·5 to 2·0 per cent, so that the average rate of growth (from

1960 to 2000) might be about 2·0 to 2·5 per cent. Does this appear a plausible perspective?

Bourgeois-Pichat: It could happen, and it did happen in Singapore, which provides an example which is generally quoted by demographers. The birth rate in Singapore was in the neighbourhood of 45 to 49 per thousand six years ago and it is now only 35 per thousand, a drop of more than 10 per thousand. It could also happen in Africa.

Brown: I agree that it could happen, but it seems to be very unlikely in Africa. In some parts of India, and in places like Singapore, there are very high concentrations of population; people are directly affected in their daily lives by the resulting pressures. In such conditions the aim of government policies can be explained to the people with some hope of obtaining their understanding and co-operation. But an African village is a far cry from a city like Singapore. I have little confidence that the course of events in manifestly overcrowded areas is likely to be repeated in Africa for a considerable time. Many countries in Africa, like Ethiopia, hardly feel the pressure of their growing populations. The people as a whole are not aware of the problem or that the rate of growth of a population can itself cause problems in a country which is sparsely populated. I feel that we are going to be faced with a minimum 2·0 to 2·5 per cent annual increase for at least a couple of generations.

Bourgeois-Pichat: Medical and educational progress may lead to birth control on a vast scale. So far, the birth control devices produced have not been very efficient in underdeveloped countries; they are difficult to apply and it is necessary to have a certain way of life in order to apply them. But recently there has been some progress, particularly with reference to the intra-uterine devices. These appear to be very safe, easy to use, very cheap, and, at least for some 70 per cent of the women, completely efficient.

If it proves necessary to apply an intra-uterine device just once to ensure that there will be no children for, say, ten years, this would transform the situation, and in Africa it would be a great help. I agree with Dr. Brown that if nothing happens, if we continue in the present state of knowledge, it is unlikely that Africa as a whole will follow the trend of the city of Singapore, which is quite different; but things may change even in Africa, if progress makes birth control methods easier to apply.

Brown: At the moment the problem of health education, which is a very necessary part of such projects, is to reach the population. Perhaps 90 per cent of the population in Africa still live in rural areas, and we are being rather optimistic if we believe that in the short time left to us we can develop health education programmes to the point where they can reach a high percentage of the population, convert people to a new way of thinking, and give them even the small amount of instruction and assistance necessary to permit each woman to practise such birth control methods effectively.

Goody: Surely the problem is that neither countries nor individuals have any incentive to use these devices. Under the conditions of relatively sparse population one finds in much of Africa, the national incentive is to increase the population, not to decrease it. As for the individual, high infant mortality has in the past given every incentive to frequent childbirth. Though mortality rates are dropping, people will continue to be conscious of them and therefore continue to see a very high birth rate as a compensation for some time to come. Moreover, because of the great emphasis placed on kinship and the system of peasant farming, people place a great value on children.

Lambo: I want to endorse what Dr. Goody has said. There is in many African countries an incentive to increase the birth rate, whether because of individual needs, local or national desires, or cultural attitudes. At the same time, it is very difficult to forecast what will happen eventually. In Nigeria during our large-scale surveys we were very surprised to find that even in remote villages people were practising monogamy and restricting the size of their families. Because of improved health conditions, the wives are more fertile and the children less likely to die; consequently the husbands are contented to take one wife, and after they have had two or three children, the family size is restricted. Sterility in women and the high rate of child mortality in Africa contributed in a large measure to the practice of polygamy.

Goody: It has been suggested[7] that polygamy is a limiting factor in fertility and not the other way around. The marriage span of a man has now increased because of earlier marriage. Young men no longer have to wait for their father's permission before they take a bride, and the women do not all belong to the old men, who may be relatively infertile. All these changes will increase fertility rates.

Bourgeois-Pichat: The high sterility observed among certain African women may be due not so much to biological factors as to these sociological factors.

Patel: Serious consideration has been given at international level to the anti-malarial campaign, and to the "Freedom from Hunger" campaign; but is it not conceivable that W.H.O. or a similar organization may soon undertake a campaign for "Freedom from Birth"? With a wide and free distribution of birth-control materials, it should rapidly bring down the population growth rate.

Goody: The two things seem to be on very different levels. In the one case you are dealing with disease; in the other you want to control an activity that in itself is basic to human existence. Moreover, in situations of low productivity and no land shortage, and in situations where the nation pays for training, it is often advantageous to an individual to have a large family.

If you are really trying to reduce the birth rate, it would be better to adopt administrative rather than contraceptive techniques. One possible solution would be to introduce compulsory education as speedily as possible and make people pay for the education of their own children, thus creating a disincentive against large families. In other words, instead of education being paid for out of a total fund, to which all members of the population contribute equally, the prolific should be made to pay accordingly.

In most of Africa today, as in Europe and America, education is now socialized; there are no school fees and hence no specific disincentive for particular individuals to reduce the size of their families. People say to themselves: "Schooling is free, so we will have as many children as we can in order to take advantage of it". School fees were one of the major disincentives in Victorian England, and they remain so today in the professional middle class, there and in many other countries.

Sutton: The school fees system has been a characteristic of English-speaking Africa, and this could certainly become a very considerable constraint on large families. In Kenya nowadays, the principal demand on cash income for many families is for school fees, and it becomes a real consideration whether another child can be sent to school. On the other hand, as Dr. Goody said, most African states regard school fees as undemocratic and try to eliminate them.

Ewing: The assumption underlying much of this discussion is that both the present economic situation and current population trends in Africa will continue, and improving health services will bring about an ever more overwhelming population problem, more and more out of proportion to any economic development. Obviously, those who feel that the basic economic structure of Africa will not be very different in the future are bound to take the view that even vast improvements in education will not affect the main issue. But if you can project certain knowledge which within the span of this century will transform the whole economic structure of Africa, so that the level of development will not be very different from Western Europe now, then I do not see any reason why the birth rate should not come to be the same as in Western Europe, for very much the same reasons.

Goody: Long-term policies may change the situation, but it seems to me that in the short run compulsory education, compulsorily paid for, would bring a change more quickly than anything else.

Bourgeois-Pichat: The population problem is one of the most important facing the world today, and the discussion here has shown that it is difficult to discuss it without emotion—it is difficult to keep an objective attitude. This is probably so because we are so involved in the problem; we are thinking of our own destinies.

While I was listening to members of this symposium, I was thinking that we were faced here with a situation similar to the one which would occur among physicists if the atom had something to say in the burst of the atomic bomb. In such a case no doubt the experiments of the physicists would be much more complicated than they are at present. Dealing with population problems is somewhat similar: each individual has too much to say on each of these problems!

4

TRIBAL, RACIAL, RELIGIOUS AND LANGUAGE PROBLEMS IN AFRICA

JACK GOODY

I N the context of the great stress that intellectuals and politicians alike now place upon the ideal of a united Africa, any discussion of the differences in language, race, religion and culture may easily be taken as an attack upon the concept of continental unity. No such intention lies behind this paper. I have been asked to open a discussion on this subject with the aim of making a realistic assessment of the problems involved. I am acutely aware that the situation varies from one country to the next: I can only hope to make some general points that apply, at best, to a majority of the peoples concerned.

The differences of language, religion, race and culture in Africa are as radical as in any other continent in the world, and perhaps more so. I want to start with language, since it is basic to humanity itself. The major cultural advances of mankind have been intimately linked with the invention of more complex systems of communication.

Homo sapiens (as distinct from earlier hominids) was probably the first to use language as we know it: writing was associated with the emergence of the city civilizations of the Fertile Crescent: the alphabetic script paved the way for the Greek achievements, printing for the Renaissance in Western Europe, the rotary press for the mass dissemination of information that characterizes the industrial societies of the past hundred years. With the advent of television and the transistor, which give communication an immediacy lacking in the written word, it is possible to inform and educate without the need for literacy. (It is a rather desiccated materialism that limits its technological analysis to tools manipulated by the hand and characterizes the major revolutions of mankind in terms of the treatment of the stone or the type of metal used: even Gordon Childe's[1] emphasis on productive techniques does not allow enough room for the technology of the intellect.)

Six major language families are represented in Africa (see Fig. 1). In the north and north-east there is the Afro-Asiatic group that includes Semitic (Arabic and Hebrew), Berber, Ancient Egyptian (Coptic), the Cushitic languages of Ethiopia and the Chadic languages of Northern Nigeria, among these being Hausa, probably the most widely spoken language of Negro Africa. The most important family of languages is the Niger-Congo*, stretching from Dakar to Durban, and including Fulani and Bantu, Mande and Swahili (though the last has been much influenced by Semitic speech).

Apart from these two main families, there are two other smaller groups: Nilo-Saharan, extending from Niger (Songhai) to Nile (Nilotic and Nubian), and the Khoisan languages spoken by the Bushmen and other hunting peoples of southern and eastern Africa. Finally there are the representatives of language families whose major strength lies outside Africa, the Malayo-Polynesian languages of Madagascar and the Indo-European languages imported in recent centuries by migrants from Europe and Asia.

Each of the major families (and especially the Niger-Congo) contains a multitude of mutually unintelligible tongues. Many of these are of very limited distribution; others such as Yoruba and Twi are spoken by large segments of a country's population. But whereas linguistic factors played a prominent part in the formation of European states, there are few countries south of the Sahara where a dominant language prevails. The scramble for

---

* This family bears some relationship to certain languages in the Nuba hills of the Sudanese Republic; in his latest classification Greenberg[2] includes both families together under the somewhat cumbersome name, Congo-Kordofanian.

Africa allowed scant room for considering the niceties of language boundaries. But perhaps not a great deal more could have been achieved if the organization into national units had been carried out by a committee of linguists under the auspices of U.N.E.S.C.O.

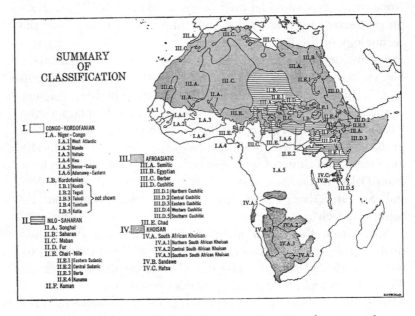

Fig. 1. Classification of African languages. From Greenberg (1963)[2].

For the fundamental problem is that the increasing range of social relationships demands a verbal code of greater extent than had previously existed. Centralized political systems, especially when the mode of communication is by writing, need a specified language of administration or at worst a restricted number of such languages. All the conquest states of Africa, whether they have been established by literate or non-literate invaders, by Arab or European, Hausa or Ganda, tend to import (or adopt) a single language of administration, commerce and learning—and this process inevitably puts pressure on the languages of smaller circulation.

The British used their own language for administration, while encouraging the use of local languages in primary schools. Other colonial powers gave less emphasis to the vernacular, insisting that most instruction be carried on in their own tongue, so that the advent of total literacy would result in the virtual elimination of local languages among the urban population, as happened in both North and South America.

In so far as one can trace trends in the post-independence era, it is the policy of "assimilation" that has prevailed. Except in North Africa there have been few moves to adopt an official language other than that of the European conquerors who established the boundaries and hence the unity of the present states. Even where one local language has been dominant, speakers of smaller languages prefer to give way to an outsider rather than to a near neighbour. Where two or more important languages exist side by side, the choice may threaten the unity of the state and such conflict is avoided by recourse to a European tongue. And as far as the progress of the country is concerned, the use of a major international language renders technical assistance easier to obtain and makes it simpler for scientists and scholars to have access to world stores of information.

At the national level the case for adopting a single language is widely accepted. In his book on "Ghana's Heritage of Culture"[3], the late Kofi Antubam describes the efforts of the Vernacular Literature Bureau which went "up and down the country directing the diabolical operation of reducing petty dialects here and there into writing . . . a multiplicity of written languages is the greatest danger to the evolution and development of a national language of any progressive country. In all spheres of activity the arduous task of weaving up a country of tribes into the larger unit of a nation demands that certain sacrifices should be made by one tribe or other within the national unit. . . ."

Antubam himself spoke the major language of Ghana, just as he wrote of the cultural heritage of its largest group. Had he belonged to a smaller tribe, he might have experienced some of the pangs of the Celtic population of the British Isles as they see their language and culture dwindling before their eyes. Indeed, as an artist, he must surely have felt more ambivalence than his words assert, for the loss of language and culture means that the social personality of the individuals involved can no longer be reproduced. A part of one's immortality is wrested away.

However, there is no doubt in my mind that his standpoint was correct: the unity of the country is certainly promoted by the adoption of a single official language for administrative and educational purposes. And there are compelling reasons why this language should continue to be the language of the colonial power (as was the case in the American continent, both North and South, as well as in that part of Asia conquered by Russia), since the use of an already established language with an international currency allows the new nation immediate access to the world bank of human knowledge. A great speed of advance is possible because of the greater use that can be made of technical assistance, university teachers and the written word. Equally a more direct impact can be made on world affairs.

But while the process of linguistic unification is highly advantageous, it also has disruptive consequences. Unless the speakers of minority languages are in a position of considerable subordination (like that of new immigrants or conquered peoples), they will clearly resist the change, for the use of a national language is bound to depress the status and utility of indigenous languages, a process which in the end is likely to lead to their disappearance. It is true that a half-way house can be found in a deliberate bilingualism which allows one language in the domestic domain and another in the political. In the case of the Celtic minorities in Europe, such a situation has persisted for many centuries. But in the contemporary world, such dichotomies are productive of considerable tensions. Local languages are likely to be found in areas of economic backwardness, both as a cause and as an effect. Their very continuation makes technological advance more difficult, and this in turn produces resentment against the cultural majority. Such pockets are inevitably foci of internal dissension, which can in turn be exploited by external enemies. In Europe, the Breton and Flemish minorities were conspicuous for their attachment to the Fascist causes of the 1930's.

A common language (or languages) is clearly as important for continental as for national unity. Since the vast majority of national languages apart from Swahili have been chosen from those of a comparatively few conquering powers (Arabic north of the Sahara, English, French and Portuguese to the south), communication on the pan-African level presents no great problems. In any case, it is most unlikely that any group of powers would consent to change their present national language for that of any other group. Linguistic unity can be enforced within a national state through the educational system, supported (in the last analysis) by its monopoly of armed force. No such monopoly exists at the supranational level and hence the political conditions for linguistic unification do not exist.

I have treated the problem of language first because of all aspects of culture it is perhaps the least tractable to change. Religious differences seem to me of lesser importance. In terms of *world* religions, Africa is divided into the Moslem north and the Christian south. But much of Africa falls outside the dominion of these exclusive creeds that emanate from the Semitic world of the Near East. And even where they are in some sense accepted, "pagan" practices and beliefs are frequently merged with official rite and dogma. Africa is the land of break-away churches, especially in those parts where the orthodox *ecclesia* is in the keeping of privileged minorities of European extraction. But everywhere the pattern of belief tends to be eclectic; few paths to supernatural comfort are rejected and in consequence tribes have their own ceremonies rather than their own religions.

The situation could change under the influence of the world religions, each advocating its singular path to salvation. The danger here lies particularly in "reformist" (or reactionary?) elements that decry accommodation with the infidel. But the possibility of new Jihads or wars of religion are becoming more and more remote. In this technological age, men's energies are channelled elsewhere; they wear their spiritual beliefs more lightly; and the patterns of world education, to which all new nations are committed, are increasingly secular in tone. The Koranic class is no substitute for the primary school, where even in church-sponsored institutions the appearances of the priest and preacher are limited to the set hours of religious instruction.

I speak here of the general trend. In the short run, religious beliefs may form the ideological base of political parties or associations (as with the old, proscribed, M.P.P. of Northern Ghana). Differences of creed may erupt in local pogroms. But nowadays this seems unlikely in the absence of added vexations of an economic or political nature. While religious commitment sometimes coincides with territorial areas and hence may encourage the fission of a political unit, the class systems that are now emerging mostly cut across religious differences. There are rich Moslems and poor Moslems; capitalist Christians and peasant Christians. Given such cross-cutting identifications, Africans are unlikely to lose much sleep over the difference between consubstantiation and transubstantiation or to riot over the loss of the Prophet's hairs. Such divisions as exist should easily be held in check by a centralized political system.

Language and religion are particular facets of culture, and it is the residuum of cultural problems that I understand to be called "tribal". In the long run, differences here seem to me of less significance, even though the Somali, the Berbers and the Ewe have been often in the news. But in the changing political and economic conditions of the twentieth century, tribal allegiances are giving way to national ones with startling speed. The power position of chiefs and other traditional authorities has been overthrown, though they retain ritual prerogatives and many continuing loyalties. The new identifications with national symbols, with flag, anthem, president, airline and the rest, are real and deep enough—indeed too real for the taste of those interested in the creation of effective polities of yet larger scale, whether on the regional, continental or world scene. It is frightening to see how easily the arbitrary lines that resulted from the competing claims of European powers have acquired the sanctity of ancient *limes*. It is not unusual to find a national leader announce a readiness to fight for the frontiers concocted by a European boundary commission less than half a century ago. Nor does this situation arise simply from the interests of politicians who might prefer to come first in a small field rather than take their chance with a larger entry. The identification is concrete, emotive, even among ordinary people. It is not so much the traditional division of language, race and culture, but rather this emotional attachment, and the premium placed on small political units by present international organizations (Togo has the same voting strength as India in the United Nations), which give rise to the deepest problem for the creation of larger entities to control the means of destruction and to meet other problems of social organization on a world scale.

But before concluding this topic, let me comment briefly on the last of the problem areas I am asked to consider, that of race. Africa was the cradle of mankind, of *homo* if not *homo sapiens*. Australoids apart, all the main racial groups are found in Africa today. Apart from the basic Negro population, there are the old-established Caucasoids along the Mediterranean littoral and pushing down into the Sahara where the type merges gradually with the Negro peoples to the south. Then there are the newer groups of Caucasoids in South and East Africa emanating from Europe and India. In Madagascar the Mongoloid immigrants from Indonesia have blended with Negro stock. In the south a handful of Bushmen hunters maintain their separate existence. Apart from these and the southern whites, the pattern everywhere is one of merging races: and their self-imposed isolation is politico-economic, rather than racial, if by the latter we refer specifically to physical differences of an inherited kind. The colour of one's skin is an all too obvious mark of distinction around which cluster conflicts of a more substantial sort. But Africa has normally resolved the physical side of things by the simple expedient of inter-marriage.

Only the southern whites have turned in upon themselves, with consequences that are all too readily apparent.

In the fields, then, of race, religion and culture generally, the traditional pattern is one of mixing, melting, merging. Only in the sphere of language are there serious difficulties here. People married out rather than in, there were few of the restrictions on dining and other forms of social intercourse that marked the more rigidly stratified societies of Europe and Asia. Divisions of course existed and I have no wish to play down their importance in traditional societies and on the contemporary scene. But such differences will I think have increasingly less significance in the future. Here the important divisions are new ones, arising around the formation of new political units, which like all other states have too great a control over their own and others' destinies for the well-being of Africa and the world. And inside these states there is developing a new hierarchy based upon education and wealth. The division between literates and non-literates will resolve itself in time, although an educational hierarchy will inevitably emerge. But there is also a stratification based on wealth which is a good deal more radical than that of Euro-American societies, and which leads to great distinctions in styles of life; while the salaries and aspirations of the town-based élite approximate to the highest European standards, those of the rural population are often closer to a medieval peasantry. At the same time the situation of the educated classes, who face the general economic and political problems of living in a rapidly developing, tropical environment, gives rise to similar intellectual problems and to a kind of pan-African culture, with its common magazines, café music, literature and debates. It is this new social situation rather than the old that generates the problems (and the hopes) of a wider unity. And the foremost of these problems lies firmly in the political kingdom.

Appendix I

LANGUAGE DIFFERENTIATION IN A NATIONAL STATE

The main possibilities of linguistic differentiation within a developing country can be summarized as follows:

(1) Domestic ("mother tongue").
(2) Lower Education (school).
(3) Higher Education (university).
(4) Official and National.
(5) International.

Domestic Languages are those an individual learns in the home: the more highly differentiated the languages are in a given region, the greater will be the amount of language learning likely to be required of individuals. Most Africans know at least two such languages; many know more. Bilingualism is widespread.

School Languages: the choice here is between the vernacular and the national language, where these do not coincide. A single countrywide school language simplifies the provision of textbooks and the transfer of teachers.

University Languages: the pressure here is towards a language of international currency, in particular English (the University of Khartoum teaches in English, even though the national language is Arabic).

Official and National Languages: Amharic is, apart from Arabic, the only local language so far adopted as the sole official language. Only Cameroon, South and South-West Africa, the Somali Republic, Burundi and Rwanda have more than one official language. Where the official language is imported, the most widespread local tongue may be designated the national language. (See Appendix II.)

International Languages: where the official language is not a

107

European language, other languages have to be chosen for international communication and even for signs, notice boards and other internal uses. One such language tends to predominate, and that is the language of university education, which in turn is usually that of the former colonial power. To use other languages, apart from Arabic, would be to create enormous problems of translation.

Efficiency of communication increases as the number of languages approaches unity. Equally, the greater the loss of indigenous languages, the greater will be the loss in terms of associated cultural institutions.

The same is true of the number of scripts employed; there is an enormous loss of efficiency when a nation has to use a double set of typewriters.

Appendix II

OFFICIAL LANGUAGES OF AFRICA

Language	Country	Population
Amharic (21 million)	Ethiopia	21,400,000
Arabic (69 million)	Algeria	11,020,000
	Libya	1,270,000
	Morocco	12,360,000
	Sudan	12,831,000
	United Arab Republic	27,285,000
	Tunisia	4,290,000
English (85 million)	Basutoland	642,000
	Bechuanaland	294,000
	Gambia	264,000
	Ghana	7,244,000
	Kenya	8,847,000
	Liberia	1,010,000

Language	Country	Population
English *continued*	Malawi	2,921,000
	Mauritius and Dependencies	727,000
	Nigeria	37,213,000
	St. Helena	4,624
	Seychelles	44,000
	Sierra Leone	2,183,000
	S. Rhodesia	3,839,000
	Swaziland	269,000
	Tanzania (Swahili)	10,046,000
	Zambia	2,515,000
	Uganda	7,016,000
French (53 million)	Central African Republic	1,280,000
	Chad	2,720,000
	Congo	820,000
	Congolese Republic	15,007,000
	Dahomey	2,200,000
	French Somaliland	67,000
	Gabon	435,000
	Guinea	3,357,000
	Ivory Coast	3,410,000
	Madagascar	5,939,000
	Mali	4,305,000
	Mauritania (Arabic)	780,000
	Niger	3,041,000
	Ile de la Réunion	349,000
	Senegal	3,360,000
	Togo	1,563,000
	Upper Volta	4,500,000
Portuguese (11 million)	Angola	4,145,000
	Cape Verde Islands	148,000
	Mozambique	5,732,000

Language	Country	Population
Portuguese *continued*	Portuguese Guinea	511,000
	São Tomé and Principé Islands	60,200
Spanish (240,000)	Spanish Guinea	204,000
	Spanish Sahara	36,000
More than one language: (30 million)		
English and French	Cameroon	4,560,000
Afrikaans and English	S. Africa	17,075,000
Afrikaans, English and German	S.W. Africa	525,000
French and Kirundi	Burundi	2,600,000
French and Kinyarwanda	Rwanda	2,695,000
Arabic, English and Italian	Somali Republic (Somali)	2,250,000

National languages in brackets.

DISCUSSION

Mulugeta: African languages are not only diverse and very numerous, but also (except for Amharic in Ethiopia) one of their glaring characteristics is that so very few of them are written. What are the broad reasons for this?

Goody: Of course writing was used in the Moslem world and throughout the Christian world of north-eastern Africa. But there was no great incentive to use these scripts to write down other languages, with a few exceptions such as those for which Arabic script is used. The Roman script never penetrated Africa south of the Sahara. Some examples are known of indigenous attempts to start elementary writing systems in West Africa, but there was no technological breakthrough to a fully fledged system of writing. .

Many of the main languages in Africa have been used in writing for quite a long time now, especially in the coastal areas. The problem is not in writing them down; it is the fact that the languages themselves are of restricted circulation.

Monod: Fulani has also been written in Arabic characters. It is true in general that there have not been written scripts before, but we now know about six African alphabets, all of them of rather recent origin. The oldest one is probably the Vai in Liberia, first used in the middle of the 19th century, then came the well-known Bamoun script in the Cameroons, which in fact is the only one which has served practical purposes and for writing books. Mande has been mentioned earlier; others are Nsibidi and Toma, and a very interesting fact was the appearance, about eight years ago, of a new alphabet created entirely by one man—and I know the man—in the western Ivory Coast, among the Bete tribe. These western African alphabets are not in fact alphabets, they are either script, i.e. ideographic, or, at the best, syllabic, which means that they must have hundreds of signs to write anything, and none of them—as far as I know—has been printed.

In the north, as you mentioned, the Roman alphabet didn't wander far across from North Africa. The situation has been a little different for one of the Libyan types of alphabets, the Tifinar script, which is still, of course, used by the Touareg, and which was used last century as far as the Atlantic coast in the west. There are many inscriptions on rocks in that alphabet in Mauritania.

As to the earliest date of the introduction of Arabic script in the west, the oldest documents we have at present are engraved tombstones, royal tombstones, from Gao; they date from the 11th century, and curiously enough, some of them at least have been brought from Spain, from Almeria, already engraved, and transported to the Western Sudan.

Goody: As far as one knows now, all true alphabetic scripts are derived from Semitic sources in the Middle East. Like the wheel, the alphabet was invented only once, but of course there were, as you say, some proto-alphabetic developments in Africa (possibly independent of each other) which can serve for very limited purposes of communication.

Brown: Chinese and related languages, although differing as much from one to another as European languages do, all used Chinese picture-based script, so that although persons could not talk to one another, they were all able to share the same literature. When Viet-Nam adopted phonetic Roman alphabetic script some 80 to 90 years ago, it became in some ways easier to teach and there was a rather easier process of learning. On the other hand the country cut itself off from the literature of the whole of the Chinese group.

Goody: A choice has to be made in this matter of the alphabet, as in Viet-Nam. One cuts oneself off from some things and opens the way to other things. The pressure of technology is now so strong that this is likely to channel the future developments. One cannot of course ignore literature, but I would remind you that one is always getting cut off from literature. The ordinary English person can't read Anglo-Saxon and can't understand much of Chaucer, because of changes in language and cultural tradition. This is a continuous process: languages are changing all the time.

The pressure is also towards adopting a Roman script; even China has been experimenting in that direction. One has to remember that the written information which has been piling up in the last few decades is overwhelming in relation to what has gone on in the past. To keep in touch, the lines of communication have to be kept as free and simple as possible.

Lambo: What about functional aspects—why do some languages survive and others die? For example, the Yoruba language and culture have survived vigorously, testifying to the fact that there are psychological mechanisms inherent in some African languages which carry inner meanings; and this fact may account for the survival of such languages.

Goody: This is true; it is difficult for us to think of speaking another language from birth, and of what one's personality would be like if one did. One's conceptual apparatus would be quite different and this is why a great deal of resistance is aroused to any questions of linguistic change.

Sutton: I think the problem is a little more complicated than you suggest, Dr. Goody. I see two types of countries evolving in Africa: ones in which there is such a diversity of languages that it is impossible to establish one of them as a national language without the difficulties which you describe; and others where there is little or no difficulty in agreeing on an African national language—Somalia is such a country and Tanzania is another. How difficult will it be for countries to live side by side when some have African national languages and some do not? For instance, Swahili is the national language of Tanzania and is being developed there as such, but neither Kenya nor Uganda has yet attempted to take an African language as a national language. Of course, the Swedes use English as a language for international communication while maintaining the use of Swedish at home, and they live at peace with England. So it is certainly not impossible, but I think we must envisage this problem as part of the future of Africa.

Goody: I was not thinking only of the establishment of one national language, but in some cases of two or three. Even when this is done, and even when a local language is chosen, other languages have to go. In Basutoland it means the elimination of other languages of smaller circulation. In Madagascar again there are languages of small circulation that will have to give way to Malagassy; and apart from this, French is widely used in schools. Such trilingualism is not uncommon in other parts. In terms of efficiency, the more languages that are used within a country, the less efficient is the system of communication. But the difficulties in the way of deliberate linguistic unification are many. One has to bear in mind the experience of Ceylon.

Mesfin: Some conflict seems to underlie our discussion. We are discussing a very speedy economic advancement, for Africa as a whole, and together with this the attainment of political unity as fast as possible. Now these two, economic advancement and political unity, seem to me to clash with the idea of cultural preservation.

If a multilingual country, for instance, decides to use two or three national languages, this is a waste of resources, because it means translation, lots of paper work, and so forth, which may severely handicap these poor countries. It will definitely also arrest the consciousness of a greater whole—the nation. Therefore I do not really know whether we are going to make sacrifices here in Africa, for the sake of economic development and political unity, in terms of suppressing or simply allowing some languages to die.

Gayer: Since I live in Switzerland, where there are four official languages, I would like to say a word about the losses in time, money and effort in having to allow for several languages within one country. Scientific developments virtually demand the use of the English language in organizations like my own, and for that matter in this symposium. However, in television and broadcasting sound channels can carry two or three languages, and also written language can be superimposed on the screen itself. This could of course help to develop the national language, as well as, say, English, but in many African countries technical facilities are just not available to handle two or three different languages, and so for an African country to use even one national language and one foreign one, such as English, leads to loss of money, confusion of paper work, and so forth. That is simply not a solution at the moment; multilingual services cost money.

Howard-Goldsmith: Dr. Goody has obviously got a good subject —his paper has been most stimulating and I think this is due not only to the subject matter, but also to the very lively and competent way in which he explained it.

Mr. Gayer has said almost what I wanted to say, that is, that this symposium cannot over-emphasize the handicap which these many different languages present for economic and political development on both a national and a continental scale. It should be made quite clear that if this continent and its constituent countries want to achieve that economic development, then they have to eliminate these different linguistic characteristics.

Quite recently, the United Nations assisted Ethiopia to draw up mining legislation, but we were told, and have since experienced, that it would not be put into effect for a considerable time because it had first to be translated into Amharic. Similar legislation has been requested in Basutoland and I just cannot visualize how many years it will take to produce that in the Basuto language.

I feel very strongly that we should encourage one language for this continent—possibly a non-African one—and if it is claimed that this would diminish the spiritual heritages of the various nations, I think that can be exaggerated too. After all, in South America there are some 12 different nations which speak approximately the same language and have entirely different national characteristics and traditions; and even in North America—Mr. Gayer may not agree with me—a Texan feels very strongly that he is a different person from an Easterner, although they both speak the same language.

Gille: Even with the most internationally used languages, there remains the problem of ready adaptation to scientific use. Every language of any modern value is forced to be more and more technical.

Goody: The difficulty lies on another level really, in securing access to world literature, most of which is in English, German, French or Russian.

Habte-Ab: Can you see in the structure of some of the larger groups of African languages the ability to develop in the technical, literary and other aspects of modern idiom?

Goody: That is an interesting problem. My own personal opinion is that there is nothing which inherently prevents this. There is nothing peculiar, I think, about the English language which enables it to express complex technological ideas. The point is that the languages of international currency are already developed in that way; so even if you decide to do the same for another language, the people using it are cut off from access to the furiously developing international literature. Or you have an enormous problem in translation, though here computers will ease the situation in the future.

Dekker: I come from a very small country, Holland, where at all schools we have our own and a choice of one foreign language, German, English or French, with the result that we have few difficulties with access to the literature of the main languages. Would it be very difficult to have, as a routine everywhere, the local language or the national language, and one of the four major languages?

Goody: Bilingual education would be perfectly possible, if expensive. But in most African states at the moment you would first have to establish the national language or languages. The question of choice in, say, Nigeria, is not of which language you are going to choose, but how to reduce the choice to two or three or to any manageable number. Ghana has made a deliberate choice in the matter: they have chosen one language for education, that of the ex-colonial power. This choice will make it easier for them to advance economically. But it is certainly not the only solution to the problem.

Sutton: It seems now that two languages can be taught together not only with no loss, but with real gain. The advantages of comparison with another language are so great that even in the United States quite radical experiments are going on now. For example, at Westport, Connecticut, Hindi is being taught, not because that is a useful language in Westport, but because it provides a better understanding of the structure of English. Where African languages are studied in, for example, Ghanaian secondary schools for essentially cultural purposes, this type of contrasting study in relation to English should be very helpful. It should then be possible to gain the advantages of adopting a national language of international currency without prejudice to the cultural development of African languages.

Goody: In most of these countries one is not dealing simply with two or three languages, but with perhaps 50 or 100 different languages. In Nigeria alone there are nearly 300, which will give you some idea of the problem. It is perfectly possible to do as Dr. Sutton suggests and have a series of languages for cultural purposes, but I cannot visualize the situation in Northern Ghana, for example, where there are, say, 20 different languages, and where each school formerly specialized in one of the very local languages. This involves both textbooks and teachers. But now Ghana can move teachers rapidly from one place to another, and can thus more readily stimulate development in all areas of the country.

Last: It is very easy for a group of experts to sit round a table and recommend all sorts of things. The practical problem is one of fitting all these items into a school programme. You propose putting two languages, or even three, into a normal school programme in an African country; but a great many demands are being made on the school which are not made in other parts of the world. We have all sorts of cultural problems to face in the school system. You seek to introduce a variety of technical and practical subjects; we already have to deal with health and sanitation to a degree which is not required in modernized countries. Practically the whole of the upbringing of the child in this generation in Africa depends on the school, and then you ask for so many languages on top of this. Right at the end of this process is the poor headmaster who is trying to find time to satisfy all these demands.

Obviously one answer lies in a radical approach to language

learning. As Dr. Sutton has suggested, if more than one language can be taught at the same time, time is saved on the timetable. Otherwise, perhaps the only answer is to take note of the Russian experiments on learning languages when asleep; we could then do our international language learning in Africa at night!

One naturally wishes to establish a national language. For example, in Ethiopia for this reason all elementary school instruction is now in Amharic. We can certainly use Amharic as the medium of instruction in the classroom, but we then have the problem of books to promote the use of the language. What does one do in an Ethiopian elementary school when the only relevant reading material is the actual book being used for instruction in the classroom? True, there are certain stories and reading books in Amharic, but in the technical subjects, in all the other subjects in the curriculum, there just is not one other book in Amharic that could be put in a school library. It requires an enormous effort to translate and create new material to back up the teaching programme. This has to be done, but it has to be realized that considerable resources have to be spent on such projects.

Goody: The cost of every additional language in Africa is very high, and the burden on the school is already very heavy, since in Africa a child does not at present accumulate much background knowledge in the home, compared with the European situation.

Mustafa: In our experience in the rather heavily tribalized parts of the Sudan—and I think this is also true of the still heavily tribalized parts of the rest of Africa—we have found that not only the language difficulties but also differences in tribal practices lead to constant friction between tribes belonging to the same race, and living under the same geographical conditions. How much do you think this would be a real challenge to any mergers between African countries? These tribes don't seem to possess any sense of nationalism, they don't seem to feel that they belong to a nation; their feelings and allegiances are mainly to the area in which they live. They don't recognize even the other tribes, and they refuse to be subjected to anybody outside the tribe. Yet the boundaries of most African states are artificial and we often find one tribe living in three different states.

Goody: I have been impressed in recent years by the great changes taking place in tribal allegiances. Of course, tribal attachments are still an important factor, but they are largely held in check simply because political force is concentrated at the centre.

In Ghana I have been surprised by the cross-cutting ties that are forming between men of different tribal groups, at secondary schools, in administrative jobs, etc. Here the use of a non-local language helps. Although traditional backgrounds remain important, new forms of social interaction cut across tribal boundaries. For example, when a child was born to any of a group of government officers I knew in Ghana, they performed an out-dooring (i.e. a naming or baptismal) ceremony which did not follow the ritual of any one group but was a merger of the natal ceremonies of them all. I do not know whether Professor Lambo has had the same experience, but I became very conscious of this development.

Lambo: This is certainly beginning to happen, but on the whole my own experience has probably been the opposite. In Nigeria, on the surface there is homogeneity and a manifest allegiance to the central government. Underneath, however, one can sense a feeling of frustration and bitterness between both classes and tribes, but especially between the latter. In many parts of Africa there is a widespread feeling of uncertainty and anxiety among tribes. The difficulties encountered in Africa seem to stem from the scramble for opportunity and the struggle to get one tribe or group into power. As a result of their struggle there is a definite undercurrent with many psychological and emotional aspects underlying the relationship between tribes, groups and persons. To the casual observer, however, this highly competitive spirit is not so obvious.

Goody: True, there is competition between tribes, but perhaps more importantly between family groups within tribes. Moreover, once people have gained their positions in a Ministry, then there is a sort of pulling together in opposition to the tribal background. Ties arise between people in similar sorts of occupations which seem to me to challenge the differences in their backgrounds to a very significant extent.

Young: Even in Scotland "tribal" antagonisms can still occasionally be seen between members of different clans.

Apeadu: All over Africa governments are trying to make different tribes and language groups submerge their identities in favour of a consciousness of their membership of the nation as a whole; organizations are being established, for example, for all the farmers of the country, all the women, all the youth: such organizations cut across the narrow older loyalties, and entrench the idea of nationhood in people's consciousness.

Mesfin: What are the really essential differences between the Caucasoid groups, the Negroes and the Bushmen that make them races in the biological sense?

Goody: The differentiation is made on a physical basis, and does not extend beyond that. The differences are in the colour of the skin, type of hair, bone structure, and soft parts of the body. These are overt features that can be measured. Our knowledge as to how they are made up genetically, apart from blood groups, is not very far advanced.

Lambo: I think Dr. Goody has covered all the essential points, but I would add that quite apart from the genotype or haemoglobin variations, etc., there are perhaps other biological differences which are not yet known. With regard to genetic differences in Africa and also within the same group, migration may be a selective factor in that those who move may be genetically different from those who remain behind.

5

SOCIOECONOMIC CHANGES IN AFRICA AND THEIR IMPLICATIONS FOR MENTAL HEALTH

T. ADEOYE LAMBO

EVEN in the nineteenth century there was awareness of the frequent association between the problems associated with social change and the incidence of mental disorder; Esquirol[1] in France and Maudsley[2] in England both testified to this fact at a time when Europe was undergoing the many social changes brought about by industrialization.

The great epidemiologist Hecker[3] and the celebrated medical historian Sigerist[4] have clearly shown that the incidence and manifestations of many mass disorders or outbreaks were related to the factors of time and place. Thus the concept that "mental disorders change with time, and that they are changeable" was established. The factor of time and place is also bound up with the problem of cultural relativity, making the problem of defining mental illness a formidable one in a cross-cultural context. In fact, psychiatrists have not yet succeeded in defining mental health and mental ill-health in terms equally applicable to all societies or cultural groups.

In spite of these difficulties of definition we have been able to make systematic and empirical observations on mental health problems occurring in Africa in association with the process of change, especially in the social and economic spheres, and a general account of psychosocial reactions is presented here.

In our social psychiatry research programmes, since particular emphasis was being laid on the social and economic aspects of change, we had to broaden our frame of reference to include the theories and methods of cultural dynamics. Herskovits[5] has aptly observed, ". . . the problem of economic development, like all problems of cultural change, is essentially one of discovering, assessing, and predicting responses of men and women to innovations that go beyond the bounds of antecedent convention". Consequently, in our research we were led to cross the conventional boundaries of our discipline, although psychiatrists by training but not by opportunity are ill-equipped to employ sociological and cultural anthropological methods.

For convenience I shall review our work only in relation to population changes, especially migration, the adjustment and adaptation of African peoples to western institutions (urbanization, industrialization, student mental health at home and abroad), and the symptomatic responses (group psychopathology) occurring in various parts of Africa.

MIGRATION

From the demographic, economic and welfare data collected by the United Nations and its specialized agencies in Africa, we know that there is a sharp rise in the rate of population growth in many African nations. Most African countries today have an annual population increase of from 2 to 3 per cent and the apparent youth of the populations is noteworthy. It is now estimated that 35 to 40 per cent of the populations of the new African nations are under the age of 15. This changing age structure coupled with economic pressure may have some important implications for the epidemiology of many diseases (for example, schizophrenia) in the developing countries of Africa.

In their present state of economic development and with the pressure of over-population in some areas, many African countries cannot meet the growing needs of their people. Consequently, many young people become migrants, seeking to obtain more money to meet these needs; in many cases, the wives stay behind and usually this is the beginning of the erosion of family ties.

The problem of unemployed youth is a growing one in Africa, although it is not an uncommon feature of young, developing economies, In some countries with intensified social and educational programmes, such as Southern Nigeria, the imbalance between the pace of social and educational development and the rate of economic growth has been acute. In 1958 Houghton quoted an estimate of 5 million migrant labourers in Africa. A recent survey has shown that this figure has increased considerably and the bulk of the increase is made up of young unemployed people. Examination of annual reports from nine African countries over a period of three years (1960–62) and reports from field workers show a steadily rising crime rate in many developing countries, and a lower peak age for crime (i.e. many more younger people commit crimes). This is undoubtedly one result of severe unemployment.

This group of people has formed part of the subject of our study, and the overt psychological reactions resulting from this situation would constitute an interesting chapter in itself. Recent surveys by Raymaekers [6], [7], [8] in the Congo and by Collomb and Ayats[9] in Senegal have dealt fairly comprehensively with much of this aspect of the problem. Sporadic or mass shifts of population to urban areas and to new industrial centres with no infrastructure, or with infrastructure such as a housing programme imperfectly adjusted to the economic possibilities and to the needs of the inhabitants, have been the subject of constant psychosocial surveillance. As many data as possible are being collected on the mental health of seasonal workers and workers taking part in big constructional undertakings and development schemes, such as the Tema harbour in Ghana, the Kariba hydroelectric scheme on the Zambezi, the construction programmes for railways and highways, the Volta River Dam in Ghana, and the Niger Dam in Nigeria. In some of these ectopic and tribally heterogeneous populations of workers, there is normally a floating population of unskilled workers without regular employment, who are, nevertheless, unwilling to leave these newly created centres to take up gainful employment in the rural areas.

In our 1957 "Survey of displaced and detribalized people in Yoruba Country"[10], we found that the morbidity rate, as measured by crime, incidence of venereal disease, indiscriminate and prolonged use of marihuana, alcoholism, psychoneurotic and psychosomatic symptoms, was highest among the group of individuals who were perpetually out of work, who did not have any member of their family with them and who could be strictly termed "migrant labourers" of long duration. We have concluded through these studies that migration—spontaneous and controlled—has much bearing on the adjustment processes of individuals passing from indigenous to industrial economies, from one social class to another, or from rural to urbanized communities. We are confident that the correlation found between certain social factors and the high morbidity rate in this "captive population" is not due to chance, but reflects a trend in a population made up of individuals who are forced to maintain a marginal social relationship to society and are generally under stress.

Taking crime as one of the valid criteria of disturbed mental health or as a psychopathological phenomenon, I can support these findings on the migration differential in mental ill-health with some figures compiled from the lists of three West African countries over a two-year period. The number of offenders who came into this migrant group, and data on their tribal and ethnic origin and length of stay in the locality, were recorded. Approximately 25 per cent (2,057) of all the migrants had previous convictions and over 45 per cent (3,704) were of different tribal or ethnic origin from the local population.

The main crimes were:
    (i) Murder—73 offenders, of whom 37 (50·6 per cent) were long-standing users of *Cannabis indica* with pronounced psychological dependence. Thirty (41·1 per cent) were

migrants aged less than 40 years. Many had been out of work for months.

(ii) Assault and battery—263, of whom 82 (31·1 per cent) had a history of abuse of hemp and 97 (37·5 per cent) were of different tribal or ethnic origin. They were poorly integrated into the community, and many had failed to maintain continuous employment. Nearly 50 per cent of this group were under the age of 30 years.

(iii) Sex offences against women—472, of whom 123 (26 per cent) had a definite history of taking Indian hemp and marginal occupation. Two hundred and seventy-two (57·4 per cent) had no fixed abode, were illiterate, and were socially destitute. Their ages ranged between 27 and 35 years.

Within the past few decades many studies have been directed towards eliciting the differences (possibly cultural, social, psychological and genetic) between people who migrate and those who stay behind. Socioeconomic differentials in the incidence and prevalence of mental disease between these groups have been the subject of intensive studies. The classic works of Ødegaard[11, 12, 13, 14], Jaco[15], and Faris and Dunham[16], to mention a few, are relevant here. Despite minor inconsistencies in the findings, the weight of scientific evidence suggests that migration, especially to urban areas, presents greater mental health risks. Our own analysis of the socioeconomic status of some migrants in Africa has confirmed the more elaborate studies from other countries which show that major differences exist between the socioeconomic structures of migrant and non-migrant populations. The observed variable ("migration" differential) may therefore be reflecting the socioeconomic differential and not migration *per se*, and when this variable is controlled, the differences in the prevalence of psychiatric problems or morbidity rate between migrant and non-migrant populations tend to disappear.

Among some African migrants powerful sociocultural mechanisms exist which act as a safety-valve tending to reduce the development of psychosocial disorders. In Southern Nigeria, hospital admission rates and two major surveys have shown that the Ibo-speaking migrant workers in Yoruba towns have maintained good mental health, comparable to that of the non-migrant Ibo population in the Eastern Region of Nigeria and better than that of the local population of the Yoruba sub-tribe. The Ibo migrant workers have for many years maintained an elaborate social network which has resulted in the formation of "chain migration". This is a form of movement which affords a unique opportunity for prospective migrants to learn current social conditions and opportunities. They are supplied with maximum social and physical infrastructure on arrival (accommodation, membership of tribal association, etc.) and employment is arranged *"by means of primary social relationships with previous migrants"*. This form of chain migration has also produced "chain occupations"—these are particular niches in the Nigerian labour structure to which successive migrants direct and guide their fellows on the basis of their own experience. Associations, community organizations, clans or other forms of segmental solidarity are the essential feature of this new social organization.

Chain migration is a powerful buffer against social isolation, social insecurity and anxiety, in spite of the "negative selection to the under-privileged occupational groups" of these individuals, and this demonstrates how "transferred" traditional institutions and cultural patterns have been effectively utilized as group resources in urban environments to promote effective inner cohesion and to prevent social ills and maladjustment in certain predisposed individuals. It has been said that "human relationships may be highly supportive, even when they are non-personal. It is the merit of a rôle structure that it can support human expectations across the gulf which would otherwise be created by changing personalities"[17].

ADJUSTMENT AND OTHER ADAPTATIONAL CHANGES OF AFRICAN PEOPLES TO WESTERN CULTURE

In Africa, the three phenomena—population increase, changing age structure of population, and population mobility (especially urbanization and social mobility)—have been incriminated as being at the root of most current psychosocial problems in Africa. One of the most striking features of the traditional cultures of Africa is their flexibility, adaptability and other intangible built-in factors for maintaining what might be described as *psychological homoeostasis* in the face of many rapid changes. This inherent property of most of the diverse cultures in Africa has been termed "psychological rebound phenomenon"[18] and has shown itself in the basic psychological structure of the African peoples. It has proved to be the determining factor for maintaining good mental health in spite of the continual social disruption and instability of the transitional culture.

The ability of African peoples to adapt and to adjust themselves to Western culture is reflected in the mental health implications of urbanization and industrialization—in the mental health of students at home and abroad, and in the group psychopathological reactions that are encountered in some areas undergoing rapid social and political changes. Adaptational failure from the standpoint of mental health should be assessed not only by the incidence and prevalence of mental and psychosomatic disorders, but also by such indices as rate of crime, delinquency, alcoholism, prostitution, drug addiction, suicide and illegitimacy.

A summary of two case histories may illustrate certain mentally unhealthy aspects of social change and certain types of social mobility.

(a) Mr. X.A.X., Government scholar, aged 31, single, was admitted to King's College Hospital, London, suffering from severe agitated depression. Earlier he had tried to commit suicide by taking rat poison. During the subsequent interview, he explained his action: "I arrived in this country and found that I was alone in the world and became temporarily panic-stricken.'' He continued: ''On arrival in London, I was most upset by the cold attitude of the English people and more especially of Nigerian friends I used to know at home. I rushed to greet an old Nigerian friend with great emotion but he rebuffed my warm attempt to associate and left me cold, looking silly. I was greatly perturbed by the apparent lack of friendly spirit.''

He went on to describe a breakdown of affective relations with the new society in which he had found himself. He said, ''Also my 'digs' were cold and the other English students, who were much younger than I am, did not seem to have much interest in anybody. I found the method of teaching strange. I became anxious, restless, sleepless and could not concentrate. Everything was unreal. A few days later I began to think people were against me, persecuting me and might even murder me. I thought I would rather do away with myself than allow my 'enemies' to get me.''

This young man came from a semi-rural part of Nigeria. Outside his indigenous social environment and stripped of all the cultural and moral support to which he was accustomed, he developed severe paranoid trends.

(b) O.Y.B., an old lady aged 72, was admitted into Aro Hospital suffering from a confusional state with delusions of persecution. She was brought in by her eldest daughter, a busy professional woman. Her eldest son, a high civil servant, lived in the government quarter in the government reservation area. There were seven children in the family, each of them fairly highly placed. The patient was once the eldest wife in a polygamous home. Until her husband died, a year before her illness, she had always lived in a big village. She then went to live in the city with the youngest daughter who was, according to the patient, far too busy to see her. She was kept in the background and away from her daughter's friends. She became rather depressed because of her loneliness, cultural isolation and the breakdown of effective communication. She noticed, for the first time, that her vision was failing and that memory for recent events was impaired.

Social advances create new demands and many ageing people lack the necessary physical and emotional resources to adopt a new rôle and accept the transformation of values.

Urban social phenomena have inevitably been incriminated as one of the main causes of increased rates of crime, delinquency and other psychopathological phenomena. Thus, such phrases as "delinquency is an urban phenomenon", "crime is the product of transition from rural to urban life", etc., have become well established. This is not strictly true but is an impression transmitted from one group of workers to another. The main error lies in the fact that tribal social life is often (and unconsciously) compared with urban social life when analyses are made. Urban phenomena are always assumed to be destructive by nature and full of problems, but this assumption is not valid. Social disorganization is the main factor whether the environment is urban or rural. Asuni[19] in his study of suicide in Western Nigeria found that the incidence of suicide was higher in rural areas and concluded, ". . . the changes going on . . . are more disturbing to the rural area in terms of disorganization, if we remember that the elders are beginning to lose their grip on the young, and the young are getting dissatisfied with the old, as well as the breaking up of the traditional ways and extended family grouping which are stronger and deeper in the rural areas".

Socioeconomic changes do not always generate disruptive situations. In fact, many examples (e.g. Hoselitz[20]) have been given to show "how the interaction between traditional norms and economic growth may lead to mutually reinforcing trends rather than to irrepressible conflict".

However, an individual coming from a rural environment to an urban area may discover that his behaviour pattern is not appropriate and he may have to alter his customs and adopt new habits in order to participate in urban institutions and structures. His capacity to adapt depends on many factors, among which his perception of the changes in his social environment is important. The way in which an event is experienced, even more than its objective content, has vital psychological consequences.

Disorganization of primary social institutions (i.e. dissolution, fragmentation and lack of functional capacity of the family) is more prevalent in urban areas than in the tribal culture, and forms the core of many social problems. Among other things the city generates a complex pattern of rôle relationships.

Many other features of the urban setting contribute to social disorganization. In many African metropolitan areas, zoning was created by the colonial powers, leading to the creation of segregated areas and the formation of "neutral zones". In the post-colonial era with rapid social, political and technological change, rapid development of many satellite communities has taken place on the periphery of large towns (e.g. squatters in Leopoldville) and these communities have provided the material for special studies of all features of social disintegration. Peri-urban satellite community developments are a new feature of Africa since independence. In many places, because of political and social disequilibrium and consequent economic recession, large groups have inhabited areas on the periphery of big cities. They have no social and physical infrastructure and no legal status for occupation. There are over 35,000 squatters in Leopoldville and the figure is increasing. They form a large section of the city constituting an "area of social disengagement". In this and other similar social groups the morbidity rate is so high and the social stress so evident that the connexion is obvious.

The special features of these peri-urban settings are as follows:

    (i) High morbidity rate, including crime and other psycho-social phenomena.

(ii) Presence of non-traditional and non-supportive child-rearing patterns:

(a) Mental and emotional factors in the development of the child are not given full play; there is no consistent relationship, and other aspects of child-rearing related to emotional security, optimum mental development and expression of drives are defective or neglected.

(b) Stimulation and opportunity for sensory, motor and integrative experience in the environment are considerably reduced.

(c) Communication, empathy, and identification with adults are not normally fostered because of the structure of the family and the group—for example, through loosening of authority (children without fathers).

(d) Expressions of affection, sexual interest and other aspects of intimate relationship are minimal or absent.

(iii) Lack of community support for coping with typical social stresses.

Raymaekers[8], who has made extensive sociological surveys into the general problems of crime, delinquency, and drug addiction and abuse within these socially tenuous communities around Leopoldville, found "an increasing tendency towards theft and violence, particularly in more or less organized juvenile gangs". In a survey of 1,808 houses in Matete, he discovered one hemp dealer for every 56 houses, without taking the undetected dealer into consideration. With regard to the increasingly high rate of juvenile crime in Leopoldville, where two-thirds of the present population consists of persons under the age of 25 years, Raymaekers observed, "The responsibility lies not with the juveniles, but in the obvious lack of social institutions, guidance and supervision. The 'technical' break between the young, urbanized generation and the adults raised in the rural traditions does not make the solution any easier."

In Johannesburg, we discovered a delinquent group composed of largely uneducated or semi-educated individuals generally called the "ducktails". Many of them are potential criminals and they usually form gangs; they are mostly unemployed, and smoke cannabis on a large scale. This sub-cultural group has its own social values and *mores*, with initiation ceremonies for new entrants into the gangs. The sexes are mixed and nearly all come from low socioeconomic strata.

Lastly, to deal briefly with the group psychopathological phenomena that are now being experienced in those parts of Africa which are undergoing rapid changes, I should like to refer to two distinct phenomena—(i) an epidemic syndrome and (ii) recent violent tribal clashes leading to mass slaughter.

(i) Epidemic outbreaks of the "laughing syndrome" in the Bukoba district of Tanganyika and in the Mbale district of Uganda have been reported. This hysterical attack is characterized by episodes of laughing and crying lasting from a few minutes to a few hours, followed by a respite and then a recurrence, accompanied by restlessness and on occasions violence when restrained.

The disease was first noticed on 30th January 1962 in a mission-run girls' middle school in Kashasha village. From that date until now over 1,000 people have been affected. Rankin and Philip[21] reported that most of the victims were adolescent school girls and school boys though adult males and females have also been involved. They further noticed that no literate or relatively sophisticated adult members of society have been affected. Children were affected in such large numbers that many schools had to close.

Kagwa[22] in his more recent observation gave the estimated age distribution as follows:

Age (years)		
Age (years)	6–10	6%
,,	11–40	90%
,,	41–55	4%

and in his comparative study of this phenomenon observes, "One striking feature is the stereotype of symptoms in each particular ethnological group. The 'attacks' and spread of similar symptoms ran along tribal lines. Even in instances where it spread over geographical borders the epidemics affected only members of the same tribe and culture." Kagwa suggested that the cause might be an unresolved emotional conflict resulting from continuous simultaneous exposure at schools and churches to new beliefs and at home to traditional *mores* and folkways.

A different type of these phenomena is seen among the syncretic religious communities in West Africa, for example. We have made observations on the higher distribution of morbidity rates there than among the normal population.

  (ii) Various types of socially and/or legally disapproved mass behaviour (phenomena such as the various manifestations of social and political unrest—embitterment between classes, violent tribal clashes between traditional enemies or between races, massive strikes, etc.) seem to be symptomatic of group anxiety, insecurity and disorganized functioning. There is nothing extraordinary in this, indeed it would be strange if it were otherwise—strange if different periods produced the same or nearly the same patterns of disease or psychosocial reactions.

Before concluding, I should like to point to the major gaps in our present knowledge of urban society in tropical Africa. Considerable but hidden phenomena require further systematic and empirical investigation. Our growing population presses relentlessly and at an accelerating rate upon inadequate resources for health protection and social welfare. The African societies are turning into an increasingly mobile people, pushing away from tribal areas into peri-urban concentrations of shanty towns in which the individual becomes isolated and alienated in a fragmented society of heterogeneous sub-culture, thereby frustrating his expectations, shattering his previous experience and forcing him to become dependent upon synthetic forms of social organization for his emotional security. All this constitutes a "threat to mental health so vast as to dwarf any other". As we are pioneers in research in this and related fields I hope some of my broad generalizations will be forgiven, although the basic facts are common to many of the transitional societies in Africa.

In conclusion, I should like to sound a positive note by re-emphasizing that the traditional cultures of Africa are endowed with a diverse range of built-in adaptive mechanisms, operating through social channels which emphasize traditional human values. In view of the pressing need for a new scientific approach, a multidisciplinary team should be encouraged to investigate more scientific ways of preserving, activating, and mobilizing all these human resources for the balanced survival of our peoples and their optimum functioning in the new world.

SUMMARY

Current socioeconomic changes in Africa and their implications for mental health have been reviewed. Sociodemographic factors (population increase, migration, social mobility), adjustment and other adaptational changes of African peoples to Western culture (urbanization, industrialization), and group psychopathological phenomena resulting from social, economic and political disequilibrium have been examined in the light of their impact on the mental health of individuals.

Through the evaluation of case histories and of data from community surveys, many psychosocial reactions and other manifestations of abnormal behaviour have been found to be associated with adverse socioeconomic factors operating within communities under stress. Thus high rates of delinquency, crime, prostitution, alcoholism, drug addiction, psychosomatic and psychoneurotic manifestations have been recorded in communities which form peri-urban concentrations, and "captive populations" (e.g. factory workers) have been intensively studied in many parts of Africa.

A multidisciplinary approach to the scientific study of current psychosocial problems in Africa has been strongly recommended and emphasis has been laid on the need for a more effective preventive programme to preserve human and other resources of the growing nations of Africa.

DISCUSSION

Acock: Professor Lambo, you apparently related a rising crime rate to economic development in the developing countries. However, the crime rate also seems to be rising in the so-called developed countries. I believe in the necessity for development, so I am rather alarmed to hear such an eminent authority ascribe a rising crime rate to economic progress. I prefer to think that a rising crime rate is a symptom of social and economic change rather than of development as such. Can you reassure me on this point?

Lambo: I agree this is a symptom not so much of development as of the accompanying social dissolution. Such disruptive social changes have been noted to accompany all the economic and social activities labelled "development". Social changes *per se* do not necessarily produce crime, delinquency and other adverse behaviour or social problems, but they may under certain circumstances be accompanied by social dissolution or disorganization which in turn often produces these psychosocial disorders.

Wolstenholme: You referred to the combination of drugs and crime, Professor Lambo. How much is dependence on drugs or addiction to drugs being aggravated by this social disintegration, and how far was it apparent in parts of Africa before development took place?

Lambo: Before major developments in the socioeconomic sphere took place, very little was heard of addiction or abuse of drugs as a national or continental medico-social problem, but since the active process of urbanization began difficulties have been encountered by young people, especially the unemployed, and drug-taking has become an established social malady.

It is extremely difficult to isolate one particular factor from the entire crime picture in Africa now. For example, we know that many delinquent children or young adults take drugs. Many of the young female delinquents are prostitutes, but some have only committed "crimes" which within their cultural contexts do not constitute crimes at all. Because of the differences in the legal systems of the colonial or metropolitan powers (French, British, Belgian, etc.) what is defined as a crime in one area may not constitute a criminal offence in another. This has made the comparison of crime statistics difficult in Africa.

Bourgeois-Pichat: I have always had the feeling that Africa has so far been a lucky continent as regards crime and juvenile delinquency, and in this respect at least has indeed been more advanced than European countries. Africans have established a series of customs that we sometimes have a tendency to regard as superstitions, but I think that ceremonies like the initiation of boys and girls, with all their atmosphere of secrecy, must have a psychotherapeutic effect. Africa, in giving up these ceremonies, may be reverting to the European situation and losing some of its safeguards.

Lambo: I think you are right. As I mentioned in my paper, there are positive cultural factors which could well be used as preventive measures. In many African societies the family structure, social rôles, and ceremonies in the traditional setting act as safety valves. These factors tend to protect individuals from social difficulties such as isolation and economic deprivation. Transition from one culture to another is a very big step in the life of an individual unless there is adequate protection and adequate provision for the changes. It has been shown in one survey, conducted by the Cornell-Aro Group[23] in 15 traditional villages, that a very high proportion of the inhabitants had well-established psychological problems, but these problems were not crippling and of course in a rural area the idea of being emotionally ill does not become so obvious as it does with people who live in cities.

Sutton: In some newer countries, just as in the United States, there is great concern over the difficulties of getting young people into employment. Under-educated young people in the United States constitute a very large proportion of the total unemployed, and so we have a problem very similar to that of the unemployed school-leaver in Africa. In the United States there are complications due to the fact that people of lower-class status, particularly in urban areas, tend to acquire attitudes and values which make it particularly difficult for their children to climb the ordinary ladders of achievement through the schools; they turn instead to patterns of behaviour that are hostile to the main patterns of society and often become delinquent. I don't know whether we have yet got a clear parallel to this in Africa—I hope not—but some of the disorderly behaviour of young people in the towns looks worrisomely familiar.

Mustafa: The material civilization prevailing in the world today has weakened family ties, because it has created a certain degree of economic independence within the family. It also relegates to a background position the spiritual values which used to govern the behaviour of individuals; it is this absence of spiritual values and the weakening of family ties which produce the increase in the rate of crime. In developing countries the rate of juvenile delinquency may be even greater than it is in Europe. Obviously we want Africa to develop, but we are not really learning from world experience; we are inheriting the material civilization which is now prevailing in the world, without doing anything to exclude the evils which accompany it. Can you suggest whether anything can be done about it, Professor Lambo?

Lambo: Very little attention has been paid to these problems by national leaders. Social ills really don't hit you in the face. It is easier to see new buildings and new roads as evidence of progress, but unfortunately delinquency, prostitution, drug addiction and other social disasters accompanying "progress" are often tucked away from full view. Many countries in Africa today continue to over-emphasize material progress but make little or no provision for the social and moral welfare of their people.

Mustafa: Perhaps the African problem is slightly different from the problem of which we see examples in England and most European countries today. As well as the weakening of family ties, there is also often the situation where the parents are less educated than the child and therefore the child tends to pay little attention to the parents; the parents cannot discipline or command the respect of the child. This is an additional problem to the ones already mentioned.

Mesfin: I do not think anybody would connect development as such with some of the ills that have been mentioned by Professor Lambo, but it is a fact that some aspects of development in many of the African countries are actually connected with or accompanied by these ills. As already mentioned, educational development has freed young people from family control, and from certain traditional and cultural values; they have not yet found or fully adopted the Western values, so that at the moment they are really hanging in the air without any values whatsoever. This is, I think, the result of education, which in itself is development.

I would like to think of development as being comprehensive; it should mean not only material development, not only literacy, not only being able to speak English or read English books or French books, etc., but also having some sense of values. The latter are being grasped very slowly and there is really no emphasis on developing some sense of values, whether they be Western or African.

Urbanization is a further evidence of development—to a certain extent it is really a process of development, but we all know how many things are involved in urbanization. It is sufficient to go round this city of Addis Ababa to see the extent to which the traditional values of the people of this country have been greatly distorted and some completely destroyed. If development and these ills that have been mentioned are really connected, the only way to avoid this is to introduce new systems of education based on the cultural values and material needs of the African countries.

Lambo: I agree in principle; there is no doubt that socio-cultural values in all societies in Africa are undergoing radical changes. I was thinking a moment ago not only of the impact which the outside world has had on the cultures of these societies, but also of the impact of traditional African cultures on each other. The point is that in Africa there are many complications—of tribe, language, ethnic grouping, etc. There is a great deal of mingling of cultures and one must expect a period during which a certain amount of disorganization and a certain amount of reorganization occur almost simultaneously. The elements of social change are extraordinary and the interactions very complex. The adverse repercussions of culture changes often resolve spontaneously but one can never be sure when this will happen. One of the most difficult questions is how to obtain a more refined and deeper knowledge of African societies and the social institutions, so that we can select certain elements for emphasis and preservation.

Apeadu: One difficulty is that governments in Africa expect too much from tribal institutions. They consider that everyone in Africa is everybody else's cousin, uncle, or nephew, and that their obligations can be quietly left to the social network. Some evils are inevitable, and in such cases imaginative curative measures are essential. I have in mind the very successful effort made in Israel to integrate immigrants: an immigrant there is really seriously taken in hand and fitted into his new society by many different measures—crash language instruction pro-grammes, teaching in citizenship, trades and finally placement in jobs, settlement in communities, and so on.

Having for some time been associated with voluntary organizations in one of the African countries, I would be the last to say that this job should be left to government organizations alone.

However, I think governments must accept the implications of economic development and realize that where there is displacement of labour, the people have to be looked after, both the young independent people who leave their parents and the parents who are left without security. Unemployment benefits and all the social security provisions that are an accepted government responsibility in modern society will have to be looked at seriously and adopted in some way sooner rather than later. There are still problems even when a job has been secured.

Michaelis: The great effort in Israel to integrate their immigrants comes from the Israeli Army. In the army the young people are taught their new language, Hebrew, and to a great extent also the archaeology and history of their country. Would you take this as a relevant example for your country or any other country in Africa? It may be excellent for Israel, but wouldn't it be difficult here in Africa?

Lambo: In Nigeria we have always looked upon the situation in Israel as a demonstration project or an experimental situation which is closely related to our own problems and those of the rest of Africa. Certainly, the agricultural programme, the development schemes, the sociocultural difficulties and the basic human problems are comparable to the problems that are present in Nigeria—a country of diverse culture and varying rates of change.

Goody: The experience of the developed countries is not enough here. Many of the developing countries tend to limit themselves to importing "social welfare", providing European palliatives for African ills—that isn't enough.

Acock: I have quite a lot of sympathy with African national leaders. I doubt very much whether many of the African countries could afford such expensive programmes. The U.K. National Health Service costs more per head of the population of the U.K. than the total national income per head of Uganda. It is important that we get the facts in their right order and I just wonder what margin is left in the budgets of these African countries to pay for these social services.

Lambo: The problem of industrial welfare as we know it has been the immediate concern of big industries even in Nigeria. The Federal Government of Nigeria does not have to provide for the workers, but one feels that foreign investors and industrial organizations who come to establish themselves in Nigeria should be required to provide the minimum welfare infrastructure for their workers.

Last: I think the answer to Dr. Acock is that in Africa we are now plagued by economists who regard people as mere factors in production, and that the question he posed as to whether the African governments could afford all these things, should have been, to my idea, whether the African governments can afford *not* to put these things into comprehensive planning. We have several examples of the point I was getting at earlier when I said that we did not understand the human requirements which we have to provide for in the basic planning of development schemes. An interesting article[24] appeared a short while ago on the experience of the Sudan. The Gezira was the site of a large development scheme which was supposed to build up into a new community—a new human landscape; but the cotton economy now depends upon a high percentage of migrant labour, which was certainly not the intention in the first place. Unless, right from the beginning or perhaps slightly in advance, we take into consideration and provide all the social and human requirements of the new communities, we are going to produce undesirable results of this type.

Young: Professor Lambo has stressed, as indeed have other speakers, the importance of the family unit in preserving the idea of family life in communities which are undergoing change. I certainly have been very impressed by the need for this in Britain at the present time. I wonder what can be done, either by governments or by any other organizations, to preserve the family unit.

Lambo: I cannot offer any specific plan for the preservation of family ties, but I will again take my lead from what has been done in Israel. There the kibbutzim have really comprehensive community services to look after the children, to keep them occupied, to give them some cultural training, etc.; at the same time the mothers are enabled to play some useful rôle within the community. All this requires well-planned social facilities. In Africa the prevalence of prostitution among the women left behind by their migrant husbands is particularly high and of course this again leads to the breaking-up of the family unit and a definite increase in the divorce rate, in addition to the high incidence of venereal diseases. On the Ivory Coast, for example, 60 to 70 per cent of the able-bodied men are employed every year as migrant workers for about seven to eight months of the year, and as far as I know nothing is done for the families left behind. The kibbutz scheme could well be examined to see whether it could be used in some parts of Africa.

Goody: Such schemes do not necessarily cost a great deal of money. Take the problem of unemployment. A large contributory factor here is the question of rôle expectations. Many of the people who come through primary schools expect to be able to go into clerical occupations, which are limited in number. On the other hand, Africa is a large continent and there is plenty of room for people to undertake more farming, more food production. One of the problems here is to change these rôle expectations which separate people into non-literate farmers and literate others. To do this might lessen the rush into the towns and the consequent unemployment.

Apeadu: Not only do African governments have to consider the question of expenditure, but they also have to look at the relative priorities of what they want to do. All we can hope is that when governments become sufficiently conscious of the necessity to do something in this field, they will rearrange their order of priorities in the development programme so that the urgent aspects of social welfare are given more importance than at present, but in the last analysis no government really has enough money for all the things it should do.

Patel: The question "Can we afford it?" applies especially to education and items like health services, but I am not quite sure that Dr. Acock's comparison earlier was properly posed. It is like saying: "Can we graft the hand of a grown-up onto a child?" The U.K. may be spending *today* on health per head of its population more than the income per head in Uganda. But in, say, Napoleonic times, it may well be that the health expenditure per head in the U.K. was not much more than it is in Uganda today. It is important therefore to change the terms of reference from a static framework to a dynamic framework. If we are taking merely a static situation, why not compare the health expenditure of the U.K. with that in the United States, where they probably spend twice as much burying their dead as they spend in the U.K. keeping people alive? Over the last 150 years, total output in the industrial countries has increased 20 to 30-fold and expenditure on health, education, roads, etc., even more. Uganda may raise its income level at an even faster pace in the years to come and thus provide the enlarged resources from which an increasing share of social expenditure could be provided.

Apeadu: If we regard development as an upheaval which should ultimately, if properly handled, bring about a better state of affairs and better conditions for everybody, we will not then feel so guilty about promoting development: even if it necessarily brings in its train certain evils, it is not something we should be apologetic about. When a big development is going on far away from a centre of population and labour has to be brought in, then one gets all the difficulties of dislocation, unemployment, families being left behind, and disruption that come with it. Where it cannot be avoided, we will have to accept the break-up of the old village community as it was, and whenever possible men should take their wives and children with them. If, as has been the case in some African countries, the worker still wants to go back and maintain his links with the tribal community after some months of working, then this again is something which cannot be helped and we are back again to preventive, corrective, or ameliorating measures.

Brown: Are there signs that the social welfare departments of governments in Africa and voluntary agencies are sufficiently aware of the various components of this problem and are taking steps to develop suitable curricula for the social workers who, one way or another, will have to be concerned with them? Are universities and schools which are training social workers doing so in a manner calculated at least to alleviate the situation? Even if there are insufficient financial resources for big programmes, attention to such details is still important.

Lambo: In Nigeria we are talking with the voluntary organizations about instituting programmes for the whole of Nigeria and about the proposed plan to start a school of social work; we are thinking of approaching international agencies such as U.N.E.S.C.O. for help. We feel that it is very important that we should turn out more social workers. These workers should be trained in Africa in order to be conversant with the current social problems of Africa, and at the same time be aware of the many potential local resources which could be used without falling back on the importation of alien ideas.

I must again emphasize that although governments may indeed be aware of the problems, such schemes are not rated high on the priority list for national planning.

Habte-Ab: It is a great relief to realize that somewhere in Africa today some fundamental work is being done, and that people are studying methodology to help the decision-makers. I think a certain line of action which has been decided by a government should not be subject to an order of priorities. From simple ignorance of what is happening the wrong order may be chosen.

Brown: While the problems of changing values in the spiritual field are rather less tangible, I fully agree with those of the speakers who think they are ultimately of the greatest importance, even if we cannot measure them. But in the meantime we have to face this flood of people into the cities, and from what I have seen in many parts of the world, outside Africa as well as in it, there are very few municipalities or governments which are making any really serious effort to ameliorate the physical situation of fast-growing urban populations.

The population of Leopoldville has more than doubled within a few years, but in 1963 the city had exactly the same number of health personnel as it had before independence.

I would like to think that this was just a matter of economics or lack of personnel, but this is not altogether the case. We tried to get the municipality to understand that attention to the squatting areas was really more important than the maintenance of the former high standards in some of the older parts of the city. This could have been done by a redistribution of available personnel, but we could not get the need for this appreciated.

More attention to town planning could prevent enormously high population densities because there is usually no real shortage of land yet around African cities. While there are economic factors in the way of large-scale development, a great deal more could be done by town-planning and by sanitary control generally than is being done at present in most of the cities which are receiving immigrants.

6

EPIDEMIOLOGY AND THE PROVISION OF HEALTH SERVICES IN AFRICA

H. B. L. RUSSELL*

FRICA has most of the health problems that beset other
continents as well as some specific ones of its own; it also
has an extreme shortage of medical and paramedical
personnel and of auxiliary health workers. There is a particular
shortage of doctors and professional nurses. In this paper it is
intended to touch only on those health problems which are related
to economic development, that is, those problems which are
likely to have an adverse effect on economic development unless
the most scrupulous attention is paid to them during the planning
phase, and those which may be exacerbated or extended by
economic development in the absence of proper preliminary
studies of the health implications.

Malaria eradication

Probably malaria is today the best example of a vector-borne
disease, the eradication of which may profoundly affect all
economic and social development planning. In Africa acute
malaria is said to be predominantly a disease of infants and young
children in whom premunition—the balance between immunity
and re-infection—has not yet been established. It is a cause of
very heavy mortality both by itself and in combination with other
factors. In Africa, on account of the habits of the vector mosquito,
eradication of malaria is more complicated than in other parts of

* In the absence in Europe of Dr. Russell, this paper was presented for him
by Dr. Brown.

146

the world. Possibly Ceylon has presented the most spectacular results of a successful malaria eradication campaign. In the words of Professor Cullumbine[1], "The intelligent use of D.D.T. has reduced the morbidity and mortality from malaria to remarkably low levels. This has brought, too, a decrease in the maternal and the infant mortalities, and a fall in the death rates from many other causes such as pneumonia, dysentery, etc." Professor Cullumbine also points out that the absolute number of deaths in Ceylon declined from 136,000 per year for the period 1943–46, to 95,000 in 1947–50, a decline of 30 per cent despite a rise in the population.

From this example it will be clear that when a malaria eradication programme is put into effect it may totally upset a country's development planning unless the results have been assessed and allowed for. The survival of large numbers of infants and children who formerly would have died means that additional facilities and services have to be provided, including education, food supplies and, later, work opportunities.

This is, of course, an over-simplification, and no doubt infant diarrhoea and other gastrointestinal diseases will continue to cause high mortality within the age group in question, but the fact remains that the immediate repercussions of a successful malaria eradication campaign may be serious unless development planning is flexible enough to absorb them.

Bilharziasis

Another very important health problem in Africa is the increasing incidence of bilharziasis throughout the continent. The pressing needs of African countries for water, electricity and irrigation have brought about a big increase in irrigation projects, the construction of large dams for hydroelectric power, and industrial and irrigation purposes, and of small dams to provide water, particularly in arid areas, for agricultural and other purposes. All this activity in the development of water supplies has unfortunately resulted in a wider dissemination of bilharziasis.

The disease is carried by freshwater snails which exist in many parts of the continent and they may also be carried from one place to another mechanically.

Unfortunately the uninfected snail may be easily infected by settlers moving into newly opened agricultural areas and generally speaking it is extremely difficult to control infected migrants. The spread of the disease is clearly caused by absent or faulty environmental sanitation and lack of education. Snails are infected by infected persons urinating or defaecating in the immediate vicinity of irrigation canals or bodies of water formed for one of the purposes referred to above. The parasite develops in the snails and an infective form known as a cercaria, capable of penetrating the skin, is released into the water. In this way people become infected while wading or walking or paddling or washing, for example. When water levels are low the concentrations of cercariae are correspondingly higher and infection is more likely at such a time.

The disease and its sequelae are extremely serious, the population becoming greatly debilitated and their work output consequently lowered. One form of the disease especially attacks the intestine and the other the bladder, but any part of the body can be affected. The sharp-spined eggs of this parasite have been found in the brain, spinal cord, eye, throat, lip, and the male and female genital organs: the liver and spleen are particularly liable to be attacked. In Africa the disease has so far reached its highest prevalence and greatest public health importance in Egypt.

There is a clear need therefore to associate the health authorities with the earliest stages of planning for irrigation or other purposes involving the impounding or controlled use of water. This is particularly important where arid lands are to be irrigated because the same factors that make an area suitable for human occupation make it a satisfactory habitat for the types of snail which carry the infection.

Mass treatment of populations has been found to be difficult in practice and the results not very satisfactory. Screening of settlers has also been tried but in practice some infected person usually manages to get through the screen. Nor can we expect very much by way of improvements in environmental sanitation until the general economy, education and living standards reach higher levels. Therefore at present the principal method of interrupting the transmission of the disease is the destruction of infectible snails by physical means and use of molluscicides. The prevention of human contact with infected waters and the provision of water supplies and sanitation also contribute to the control of the disease, especially in areas where irrigation farming is not practicable. I do not propose to discuss the methods of control and treatment of already infected areas of water, but I would like to ask the question recently posed by a colleague of mine, namely, ''How many planners of irrigation schemes pause to consider that in a typical area of perennial irrigation the canals serve not only as a source of water for crops but also for bathing and all other domestic purposes including the disposal of the human excreta and other wastes? It would be hard indeed to contrive a better way of ensuring the transmission of filth-borne diseases.''

Guinea worm infection

Guinea worm infection is a condition not generally regarded as very important, but I have seen whole villages crippled by it and unable to work at important times of the year when they need to be out on their farms, and the result may be economic disaster for small communities. It is not a difficult condition to deal with. Human beings are infected by drinking water containing infected water-fleas, and here again the provision of wells or some other appropriate safe water supply will eliminate or make it much easier to control the infection.

MODERN TRANSPORT AND THE SPREAD OF DISEASE

The construction of trunk roads and the development of inland water-ways are economically beneficial, but at the same time dangerous to health. This is particularly so where they are intended to link areas such as north and west Africa which have been isolated by physical barriers since the beginning of time, or across which travel has in the past been so slow and painful a proceeding as virtually to eliminate the possibility of serious disease spread by this means. The real dangers that will arise from the development of fast north-south and east-west highways in Africa are smallpox, meningococcal meningitis, typhus and relapsing fevers, bilharziasis and other parasitic diseases, gastro-intestinal diseases and, depending on the epidemiological situation in countries with connexions to the south, yellow fever and plague. The health administrations of countries along the routes of such highways—in particular trans-Saharan highways—should be consulted at every stage of planning and development, appropriate measures being drawn up for a good system of hygiene and sanitation, including the provision of safe water supplies for residents and travellers. Vector control measures and anti-epidemic measures may also prove to be necessary to protect recipient populations.

Population mobility also possesses other peculiar dangers in Africa. In areas where human trypanosomiasis is present or where favourable ecological conditions for the tsetse fly exist, a mobile population adds considerably to the risk of outbreaks of sleeping sickness in man unless appropriate measures are taken to provide an environment unfavourable to tsetse flies, or tsetse fly control is undertaken. Population mobility relates closely to population density and the patterns of settlement and migration are factors that must also be taken into account when development of areas within the tsetse fly belt is being planned. Another disease that may become extremely important in Africa as the population becomes more mobile is that known as Bancroftian filariasis. This disease is caused by a parasite carried by a mosquito with a propensity for breeding in small domestic sources of water. It causes elephantiasis, a gross swelling of the arms or legs or of the external genitalia, sometimes including the breasts in women, and it is found over a wide range of tropical Africa. In some parts of

Asia the increasing mobility of the population has meant that filariasis is being found as a local infection in many areas where it was not previously known to exist. For example, during my last visit to the city of Bangalore in India cases were for the first time being reported which must have been contracted in the city. Previously filariasis has been mainly a disease of the coastal regions of India. Once this disease is established control of the vectors is difficult and expensive. Fortunately, mass treatment may go a long way towards eradicating it. However the proper town planning and development of urban areas and the organization of health services for them would go far towards reducing the risk of infection with filariasis and would prevent a great deal of unnecessary suffering.

Smallpox

Smallpox remains a very serious problem over wide areas of Africa and its spread is likely to be facilitated by the development of fast road systems unless energetic measures are taken to eradicate it. Freeze-dried vaccine is now available which is stable and can be carried for long periods without cooling or refrigeration, thus enabling it to be taken to remote places. However, it is important that smallpox eradication procedures should be devised which will ensure that all the population at risk are vaccinated and that their vaccinations are successful. The hit-and-miss method of vaccinating travellers at river or frontier crossings or other strategic places has little place in the eradication of smallpox since nobody knows what happens either to the traveller or his vaccination as soon as he is out of sight of the vaccination station. Smallpox is a costly and unnecessary scourge which with organization could be liquidated in African countries, thus putting an end to the continued drain on money and personnel in attempts to control it. Smallpox has a high mortality and causes blindness and other complications, thus adding to the burden of the unfit. It also dislocates the normal functioning of any community in which it occurs.

EFFECT OF THE BEEF TAPEWORM ON THE MEAT INDUSTRY

One hears a great deal in Africa today about the development of meat industries and many countries hope to become exporters of meat to markets inside and outside Africa in due course. Alongside the establishment of slaughterhouses, secondary industries based on by-products can be set up. Some countries have established meat-canning plants as well. It is necessary to point out that where the beef tapeworm is very common, a fresh meat industry is unlikely to be developed unless some steps are taken to reduce the incidence of this parasite in cattle. On aesthetic grounds the great meat-eating countries of the world would be likely to reject tinned meat which they know to be produced from "measly" beef, more especially where alternative sources of supply from known clean meat are available. The remedy in this case lies in improving environmental sanitation in cattle areas, and in particular in educating the population in the sanitary disposal of excreta. Too often villagers use the pastures around their houses or villages for the purposes of defaecation and then bring their cattle onto the same area at night for safety. Some method needs to be devised to break this chain, particularly where people are accustomed to eat their beef raw or very under-cooked. From faeces to food is not a chain of events likely to gratify the tastes of advanced populations.

PROVISION OF HEALTH SERVICES

Data concerning the personnel available to staff health services in Africa were supplied to the World Health Organization for its Second Report on the World Health Situation, 1957–60[2], by 30 countries, of which only 23 attempted to relate the number of doctors to the size of the population and none of them indicated how many of these doctors were nationals of their countries. Also, a number of countries included medical assistants under the heading of doctor, and the figures provided for nursing personnel did not distinguish professional nurses from midwives and nursing auxiliaries. If these facts are borne in mind when the available data are examined, it is clear that a very severe shortage of all categories existed during the period under review, a shortage which has probably become more, rather than less, acute during the past four years. How then can the essential curative and preventive services, which constitute the health services of any country, best be provided in order to deal with the existing situation, and what should be the future policy for training personnel for African health services?

Medical education of doctors and nurses

The type of medical education which has so far been provided for African doctors—and I am not now speaking of medical assistants—has been either that provided for medical undergraduates in the more highly developed parts of the world or that based on the same kind of medical education transplanted to Africa. By and large, therefore, African doctors, like many of their Asian colleagues, have been trained to practise medicine in the European tradition. One of the results of this is that African doctors often find difficulty in accustoming themselves to working in their own countries and in fact try to reproduce for themselves the working conditions under which they have been trained. They are trained mainly in the field of clinical medicine but in practice have to work in countries where the problems are largely either mixed or purely preventive. For some years, however, people concerned with medical education in many countries have been aware of this problem and it is now coming to be realized that the medical curriculum must be adjusted in Africa to ensure that students receive a carefully balanced picture of the curative and preventive aspects of African illness and disablement, with not too much emphasis on the hospital and clinic and plenty of emphasis on the social and community aspects of disease. In Africa the general practitioner should in fact be the mainstay of the health services and through a broad medical education he should be able to appreciate the public health aspects of problems which confront him and not think of medicine as something which is practised only in a consulting room, clinic, or operating theatre.

The same considerations apply to the training of nurses. Traditionally these are professional workers in hospitals and indeed hospitals are seriously understaffed. Nevertheless public health should be integrated into the training syllabus for nurses so that they too may be fully aware of the patient as an individual with a home, a family, and a social background of which notice must be taken, and not merely as a number on a bed or a walking treatment sheet in a clinic. Africa cannot afford the luxury of a one-sided approach to health problems and it is essential that all its professional staff shall be as broadly trained as possible. It is of some interest that the number of female nurses in a country provides an indication of the degree of that country's development. This is because professional nursing education presupposes that women have reached a certain level of education which is sufficient for them to enter professional life.

When we speak of medical and nursing education we are dealing with professions which require students of the highest possible educational level and which provide courses of instruction lasting for doctors for at least five years, and for nurses three to four years. It will obviously be a long time before Africa can provide itself with the fully qualified staff required for its health services on this basis, and the alternative is to make use of whatever personnel is available at lower levels of education. These workers might be trained to provide the bulk of required health services and could relieve the doctor and the professional nurse of much of the burden of routine clinical work in hospital outpatient departments, clinics, rural health centres and the like. Thus, many countries have experimented with the use of medical assistants and found them very useful. However, they too are often only single-purpose workers trained to relieve the clinician of some of his clinical work. Ideally, this type of worker—and I believe that Africa can use them in very large numbers—should be given a balanced picture of the diseases and conditions which he is taught to handle, and his general training should emphasize public health and community medicine. He may require as long as three years of training—some countries give an even longer period—but there should always be a sufficient gap both in his educational level and in the type of training so that he understands himself to be, not a doctor cheated of his proper status, but a paramedical health worker in his own right. Governments employing this type of worker should be careful to ensure that a properly planned career and promotion structure is set up for the grade. The selection of trainees for this type of work requires careful consideration. For work in rural areas people should be chosen who preferably will go back and work in the areas from which they come. Selection by examination and educational level alone generally favours the youngster brought up in a town and experience in many countries has shown that such people are often not only out of touch but also quite out of sympathy with rural populations.

As regards nurses, here again a number of countries employ auxiliary staff in order to make the best use of available personnel at all levels of education. Auxiliary nurses or nurse-midwives usually carry out very well the nursing duties which they are taught to do, of course under the supervision of professional trained nurses. It is generally desirable that such people should be trained in their own language and not in a foreign tongue. For one thing the latter restricts the choice to a specific level of education in most countries and also tends to limit it more definitely to the urban areas. In India a grade known as an "auxiliary nurse-midwife" was trained on a $2\frac{1}{2}$-year syllabus which proved invaluable in developing health services, particularly in rural areas.

Training in environmental sanitation

The training of personnel for work in the field of environmental sanitation is of course of special importance in Africa, where so many of the besetting health problems are related to major sanitary defects, and most African countries have trained cadres of such workers. However it must be realized that the adoption of higher standards of environmental sanitation depends on many things, most of them not concerned purely with health. No amount of talking or lecturing will persuade people on a very low economic level to adopt measures for which their social situation does not make the need clear: as the standard of living rises, so does the call for better sanitation and housing and improvements in the environment. The first need therefore is a buoyant, rising economy, and the rest will surely follow. There is of course some difference between the type of work performed by a sanitarian in an urban area and one in a rural area. The urban community requires continual sanitation inspection to ensure that standards are maintained. The rural community needs above all health education and provision of safe water supplies as well as immunization against certain endemo-epidemic diseases. The rural sanitarian should be able to provide these, as well as other sanitation services which the community may need. Where the need is not felt, the sanitarian should endeavour to make it so.

At the moment sanitary engineers are trained in Africa only in the United Arab Republic. Doubt has been expressed by some as to the necessity and desirability of training engineers specifically in this field at the present time, but when one thinks about it there are many fields of activity, notably in urban areas, where the services of sanitary engineers are essential, such as town planning, housing, pipe-borne water supplies and cleansing. Sanitary engineers have a very important part to play in the design, implementation and maintenance of all these activities and systems. It seems to me essential that as soon as possible schools should be set up, one in an English-speaking and one in a French-speaking area of Africa south of the Sahara, so that engineers may be trained in their own environment amongst their own problems.

Apart from these categories of workers, there are of course many other paramedical and auxiliary health workers who are essential to the organization and running of any health service. They are the people who are required in order that hospitals and laboratory services may run smoothly and efficiently, and it is usually possible to find sufficient candidates to train for such jobs.

When we come to consider who shall train the types of worker whom we have discussed we enter the field of economics; for medical education, although it has prestige, is also extremely costly to start and to maintain; it is a wise country that knows its own limitations in this field and joins with its neighbours in providing educational and training centres at sub-regional level for its professional health staff (for example doctors, nurses and sanitary engineers) and other grades of specialized staff such as radiographers and certain levels of laboratory workers. Training facilities provided on this basis would surely be the most economical means of developing health services in Africa at the present time, in circumstances where a non-African language is the one of choice for teaching.

These are some of the problems facing Africa today in the development of its health services and related to the present pace of economic development on the continent. We must ensure that we do not penalize future generations by failing to co-ordinate the planning of many facets of national development in these countries.

SUMMARY

The main health problems of Africa which are likely to be adversely influenced by measures of economic development, or which may themselves have an adverse effect on that development unless adequately anticipated in any plans for national development, are discussed.

Mention is made of the likely effects of a successful malaria eradication campaign and of the effect on the incidence of bilharziasis of the increasing construction and use of irrigation systems unless specially designed with this problem in mind.

Problems that may be posed by the construction of trunk roads and the development of internal water-ways are referred to. Conditions such as trypanosomiasis, filariasis and smallpox are discussed in this connexion.

The presence of the beef tapeworm is discussed in relation to the development of export trades in hides and fresh meat.

The problem of finding the trained personnel needed to develop adequate health services is examined. Emphasis is laid on the need to ensure that in medical and other health training a balanced picture of the preventive and curative aspects is given to students. The desirability of developing an integrated approach to health problems is emphasized as the most economical way to use available personnel. The development of sub-regional educational and training centres for professional health personnel is proposed.

DISCUSSION

Michaelis: Would the experience of Australia with the flying doctor service be of benefit in Africa? The somewhat expensive service of doctors flying in special aircraft to the site of an accident would probably be quite uneconomical, but what about the auxiliary services—the very small radio station in either a village or a house which could contact a special centre for medical advice and consultation? This can be a relatively cheap way of getting medical advice in remote areas. I understand that there was some such experiment in Nigeria.

Lambo: The experiment has gone very well indeed in Northern Nigeria, especially in isolated villages and hamlets, where the question of transportation has become a problem of major importance. There are of course difficulties in maintaining the aircraft and in getting suitable and willing pilots.

Brown: Communications are crucial if there is an outbreak of communicable disease. Measures are analogous to those of a military operation, and every hour is important. It often takes three days or more for a man on foot or a mule to get to the nearest health centre, and from there again more hours or days by whatever transport there is to the nearest town with a telephone. Often it is a matter of four or five days before a competent authority can begin to take any action, and then they have to go all the way back along the line. As an epidemic may well have been going on for a week before the local people realize anything is wrong, the outbreak has probably done most of the damage it is going to do before help arrives. Then of course we have the added problem of getting a correct diagnosis early. Health personnel cannot know what to take with them if they do not know what they are going to face.

It is as well to have some idea of the gravity of what we are talking about. Malaria is common enough, but in Ethiopia in 1959 an epidemic was superimposed upon the normal incidence of the disease, and the estimated number of deaths in about 18 months was a minimum of 100,000 and may well have been higher than 300,000. In such a situation health personnel without communications are helpless.

The yellow fever epidemic in Ethiopia a little earlier was not so vast in magnitude, but in the areas where it struck, it struck very hard. The Pasteur Institute Report on it reads like Thucydides' description of the plague in Athens in 430 B.C.—some villages just disappeared, or often only a few families were left. Here again people were struggling with this overwhelming catastrophe in isolated, almost unapproachable country, with no radio, no telephone, no nothing!

Michaelis: What about a regular daily service by crystal radio stations to solve this problem of communications? I do not know the technical problems here, but originally in Australia it was a pedal service, run by pedalling a bicycle wheel which generated the electric current. Something equally simple and equally cheap would no doubt provide the necessary communication in the event of a major epidemic.

Would the malaria epidemic you mentioned have been quite so severe if its existence had been known in the very early stages?

Brown: I think if we had known in the earlier stages, it would have made some difference. What would a radio network of this type cost? Are we talking about 10 dollars or 10,000 dollars?

Michaelis: It might not be more than 50–60 dollars; if the sets were mass produced it might even be cheaper. Nowadays, of course, batteries and transistors are used, which use even less current, but in various parts of Australia since about 1929 thousands of generators have been run just by pedalling a bicycle wheel. The range of such a radio is 100–200 miles, depending on the land configuration.

Young: Is there somewhat of a paradox in that the treatment of epidemics is difficult because of the lack of communications, but on the other hand improved communications increase the risk of the spread of epidemics?

Brown: Yes, but when communications are improved, we hope there will also be improved general development, which gives a better chance of control.

Dr. Russell sounds a warning in his paper. If a Trans-Saharan Highway is to be built, then it should be realized from the beginning that it is going to create some important health problems. Don't let us have a situation there like that which occurred with the bilharziasis problem in the Gezira Plain project, where, as it were, a happy Minister of Agriculture goes to his Prime Minister with a smiling face and says: "Look how wonderfully we are getting on!" and then two or three years later a very melancholy Minister of Health goes in to see the Prime Minister in his turn and says: "Can I have so many millions to clear up the mass of human disease that this project has caused?"

Dr. Russell has drawn your attention to this kind of problem, but I would just like to read you one short paragraph from a paper about the Gezira Plain project:

"From the inception of the scheme the inherent danger of the establishment of bilharziasis in the Gezira was realized. It was stated in the Sudan Medical Service Annual Report for 1925 that if this were to occur the result would be disastrous and probably be irretrievable. It was realized that conditions were eminently suitable and that an infection might ultimately not only approach the situation prevailing in the Egyptian Delta but even surpass it in severity, in view of the warmer water temperatures all the year round and the resultant probability of growing infection. The history of the taking root of the disease in the Gezira within the past 30 years is a most dismaying example to all authorities facing a similar problem now and in the future.''

I won't go on with the rest of it, but it has been costing a good deal of money to try to keep this disease out.

Sutton: How long did it take to get established?

Brown: The snails were found within a year or two of the commencement of the project, and then infection got in and there was a slow increase. It was not recognized as a serious public health problem for the first ten or fifteen years. As the years have gone by the rise has been steady but slow. More health resources have been brought in to deal with it, but they have not yet, as far as I know, fully halted the rise. I don't know so much about the benefits of this whole project, though I understand that there are considerable achievements in the overall view, but some of the benefit is being lost now because the people may well not be healthier or happier than they were when the project started.

When we were discussing Professor Lambo's paper I was very glad to hear somebody use this word ''happiness''. Whatever we do to promote social and economic development our ultimate aim is to increase the sum total of human happiness and contentment. To increase the gross national product is not an aim in itself; the aim to which we are moving is a happier and more contented world, and a double income does not compensate a man with a chronic disease.

Apeadu: Just as a matter of interest, without going into great detail, what should they have done that they did not do on this project? What did they delay doing?

Brown: I think there was some realization of the problem from the beginning, but control measures available in 1925 were inadequate to prevent the spread of the disease. This is still an important unsolved problem on which much research work is being done.

Two specific examples may give point to a discussion of this kind. In Ethiopia recently a report appeared of a survey carried out in the township of Adowa with a population of about 10,000. Through this village flows a small stream, perhaps 2·0 to 2·5 metres wide. The population themselves through the local Governor-General approached the health personnel stating: ''We have a problem and we don't know what to do about it''. A rapid survey showed that 60 per cent of a sample of the population had infected stools and 80 per cent had positive skin tests.

Bilharziasis is spreading quite rapidly in some parts of Ethiopia and the Awash Valley Authority is most certainly going to have to watch this particular problem very carefully. But if you ask the World Health Organization for a definite assurance that specific measures will keep the disease out, the answer still is ''No''. The best advice we can give is that basic health services should be provided as part of the general programme for socio-economic development—particularly health education and good sanitation. In Adowa school, for example, there are some 2,000 children but only one latrine used by 37 teachers. The students defaecate in or near the stream in which the population also wash themselves and their clothes and from which they even take drinking water. This is a real-life situation; there are hundreds of little towns like Adowa in Africa.

Mustafa: The reference which has been made to the Gezira scheme raised a number of very important problems, and every point raised in the first part of Dr. Russell's paper is illustrated by what has happened in the Gezira. We had a number of epidemics—smallpox, bilharziasis, malaria, and other things—which adversely affected the economy of the country and did much to reduce the benefits of the scheme, but the lessons from that particular scheme were fairly well learned.

When the new extension of the scheme was started, a number of measures were taken which were specifically designed to avoid the early catastrophes. These included, of course, a supply of safe water for each community, but of equal importance was the establishment of what are called social development centres. The purpose of these centres is to try and educate the tenants, telling them not to use the canals for bathing or defaecating, and teaching them the basic rules of hygiene and sanitation. On the staff there are men to teach the men and women to teach the women. This is also being done in the newly established agricultural settlement in Khasm el Girba. Although bilharziasis has not been completely eradicated from this area, the situation is definitely better than it was in the Gezira scheme. My point is that if we become aware of the problem and take some measures to avoid it, it can be avoided to some extent.

Brown: What proportion of the cost of the Gezira scheme has been expended on health services?

Mustafa: The whole scheme is run on a partnership basis between the government and the tenants. The income is divided in such a way that the government takes 40 per cent and the tenants take 42 per cent, the administration costs about 8 per cent and the other 10 per cent is devoted to social development (including health), so the government and the tenants are each partly paying for it.

Dekker: The provision of a community water supply in rural areas should not be undertaken on its own, simply as a technological programme, but should be fully integrated into a scheme for improving life in rural areas generally, and should form part of a community development programme. I have seen more than one village in Africa where, after provision of a community water supply, health conditions deteriorated instead of improved. Mosquitoes bred in the village itself instead of two miles away at the site of the previous water supply. Sufficient education and improvement of community life as a whole must be achieved simultaneously to have any effect on health.

In a recent paper[3] it was estimated that the total cost of supplying the present population of Africa south of the Sahara with a safe water supply would be U.S. $7,000,000,000. This surely would have an alarming effect on the budgets of governments or on the financial resources available for development generally, and proves again that even though health measures should really be considered as part of development, for simple financial reasons they cannot be given top priority.

Lambo: Yesterday I learned for the first time of the acute water shortage in the continent of Africa, and I have been thinking that in the United States of America vast areas are acutely short of water partly because of industrial pollution. Pollution of rivers has lately appeared also in some parts of Africa—certainly in Nigeria where industries are now being sited near rivers in which there is already evidence of the harmful effects of waste products. I feel that the countries in Africa should be made very much aware of this; it will probably add in the long run to their difficulties if it is allowed to go on now without proper supervision and control.

Brown: A consultant in Addis Ababa reports that the problem is a growing one. Of course it is particularly serious where there is a big seasonal difference in the rate of flow, so that what is relatively minor pollution at one time of the year becomes a grave problem when in the dry season the rivers dwindle to small streams.

I am sure Dr. Russell would agree that the provision of an adequate water supply should be part of an overall programme and not just a health undertaking. Where a water supply is created it must be safe water; whether it is through irrigation canals, pipe supplies or whether it comes from wells, the final result to the population must be an asset and it is not going to be an asset if the water brings disease. Hence the need to look at the health aspects every time one thinks about creating a pool of water or a running water supply somewhere, since without health education the water will be used to bathe in, to defaecate in and for every conceivable purpose in addition to that for which it is primarily provided. Health departments have to be alert and vigilant not only about their own tasks but also about the plans of every other department in administration or government.

Last: Once again we have arrived at the point where in development schemes in Africa some kind of comprehensive action and study are required. We have the connexion between the provision of water and the spread of malaria. The Highways Department constructs a road, the population then migrates towards the road and areas where the Ministry of Education has built schools become depopulated. One then has to build a new set of schools. All sorts of interactions result from any sort of development scheme. It seems that the idea of comprehensive planning to which much lip-service is now paid by governments is, in fact, still very much in the textbook stage or confined to university circles.

We must have a structure within governments which reflects the need for comprehensive planning. I wonder how many African countries at this moment have such joint development relations between different Ministries at the level at which it is going to be effective—I don't think it will be effective at ministerial level, but perhaps at the head of department level where joint action needs to go all the way, through research, planning and implementation. Unless this sort of structure is set up, then all our development programmes in Africa are going to be delayed and hindered and some of them are going to come to disaster quite unnecessarily. Most African countries have taken over the administrative structures of Western European countries without relating them to the special needs of an underdeveloped and rapidly developing Africa.

Brown: I should like to suggest one way of looking at the investment in health. If we imagine a rectangle representing activities influencing development in a country, and another rectangle representing the health programme, then there is an overlapping portion (Fig. 1). Part of the health expenditure contributes directly to economic development (the overlapping part). The remainder represents social benefits. The individual is not much missed—just one more person dead and gone, and his departure really does not make much difference to the economic development of the country. But the individual has a

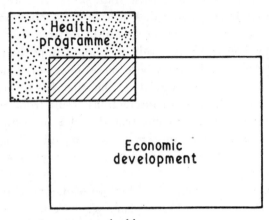

Fig. 1 (Brown). Investment in health.

 The part of the health programme which contributes directly to economic development, e.g. malaria eradication.

The part of the health programme which is a part of the social services, e.g. hospital services.

Both parts are intermingled and cannot be separated, but a given programme can be designed to accent one or the other.

social value which everybody recognizes. In a rich country there need be a relatively small overlap, but in a poor country it should be fairly large. When it comes to priorities between the sections in budgeting expenditure in the health field, the first question is how much can be spent on the health programmes which contribute directly to economic development (as somebody said: "A government cannot afford *not* to do it"). Then what is left over can be allocated to the programmes—like hospitals—which contribute to social services.

The population always exerts rather greater pressure towards the activities represented by the " social " area of the rectangle, and it seems to me that governments have to choose between two issues: (1) how much of their health activity is going to be oriented towards curative and how much to preventive medicine, and (2) in countries like Ethiopia, are they going to make an effort to cover the country with relatively low-grade trained personnel, or are they going to concentrate on a few highly trained personnel and leave the rest of the country more or less untouched until such time as money becomes available and the high quality can spread?

I think I am right in saying that the Soviet Union decided that it would strongly emphasize the preventive aspects of medicine right from the very beginning, and cover the whole country first with relatively low-grade trained personnel, in the hope that the quality could be raised later. The countries in Africa have just these same decisions to make now. The relative importance of training doctors and nurses to professional level and of training auxiliary personnel—these are decisions to be made at the highest level of government policy. A government should indicate to the health department its general policies and how much money it is prepared to spend on health. Health officials can then make their plans accordingly.

Lambo: Improved intercommunication by radio and by plane is one answer to epidemics, but this will not solve the problem which should be tackled by health education in Africa. When this is done, it should be done within the cultural framework and not by importing into Africa intensive health education programmes based on those in Great Britain and the United States, because that would definitely fail. To give you an example, public health officials several years ago visited some villages in Africa, called the elders together and gave them a talk on the importance of having pit latrines in the villages as a major public health measure. Without much persuasion the latrines were dug by the villagers and the advisers went on their way. After a month they came back to find that although the pit latrines were dug, nobody had used them at all. The advisers had forgotten to take into consideration the cultural concepts of the people, such as their belief that one's waste products—urine, stools, nail parings, etc.—could be used by an enemy if the enemy knows their whereabouts.

I have been thinking of the problem which we have been investigating in Nigeria—the estimation of neurosis in industry. I am on the Nigerian Aptitude Testing Council and I am very much aware of the fact that many expatriate officials in Nigeria and elsewhere in Africa have been complaining of the inefficiency of African workers, their frequent or chronic absenteeism and so on, and it is our major work to investigate this.

The many handicaps African workers really face are obvious to most of the people sitting round this table; there are not only emotional or psychological problems, but also physical ones. Most people are loaded all their lives with parasites, they also subsist on low wages, and undernutrition is prevalent.

Wolstenholme: As we are coming towards the end of this discussion, it might be worth while making a slightly more cheerful remark.

It is being suggested that everything that we do in Africa is going to have some dire effect, and I should like to add a comment on Professor Lambo's mention of multiple and chronic illness. It has been said that he is a lucky African who has only one disease. In vast areas of Africa nutritional deficiencies aggravate the debility due to parasitic diseases and other infections, such as tuberculosis and syphilis. The detrimental effects on the people's general level of energy and initiative are incalculable.

Just imagine what positive results might be expected if health services and health education could eliminate even one of the major causes of debilitation. People in Europe are often inclined to think that any African who is lucky enough to enjoy the sun is incurably lazy; people in the southern states of America were similarly regarded until the Rockefeller Foundation, in its first great medical work, brought about the eradication of hookworm—the almost universal prevalence of which had been indignantly denied by most people living in the south—and so stopped this anaemic drain on energy and well-being.

My own belief is that there is waiting to be released in Africa a tremendous force of energy, not only for material development but also for richer enjoyment of human happiness.

7

LAND AND AIR TRANSPORT WITHIN
THE CONTINENT OF AFRICA*

A. M. HEGAZY

D EVELOPMENTS are taking place in Africa which are creating a new status for African countries, both within the continent and on the world stage. These countries have varying problems, varying interests, and are in varying stages of development, but they all have obligations and responsibilities. Undoubtedly the pattern of the African community is changing quickly in the political, economic and social fields.

Both for internal consumption and use, and to a greater extent for their export earnings, African countries depend predominantly on primary products such as foodstuffs and raw materials, but world demand for primary products tends to grow more slowly than the demand for manufactured goods. Apart from subsistence agriculture, therefore, there is typically a heavy dependence on exports of primary commodities to unstable world markets.

Economic growth and the achievement of a higher standard of living depend primarily on land and air transportation for both passenger services and goods traffic. A growing need for better means of transport within the African continent and to overseas countries may therefore be expected.

Although trade statistics in general are not very accurate, the broad proportions of present trade within Africa are as follows:

---

* Dr. Hegazy was unable at the last moment to attend the meeting. His paper could only be made available afterwards and there was therefore no discussion of it at the meeting.

Almost 60 per cent is accounted for by food, drink and tobacco; about 15 per cent by raw materials; rather more than 3 per cent by fuel; about 3 per cent by chemicals; about 1·5 per cent by machinery, and about 18 per cent by other manufactures. In absolute terms, trade within the sub-regions in food, drink and tobacco and other manufactures can be expected to increase sharply[1].

The crucial problems facing the African people centre around the ways in which the pace of economic development can be increased:

(a) by the expansion of the agricultural sector, particularly in terms of higher output per head, resulting naturally in higher national incomes and purchasing power;

(b) by better exploitation of mineral and natural resources, leading to increased use of raw materials and the growth of industrialization;

(c) by commodity exports, which are the main source of foreign exchange earnings but which are subject to great fluctuations in world markets, both in the quantities which can be sold and in price levels. In general the prices of the export commodities of the developing countries tend to be stable or move downwards, while the prices of imported manufactured goods move upwards.

Inevitably, as history shows, industrial growth proceeds in stages up to the manufacture of capital goods such as machinery. The necessary process of industrial growth and other developments in the various sectors of the African economy—agriculture, construction and tourism—will call for parallel developments in the means of transport and communication, which are also of vital importance for security and defence. The scope of transport studies is wide, but it is important to assess what each country wants to achieve, both for freight and passenger services, and to decide priorities. A national plan for transport facilities, routes and organizations is essential, and this should be linked with social and economic programmes.

There is no single recipe which will solve the problems involved, but there are general principles which could help in this direction. African states could benefit from developments already taking place in some of the merging countries in Africa and in other parts of the world. A plan for land and air transport could be drawn up first on a national basis, then for sub-regions, and finally for Africa as a whole, and the responsibility for the necessary studies could be decided at each level. Individual states could have local committees employing specialists to study various aspects and problems of local transport, and to suggest programmes of action.

In the sub-regions and within Africa as a whole the responsibility for the study of transport development has already been assumed by the standing committees on industry, natural resources and transport of the Economic Commission for Africa. Specialized transport agencies and bodies, whether of rail, road or air transportation, could help in the progress of such studies. The main theme of work centres on the subjects discussed below.

THE IMPORTANCE OF CO-ORDINATION AMONG THE MEANS OF TRANSPORT

The various means of transport should be considered as an organic whole aiming at serving the national economy and defence; co-ordination of economic and social development programmes is necessary to avoid the destructive competition between different forms of transport which complicates traffic planning in most countries of the world. The most difficult point is that the public wants maximum service in the transport system as a whole.

It is for this reason that railways are supposed to work as a public utility serving all areas of the country at a uniform tariff. Discrimination in tariffs between services on lines with a very high traffic density and those with a very low density is unacceptable to the public. Limitation of competition from privately-owned bus and lorry services is similarly unacceptable.

Privately-owned bus and lorry services naturally concentrate on the operation of services where traffic is densest, and this is very well demonstrated in most developing countries.

Such problems should be studied carefully and a plan of transport co-ordination drawn up. Our experience shows that some organization or body on a national level should be formed to advise on the following:

(a) Co-ordination between the various transport projects in such a manner as to serve the national interest;

(b) Establishment and modification of tariff rates and fares;

(c) Fair distribution of freight traffic among the different means of transport, aimed at achieving the best results for national welfare;

(d) Co-operation between the various means of transport for the undertaking of services within a particular zone or between several zones; committees could be established for such purposes as planning, projected tariffs, and other executive problems;

(e) All matters which may arise concerning the various means of transport.

THE ECONOMIC UTILIZATION OF MEANS OF TRANSPORT

Means of transport are the first necessity in the life of the community, both for passenger travel and the transport of goods. It is the latter that we must consider especially. Agriculture has been transformed because it is now possible to send its products to markets far away, and the great manufacturing organizations can only remain in existence because they have wide markets in which to sell the output of their factories. All this depends on cheap transport, but there are limitations.

Air transport is a highly competitive industry and this competition will grow with the years, as will the potential traffic. To meet this challenge of increased competition and growth of traffic a number of world airlines are now pooling their services and working towards a complete integration of their resources.

The secretariat of the Economic Commission for Africa has discussed the need for establishing a pan-African conference or council for the co-ordination of air transport in Africa. Governments and their airlines should encourage such a move.

Transport by road depends largely on the development of motor-cars and improvements in road construction. Especially for short distances, a good deal of traffic that used to go by train now goes by road; an important saving in the cost of loading results. The fundamental economic condition of road transport is that, like water and unlike rail transport, the capital cost does not fall on the transportation enterprise. This alone widens the scope for competition.

Railways need both a huge capital outlay and state authorization for the laying of the track. Interference by the state is therefore inevitable. The cost per mile is considerable, yet the longer lines, which constitute the main communications of a country, are the most essential. The capital required, however, is not only large in itself, but large in relation to the revenue of the business. The carrying capacity of a railway, once built, is so great that only in a few of the most densely inhabited spots of the earth is enough traffic found to justify the existence of rival lines. This is certainly not the case in Africa.

The principles on which the fixing of charges should be based are complex, but in all leading railways the economic position is the same in essentials. The basis that has been reached may be described as the public service principle: the price of railway transportation should be as low as is consistent with the permanent welfare of the undertaking. Profits are not allowed to rise to an undue level, but they should not be cut down so low as to make it difficult to secure fresh capital for expansion. Reduction in charges can only be obtained through growth in business and the gradual improvement of techniques.

In the field of technical developments certain recommendations are usually advanced concerning standardization of technical specifications for African countries. Such developments could be achieved through the collection and investigation of existing information: periodical meetings should be held between technicians from the different African states, and between these technicians and their colleagues in developed countries.

THE NEED FOR TRAINING

Most African states lack qualified personnel and workmen who are highly trained in the different technical fields. Training would raise the productivity and efficiency of both the employer and the workers and lead directly to higher standards of performance and to regular working. Consequently all interested governments and specialized transport administrations and agencies, whether private or public, should give careful consideration to training, sparing no effort or financial assistance or the support of external experience in order to attain their objectives in this respect. A new generation will thus be created, capable of bearing the burden of the new projects, and supplied with the necessary technical and theoretical skills.

A complete training system should be established, and training programmes in the various countries should be drawn up. Responsible bodies should permit exchange study programmes or the exchange of personnel, and should take advantage of the main centres or training schools existing in some of the African countries. Training programmes should be prepared for three distinctive groups:

(a) *Recruitment training.* All the personnel required for the different services and occupations should be given recruitment training according to specified programmes. Basic and theoretical training should be carried out in the main training centre, or in one of the centres attached to it, whereas practical training for the actual jobs should be given in the training centres attached to the main workshops and operating sections.

(b) *Promotional training.* This group includes vocational training suitable for nominees for higher positions. The trainees will then be examined in order to choose the most suitable for promotion from among them.

(c) *Refresher training*. This group includes personnel who are below a satisfactory standard and who need to increase their theoretical and practical knowledge.

Effective training schemes represent a good investment of skill and capital.

THE FORM OF TRANSPORT ORGANIZATION

State ownership is usually suggested to be the best form of organization for coping with development plans for public utilities, but there are drawbacks.

First, the management is usually inferior to that of private companies. The administrative heads have not the same personal interest in success, and even if this is adequately replaced by public spirit they are always hampered by officialdom, and are not allowed to use their judgment as promptly and independently as in private enterprises.

The other drawback is even more serious; it is the tendency for political pressure to be used to acquire transport facilities, particularly in places where the traffic does not justify them, and to obtain abnormally cheap rates for the advantage of particular places and industries. The history of state railways is one of constant attempts to find a form of administration that will avoid these defects. There have been some marked successes, particularly where there is a tradition of honourable and intelligent work in the civil service, but the problem is by no means solved. Where state ownership and control is inevitable, the most promising method tried is to place the public utility under a board as free as possible from party politics and independent of the government of the day, the members of the board being paid highly and given security of office for a number of years, in the hope that able and impartial men will come forward. This method has had some success in promoting honest and businesslike administration, but it depends ultimately on the degree of public spirit and intelligence prevailing.

This type of authority aims at effecting sound and proper conditions with greater efficiency and freeing the organization of the restrictions of routine governmental work. Such organizations have their own independent budgets, drawn up according to procedures followed in commercial enterprises. This enables them to allocate the necessary funds for depreciation, thus avoiding the accumulation of deferred renewals that often occurs. In the meantime, it is possible to maintain the balance between revenue and expenditure so that it may not be a burden on the state budget.

THE NEED FOR CO-OPERATION

This reform in national transport facilities must be coupled with co-operation between African countries. During the meetings and conferences which have already been held on this subject it has been recommended that African states should study means for developing their respective transport networks, and that they should give priority to areas completely lacking such facilities.

It has also been recommended that African states should study, in collaboration with their neighbours, the possibility of linking their networks, and that such links should not be effected until after economic efficiency has been achieved. This will of course lead to other problems, both economic and political. The question of the expenditure to be borne by individual states in completing the missing links between railways and roads shows the need for a collective policy for the whole continent. The African organizations already in existence, whether they belong to the United Nations or are independent, will surely solve many of the problems of intra-continental transportation. Conferences must be held on rail, road and air transport. Such meetings will create mutual understanding and help members to exchange their experiences, to the benefit of all Africans.

The more advanced countries of Africa must now co-operate in helping to build up an efficient and economic communications network, to assist the less developed countries. African countries need urgently to establish a network of roads and railways to move primary products within the continent for export as well as to move capital and consumer goods required for the economic and social development of individual states.

Transport of passengers at an economic rate, and the most suitable means of transport, should be studied carefully. International organizations specializing in these fields should work hand in hand with African organizations and individual African states to develop and nationalize land and air transport.

Finally, it would be unrealistic to expect that some panacea will emerge at this symposium which will answer all transport questions to the complete satisfaction of all African interests. While the problems are real enough, they affect different nations differently. There are economic, social and political differences among the African countries themselves, and at such meetings as this we are bound to evoke divergent views, attitudes and philosophies. Out of all this will develop ideas for action which will go far towards achieving the unity of Africa, the ultimate aim of all nations of the continent.

8

TELECOMMUNICATIONS IN AFRICA

THE problems of Man and Africa are being discussed here at a timely stage of the emergence of this continent. The picture to be presented in the field of telecommunications by a unified, integrated Africa will not, I feel sure, be different from that to be found in any reference textbook. It would, however, be fascinating to review the way in which this continent reached unification in the field of telecommunications. The picture would truly be one of gigantic problems surmounted, and of tireless effort, a story to fire the imagination of any thinking person. The problems overcome are not only those of tele- communications itself, but also those of the fields of medicine, agriculture, education—in fact every field of human endeavour— because none of these can really succeed on a modern scale without relying heavily on the steady help of telecommunications. Any worth-while progress in any field whatsoever will be depen- dent on the availability of an efficient and reliable telecommunica- tions network, so the subject of "Telecommunications in Africa" is of tremendous importance to us all.

Telecommunications form the cornerstone of unification. This cornerstone is already to be seen in Africa in its rough shape, and the present telecommunication scene there shows important differences from the situation encountered on other continents. One of these differences is the fact that although Africa is by no means unpopulated in the interior, the majority of communication channels are peripheral. Another is that connexions between nations of the African continent must be carried out at overseas relay points—few direct links exist. The lack of telecommunications access between different regions is serious because telecommunication contacts between nations and their people are difficult, costly, or even, in some cases, impossible. Apart from anything else, this means that the prospect of a united Africa communicating with its peoples is remote until the telecommunication backbone is established. It follows that unity of the people is only practical with integrated continental-scale telecommunications.

Here I will review the problems, set out what has been achieved, relate the planning efforts and discuss the short- and long-term goals.

Although telecommunications problems in Africa may appear simple, in fact they are not. It is commonplace to organize the extension of telecommunications facilities in a region in which they have been found to be inadequate. However, the African problem is to plan the installation of networks costing millions under circumstances in which very few, if any, data exist as to what are the real present or future requirements. There is not even a basis on which to consider at what rate the need will grow. When these facilities are freely installed in a city or a country in which they have previously been scarce, the rate at which demand will grow is very difficult to forecast. The use of them is at first disappointing because they are unfamiliar. Also the scheme may be thoroughly uneconomical because a commercial structure demanding these facilities does not yet exist. So we must develop new yardsticks to measure demand in these circumstances. In countries in which these facilities are already commonplace, the extension criteria are different, and such criteria cannot be followed in many parts of Africa, as the demand for greater service will grow much faster than it does in other environments. The danger therefore exists that there will be a tendency to underprovide, on a theoretical basis. This allows problems to recur unnecessarily, and makes the long-term cost high. On the other hand, it is widely realized that budgetary limits demand that available finances be stretched to provide as much as possible. This also tends to lead to underprovision on practical grounds. So both theory and practice would promote error if the special circumstances of Africa are overlooked.

The planning engineer in Africa has this peculiar problem. He is subject to serious pressures to underprovide his circuits and he is confused by his training and experience which impel him to justify his circuit requirements on economic grounds. He must therefore use a new philosophy and fashion development plans that will make the networks a part of a continental whole. Government and business efficiency are determined by the provision of telecommunications facilities.

A big step in the direction of planning and co-ordinating African telecommunication facilities was taken in 1960. This was done by the Sub-Committee for Africa at the First Planning Assembly of the International Consultative Committee for Telephony and Telegraphy (International Telecommunication Union). The Plan for Africa was established by the Sub-Committee at its meeting held in Dakar in 1962, the Chairman of which was the representative of Ethiopia—Mr. Gabriel Tedros. This was a notable milestone, because a general plan was conceived for the overall development of telecommunications in Africa. After all means of providing telecommunications facilities had been reviewed, the Plan which would best meet the long-term requirements was established. For historical reasons, many of the present circuits pass through European exchanges and are not efficient for relays to neighbouring countries. The new network plan is to link African countries two by two, either by direct circuits or by suitable traffic concentration points. The Plan envisages the wide use of overhead open-wire carrier lines, supplemented by radio relay links and submarine cables. I will not elaborate on the technical difficulties of establishing such networks as they are sufficient for a separate technical paper in themselves.

Most of the present African links are via high frequency radio. The need of Africa for suitable multi-channel systems which are impossible with high frequency radio is recognized and is met in the long-term plan. In the meantime, however, high frequency radio has to be extended to fill the gap.

The Dakar Plan implementation requires a large financial outlay and even so could not be achieved for many years. The interim measure is a crash programme to provide telephone and telegraph services between the capitals of Africa via high frequency radio. Its purpose is to close the serious telecommunications gaps between countries of the African continent now. This crash programme is in the process of being set up under the direction of Mr. Robert K. A. Gardiner, Executive Secretary of the Economic Commission for Africa, and Mr. Gerald C. Gross, Secretary-General of the International Telecommunication Union. The I.T.U. team of engineers which is completing a survey of the requirements of the continent and assisting in the establishment of the intercontinental high frequency network is working from the headquarters of the Economic Commission for Africa in Addis Ababa.

The situation which has resulted provides continental telephones and telegraph for all African countries and is best illustrated by Figs. 1 and 2.

The long-term goal—the same for Africa as it is for the other continents—is for quick, reliable and cheap communications to be available in all parts of the world where they are needed, and for all parts of the world to be directly accessible from anywhere. Since Africa is more than twice the size of Europe, and contains some probably uninhabitable regions, there is a serious possibility that satellite communications *within* the continent could be effectively used in the foreseeable future. The provision of telephone and telegraph channels by means of satellites is economically feasible only if large numbers of them are required between well-defined areas. This situation is likely to exist in Africa after a certain stage in its economic development. It goes without saying that an essential prerequisite of such continental-scale communications systems is a close and stable association between the participating nations. No one nation would have any interest in carrying all the great costs involved, but if the costs and the benefits could be shared among a community of nations such a project is feasible.

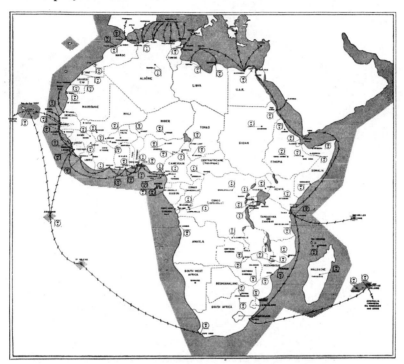

Fig. 1. High frequency and submarine cable links.

All types of telecommunications are vital to the economic and political growth of Africa. In addition to the intercontinental and national networks of telephony and telegraphy services, efficient aeronautical and maritime communications are needed. National broadcasting and television services are critical in respect to education. In respect to television, the I.T.U. played its vital rôle in 1963 when, with the assistance of headquarters, delegates of all African nations met in Geneva for the purpose of establishing a television and frequency modulated broadcasting plan. This plan provides for the establishment of stations, and for the frequency assignments required for all African countries during the coming 10 to 15 years. When this meeting was a success, African

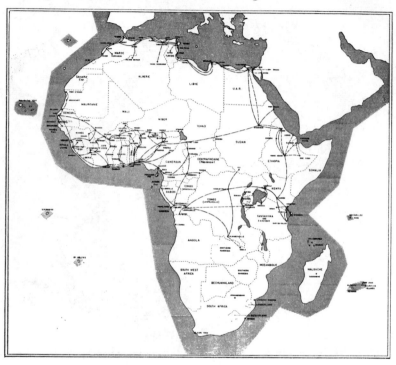

Fig. 2. Cable, overhead or radio relay links.

unity took a great step forward. The Plan was a triumph of sheer hard work, of dedication to an idea. The proposed allocated stations for Bands II and III are shown in Figs. 3 and 4, from which the provision for stations throughout the continent can be seen. Some stations already exist or are in process of installation in this band, and they are included in the layout. The virtue of this kind of planning is that if all nations of a continent are considered together, an electronic computer can calculate the effects of each

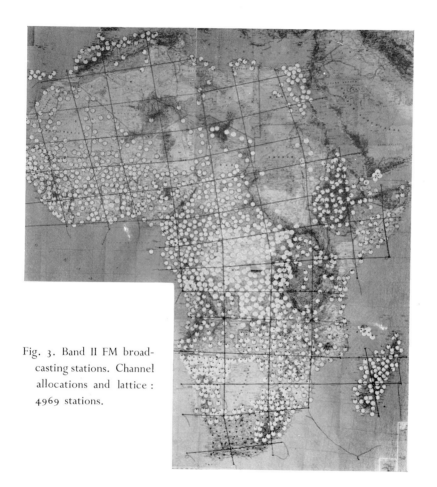

Fig. 3. Band II FM broad-
casting stations. Channel
allocations and lattice :
4969 stations.

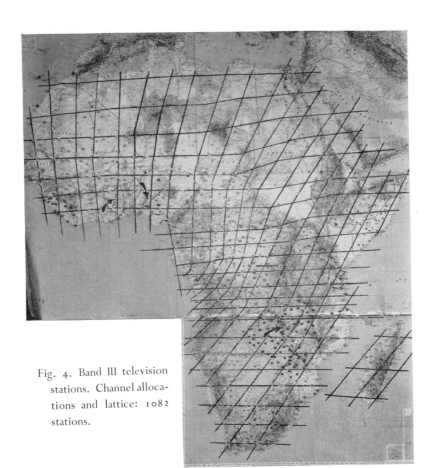

Fig. 4. Band III television
stations. Channel alloca-
tions and lattice: 1082
stations.

station on each other station. Such a feat is beyond practical limits for ordinary human calculations. This use of a computer was demonstrated at the conference in Geneva, and Africa is the first continent so planned.

One particular aspect of radiocommunications that I have discussed in the space available concerns the provision of telecommunications so that people can communicate with one another over the public networks—that is what we call point-to-point service; the other aspect relates to broadcasting, television and amateur radio services. The broadcasting and television services make it possible for the people to be informed—a critical medium of education and information. The amateur radio service likewise makes it possible for radio amateurs throughout the world to talk with one another informally—a two-way communication—and this is also an instrument of technical training and education. Amateur radio is thus midway between the point-to-point service and broadcasting. All of them contribute to common understanding among peoples.

Finally, since I have been talking of matters that involve learning, and hence teaching, there is one thing to say, very seriously. Those of us who have knowledge to impart must learn how to teach, and those of us who seek this knowledge must learn how to learn. All of us must be honest in recognizing our limitations, and in so doing we must learn the most difficult lesson of all—not to overestimate our own knowledge. This is, I think, the outstanding moral to be drawn from the growth of knowledge in this twentieth century.

When we speak of telecommunications, we are not merely talking of telephones and telegraphs, of electronic circuits and electromagnetic energy: these are only the means of expression of the art of telecommunications in our time. What we are really thinking of is the very warp and fabric of civilization, the common denominator that makes the human spirit aware of itself. Without communications, no man learns from another, no man knows of another's need, no man can reach out beyond his environment to a better world. Telecommunications are so much the essence of life that they are overlooked when we consider the things to be done in building a nation. When a man thinks of the things he hopes for, he thinks of health, of education, of happiness; he overlooks the basic fact that for any of these to mean anything he must be alive. The life of a continent is telecommunications: with telecommunications the continent is alive and dynamic.

DISCUSSION

Lambo: In our work in Nigeria we use a variety of complex apparatus. Is any programme available for the training in Africa of African personnel, at all levels, for the technical maintenance and operation of many of these research instruments? This is also particularly relevant to the long-term programme of tele-communications. Are African universities and governments being pressed to provide facilities and training programmes to enable maintenance work to be done locally in Africa?

Gayer: Very important work is being done in nearly all of the countries—your own country, Nigeria, and the Sudan among them. The telecommunication training schools are actually operated by the postal and telegraph organizations, but the International Telecommunication Union uses special assist-ance funds to provide instructors and equipment, and in some cases has helped to organize the schools themselves. People are trained at trade level to operate automatic exchanges so that the maintenance and operation of equipment within the countries can be done by the people themselves. In some countries the general manager or director is at first a foreigner and then local engineers take over the responsibilities as time goes on. This programme has been working for about ten years, and a few such efforts in Africa even date from before the war.

In many cases telecommunications have been omitted from the university curricula, and so the engineers have had to be trained at telecommunication centres abroad. Usually they first finish their engineering degree and then go abroad for advanced studies and specific training. In the University of Khartoum, on the other hand, they have a two- or three-year period of training, but after one year are brought back to work for a while before more training. So in the Sudan there is a good local programme that is being handled by the university, and in this way the gap in the training of the technicians is slowly being bridged. However, requirements are very great in comparison with the build-up.

Young: The cost of television receivers at a time when television is being developed is a significant point that should be borne in mind, as the availability of the foreign currency needed to buy receivers abroad could be an important limitation for the development of television in general. Could not the development of television occur speedily once the technical training of those needed to make receivers was sufficiently good, whether or not foreign currency was then available?

Gayer: In Egypt and India the difficulty of obtaining foreign currency demanded the creation of industries, at first for the assembly of component parts, but already the complete production of television sets is being undertaken.

The difficulty in a country like Ethiopia is that only a comparatively small number of receivers will be required for a number of years, and yet a complete service must be provided. One can argue nevertheless how important it is to have television for education in any country, and fortunately this can be effected at limited cost if sets are provided for various community groups and meetings.

I should add that I.T.U. has what we call a cheap receiver programme and we are encouraging countries to get together and set up a community area of production for these receivers. But there are difficulties in getting a group of countries together because trade of any kind is limited between many of them as yet.

Last: It seems to me that television has a very great potential for education in Africa. It is very difficult to see otherwise how Africa's educational programme is going to be fulfilled at the rate we would like to see it fulfilled. One of the chief bottlenecks is the very high cost of teachers, particularly at secondary level, and one of the possible answers to this problem is the full use of television, particularly in secondary schools, coupled with programmed learning. Have the long-range discussions on the technical side of telecommunications in Africa given consideration to the possibility of solving some of these educational problems?

Gayer: There are indeed great potentialities in using television for education. A few years ago at a symposium at Montreux, Switzerland, a package transmitter operating unit was demonstrated which is specially designed for educational purposes. The equipment is set up very quickly in a corner of the room and the receivers are placed around the school. It makes an excellent supplement to the educational process.

Only last week (September, 1964) in Lagos, U.N.E.S.C.O. held a meeting at which the African countries got together to see how television could be used for educational and informational purposes, and in what way the funds available could be applied to stimulate interest and to obtain the necessary experts. They also discussed how the programmes could be directed towards bringing different countries to the same level of development in the establishment and the use of television. I think economic considerations are not so much of an obstacle now, because fewer receivers are needed if they are installed in schools; also, now that big-screen receivers are available, great progress has been made in this field.

Sutton: We in the Ford Foundation have a great interest in the use of educational television and educational broadcasting, in many parts of the world. Our present concerns are not so much over equipment as over satisfactory programme production and reception. It is often forgotten that very considerable effort is involved in the production of any substantial number of television programmes for the schools, and in getting together satisfactory staff who can produce steadily, in sufficient quantity, programmes that really matter.

Furthermore, in the United States and other places where television is used, we have found it is not much use having well-produced programmes unless there is good liaison with the schools and an understanding on the part of the teachers of the uses of educational television programmes. It is certainly true that the value and the use of superior teachers can be multiplied by using television, but this does not mean that teachers can be eliminated. You must have teachers who can fit these programmes into their other instruction, and they themselves must be instructed in the proper use of television. This constitutes a very considerable strain on the education systems that we have in Africa.

The possibilities of educational sound broadcasting perhaps look a little better, and correspondence courses in conjunction with radio can help in important ways. One small point is that transistors have made an enormous difference in places without a local power supply. The possibilities of educational broadcasting have been greatly increased by this technological advance.

Gayer: In the example I gave in my paper I described how television and broadcasting were planned for Africa by giving all the delegates at the conference a chance to put forward their ideas until they converged into a plan, but then the plan was checked for technical soundness by the use of computers. For the European plan, on the other hand, it took two conferences and over two years of negotiation to reach agreement after each delegation had made its own calculations.

Gille: You have already referred to the important meeting which took place in Lagos on the introduction and development of television in Africa. This meeting, convened by U.N.E.S.C.O. and attended by thirty participants from African countries and by a number of observers from countries outside Africa and from international organizations, discussed such problems as the contribution of television to the future of African countries, the contribution of television to education and the dissemination of knowledge, regional co-operation, economic and educational planning and the development of television, and so on. In formal education, for instance, it was noted that television was already being used in some countries and that many others were proceeding to introduce special programmes for the schools. These programmes have proved particularly valuable in science teaching. Concern had, however, been expressed that the educational rôle of television could not become really effective until schools and community centres were properly equipped with suitable receivers.

Gayer: As I mentioned, the programming is a very difficult matter, especially in regard to television. U.N.E.S.C.O. is willing to help out on the production of educational programmes, and sound broadcasting is of course very widely used and can be programmed far more easily than can television.

Mustafa: I was naturally pleased to hear you talk about the technical training efforts in the Sudan, but I do not think the Sudan is unique in that sense. The main problem to my mind is one relating to national telecommunication in Africa generally. Most African states consist either of desert or jungle or both, and enormous difficulties are encountered in establishing a satisfactory internal system of communication under these circumstances. To overcome sandstorms and torrential rainstorms we need technical facilities which involve the spending of millions of pounds where pennies cannot be afforded.

Also, we are all concerned in Africa about the unsatisfactory position which now exists in regard to the international telecommunication system. We find it very much easier to relay messages to the United States or to Europe than to other countries in Africa. We have such links of communication with the outside world because until very recently most African states have been dependent politically and economically on those parts of the world and independent of each other.

Pan-Africanism is a fairly recent trend, but it has already made people aware of a number of problems including the need to establish an efficient system of telecommunications within the African continent. A certain degree of economic interdependence within the continent would virtually compel African states to do something serious about continental and intercontinental communication. As you suggested, the use of satellites may be the answer in the foreseeable future.

Gayer: The Sudan is a big country with great regions of sand, and with heavy rainfall in flat areas, and it may be used as an example in the argument about cables or overhead lines versus radio relay techniques. To have trade between African countries there must be unity, and for this there must be telecommunications. The only way to carry out a crash programme to install telecommunications is to use high frequency radio. Overhead wires and cables, radio relays—these are essentially long-term; they are slow to install, costly, and they have to be related to the demand for the services. But in the meantime the demand could be met on an urgent basis by the use of high frequency radio links. Such a service is not perfect; it depends on propagation conditions which are very variable and it does have certain limitations.

We hope to use the E.C.A., I.T.U. and other organizations to assist the efforts of the countries themselves, in such a way as to meet the present urgent needs. But in the long term there must be normal development on a full continental scale, and for this the use of the synchronized satellite may well be the answer. Distances are so great in Africa that it seems suitable for satellite applications, but very costly for the radio relay solutions that are proving to be the most economic and satisfactory method elsewhere.

Michaelis: Could I make some general comments on the whole field of the physical sciences and engineering in Africa? We have just heard what space research might give to Africa and perhaps I might continue from that point.

Miniature atomic reactors no larger than a big table are now in existence. The first were shown at the Third United Nations Conference for Peaceful Uses of Atomic Energy at Geneva in September, 1964, and although they are only prototypes at the moment, just as the transistors were twenty years ago, the development of these small sources of power may in years to come have a very profound effect on the speed of industrialization in underdeveloped countries.

At the same conference another very important indication was given of the future contribution which atomic energy could make to desalting—taking the salt from sea water to obtain fresh water for irrigation purposes. We heard earlier from Mr. Last that over 60 per cent of farmers in Africa have grave water difficulties. Nuclear desalting in the more advanced countries, particularly in America, is being thought of on a very large scale indeed, of 1,000 million gallons of water per day, and 2,000 million kilowatts of electricity. These sizes of course are far too large for merely local uses in Africa, but within ten years engineering advances may produce smaller units.

Also, it was announced for the first time at the Geneva Conference that the United Arab Republic and Tunisia had invited tenders for the building of atomic power stations, but these are to be used only for the generation of electricity.

Another engineering project goes under the rather extraordinary title of "City of the Sun". The idea is to use the oil resources of Africa on the spot, where they are actually found. For example, in the Sahara, where there is abundant oil, one could make electricity from oil. Water rich in salt has also been found in the Sahara and it is fairly simple chemistry to produce sodium hydroxide and chlorine gas by electrolysis of the salt solution. By the well-known process of using nitrogen from the air and hydrogen from oil, one can produce first of all ammonia and then nitric acid and a whole range of other nitrogen compounds. Eventually a petrochemical industry could result from the raw materials of oil, nitrogen and electricity, even in the Sahara.

These are just a few engineering possibilities for the future of

Africa, which I feel should be widely discussed in other meetings by African scientists and engineers.

This brings me to my last point, which is the communication of science here in Africa. Perhaps I may suggest that the example of the British Association for the Advancement of Science, which has been widely imitated during the last 130 years elsewhere, might also be followed in Africa. Many of you will know that the Association has annual meetings in different university cities in the British Isles, and that it is divided into some twenty sections dealing with the physical, biological and social sciences such as education, psychology and economics. The British Association was brought into being in 1831 because of the desire of scientists to have a wider platform for their views, to get their ideas across to politicians and to see that their knowledge was used properly. May I put it to you that a situation not unlike that in England in 1831 may now exist in this continent? If communication of science in Africa is a serious problem, the foundation of such an all-African association for the advancement of science may well be the first useful step.

Young: I am sure that the British Association itself would be wise to take note of the growing importance of television.

Michaelis: At the 1964 meeting in Southampton Lord Brain used television for the first time in the history of the British Association to have a completely nation-wide audience for science in Britain, and presidential papers were televised every morning.

Lambo: I would just like to sound a short note of warning. From my own experience of the application of high-powered technical knowledge in a young country, I know that some people tend to feel that this is a hidden magical power capable of solving all our problems in Africa. Certainly broadcasting and television will not replace the teacher. In many African countries such aids and new devices will valuably reduce the basic needs of personnel, but careful studies are needed of the psychological and social repercussions which may follow the widespread use of such new measures.

9

AFRICA'S EDUCATIONAL
NEEDS AND OPPORTUNITIES

FRANCIS X. SUTTON

INDIVIDUAL OPPORTUNITIES AND NATIONAL NEED

URING a recent period in Africa a remarkable unanimity
and simplicity characterized educational policy. A
universal right to education was one of the tenets of the
independence movements, and the great awakening of ordinary
Africans to the desirability of education raised powerful demands
for more schools and teachers. When the irresistibility of the
independence movements became clear, the thinness of past
African education became alarming. It did not take elaborate
statistical analysis to show that if colonial territories were to
become modern countries they had to have far more well-
educated Africans than they had had. Everyone concerned with
education quickly agreed that a simple "more" was the keystone
of policy, and an immense expansion ensued.

The resulting increases in educational expenditure did not
immediately lead to harsh necessities for decision, for at least
three reasons. In the first place, total revenues in many African
countries were rising. Secondly, there has been substantial
foreign aid for education, and planning of educational expenditure, in the expectation that such aid would continue and expand,
has been encouraged. Thirdly, the period of expansion in African
education has been one in which a new consciousness of the
importance of education to economic development has been
growing throughout the world. The intense concern with the
supply of trained manpower that now characterizes discussions of
development strategy came along in the 1950's and it encouraged

higher educational expenditure by emphasizing the investment aspects.

All these factors encouraged the buoyant expansionist spirit during the late 1950's and early 1960's, although inevitably educational expenditure sooner or later caused pressures on national budgets. In Africa, education now commonly takes more than 20 per cent of the national budgets. This is higher than in most places in the world and is regarded by economists as about as large a bite as education can take in a balanced development programme, if indeed it is not injudiciously high*.

Limitation of total resources sometimes showed itself starkly at early dates: a 1959 study in Upper Volta[1] showed that 23 per cent of the national budget was being used to keep only 6 per cent of the population in school, and the introduction of free universal primary education in Eastern Nigeria in 1957 had to be stopped a year later when grave budgetary problems arose. But optimistic expansion has tended to override many of these difficulties and it is unlikely that budgetary problems alone would arouse the degree of concern over educational strategy that now exists in Africa.

The optimistic view of educational expansion assumed that the greatest possible gratification of the demand for education was in the interests—both short and long term—of national development. Doubts to shadow this optimism have not been long in appearing. Many Africans seek education in the expectation of obtaining a job after some years in school—how many years has depended upon the number of Africans already educated, and it is notorious that the requisite standard for success in job-seeking has risen sharply all across Africa. Because serious labour-force

---

* It is often noted that the Eastern and Western regional governments of Nigeria have devoted more than 40 per cent of their budgets to education. But this has only been possible because various governmental services are maintained on the Nigerian federal budget. (A similar situation prevails in the United States where 50 per cent of state revenues are commonly devoted to education.) An investigation in 1959 indicated at that time that a little over 20 per cent of the total Nigerian (federal and regional) budgets was being devoted to education.

studies do not exist there is no precise information on the numbers of Africans at various educational levels who have been unable to find jobs. But in the middle of the 1950's in West Africa and a little later in East and Central Africa it became a familiar finding that a great many boys who had completed primary school could no longer obtain jobs. It was also learned, as early as the Ashanti Survey of 1945–46, [2, 3] that hardly any of the boys who had completed this much education were ready to return to their home areas and become cultivators.

The now painfully familiar problem of primary school leavers increasingly hopelessly seeking jobs in the crowded towns existed before the latest expansion of primary education. It was very familiar to African leaders, who at first found the school leaver a welcome recruit in the nationalist movements. But the perspective on these youths changes when African governments come to power. If they are left as dispirited urban unemployed they have a grave potential as an opposition force. African governments are now very conscious of the unemployment which plagues them, and aware of the danger that education will aggravate it. There is great reluctance to turn back from efforts to educate as many Africans as possible, but the dangers of the wrong kind and the wrong distribution of education are now widely denounced. As a result, a better balance has been sought between primary education on the one hand and secondary, technical and university education on the other.

The experts on development have put great stress on the need for high-level manpower and have pressed the African governments to devote more of their resources to the higher levels of education. This was the principal theme of the Addis Ababa Plan formulated at a meeting in 1961 of African ministers of education sponsored by U.N.E.S.C.O. and E.C.A. The Ashby report[4] on higher education in Nigeria argued the same way, and the concentration of United Nations and other aid programmes on secondary and higher education represents a similar judgment on priorities. There has been a strong African response to this emphasis in educational planning. Heavy investments have been made in secondary, technical, and higher education which offer promise of relieving the great shortages of highly trained people that still threaten to hamper African development in the years ahead. In some instances at least, this expansion of secondary and higher education has been planned in full recognition of the budgetary limitations it imposes on the further expansion of primary education. Furthermore, planners are now seeking to measure further expansion of primary education not merely to the residual funds left after the demands of other forms of education are met, but also to the foreseeable employment opportunities. The recently published Tanzania five-year plan, for example, calculates educational investments so that manpower needs and employment opportunities will be in balance with the output of both primary and higher schools within foreseeable periods.

The need for balanced planning of this sort seems axiomatic. But it necessitates demands for austere restraint on educational opportunities that will be hard for African peoples to accept. There is a dilemma between the radical socialist spirit of modern Africa and the doctrine of costly education for the few at the expense of equal opportunities for the many. Hope of progress through education of large numbers is not going to be relinquished. The "school leaver" problem is not willingly taken as evidence that there is too much primary education, but that education has been of the wrong kind. African leaders now denounce the education of "pen-pushing" left to them by the colonial powers which makes boys and girls want to be clerks in the towns. They call for a new kind of education which will hold people on the land, or make them into skilled workers or small businessmen if they live in the towns.

This reconciliation of educational opportunities for the masses of the people with the needs of national development is the most urgent problem now facing educational planning in Africa. If it is to be solved there will have to be close study of the quality and character of elementary education in relation to the needs of economic development. It is my hope that this paper may make some small contribution to this study.

The hope of balanced educational planning is that the common people will have indirect benefits from national development brought about by those who acquire higher levels of education. But the great expense of any education beyond primary levels means that its effectiveness must be sharply scrutinized. President Nyerere has recently reminded the students at University College, Dar-es-Salaam, that it costs £1,000 a year to support each one of them, and the national income per head is about £20 a year. The fear is widespread in Africa that in the effort to produce the professional men, administrators, and researchers who are urgently needed, a privileged élite, remote from the masses, will be produced instead. It would indeed be tragic if the sacrifices now being made to develop a balanced system of educational institutions should fail to produce men and women who can build modern nations. The higher forms of African education must be of the right kind, and as a second main concern of this paper I shall try to make some suggestions about where the right kind may be found.

MASS EDUCATION AND DEVELOPMENT IN AFRICA

The growth in the number of children being educated in Africa has, in recent years, greatly outstripped the growth of employment available in African economies. There is, I believe, no African country which has shown in recent years a decline in the numbers of children in school. But there are several, including ones with impressive rates of economic growth, where total employment has declined. Zambia is an example. The total numbers of Africans in wage employment there in recent years have been as follows*:

| 1946 | 140,776 | 1956 | 263,132 | 1962 | 229,300 |
| 1951 | 228,676 | 1961 | 236,422 | | |

---

* These and subsequent figures are from Barber (1961, p. 198)[5] and U.N.E.S.C.O.'s Northern Rhodesia Report (1964, pp. 12–13).[6]

The decrease in employment since 1956 has not been due to economic depression, or to relative increases in the employment of Europeans. The economy has continued to expand, but under conditions of increased productivity per man rather than through increases in the numbers employed. In the copper-mining industry, which dominates the Zambian economy, output increased by 22 per cent between 1957 and 1962 while the work force dropped by 18 per cent. An even sharper fall has occurred in employment outside mining, which dropped 30 per cent in the same period while output per man increased by 50 per cent.

Zambia is not alone in facing this sort of unemployment problem. Other African countries have shown similar tendencies to grow without corresponding growth in employment. Indeed in recent years, absolute declines in total employment have been experienced in Tanganyika, Kenya and Uganda, and apparently also in some other African countries not so well known to me. In Uganda total employment declined from 243,000 in 1958 to 231,000 in 1962[7]; in Tanganyika it fell from 417,000 in 1960 to 341,000 in 1963[8]; in Kenya from 614,000 in 1957 to 581,000 in 1962[9]. The same sort of increase in productivity per man which has been noted in Zambia is apparent in East Africa. Manufacturing output has been increasing at 4 per cent since 1957 while employment in manufacturing has declined by 2 per cent per annum during the same period[10]. The tendency for employment to grow slowly even when good progress is otherwise being made seems to be very general. It is one of the most troublesome features of economic development, not only in Africa, but throughout the developing world.

If one accepts this conclusion that rates of increase in employment are likely to lag behind rates of increase in national product, it follows that in African economies only modest fractions of the population will move out of the rural subsistence sector into paid employment during the next 10 to 20 years. Allowing for population growth it is easy to show (see Appendix) that annual increases in employment of 5 to 6 per cent are necessary to double percentages in the modern sector in the next generation, and such rates obviously press hard on likely rates of growth in national product. Since many countries now have 70 to 80 per cent of their population in the subsistence sector, most of these people will continue a rural existence for another generation.

From this it is clear that the future of the majority of Africans in the next decade will depend upon self-employment, and this mostly agricultural. Education for most Africans cannot, in the short run, be a preparation for employment. It will either be a preparation for unemployment or for some form of self-employment, mostly agricultural. Moreover these calculations emphasize that the hope of economic advance for large sections of the African population depends on advances in agricultural production, particularly in what has thus far been the subsistence sector of African economies.

Answers to the question, ''What can education for the masses do to assist African economic advance?'' must therefore first be sought in rural areas where most of the people are and will remain. The broad nature of the tasks to be done there is well known. It is now obvious that African agriculture requires major transformations, not merely to bring advancement, but to avoid deterioration of the soils and the livelihoods that derive from them. Although data are still deplorably poor, we now believe that rates of population increase in Africa are substantially more than they were thought to be only a few years ago, attaining 3 per cent per annum or a bit more in many places. Serious pressures on the land are resulting. The fragility of African soils and the dependence of traditional cultivation on long recuperative fallows requiring large amounts of land per cultivator are familiar facts. As population density increases, traditional practices threaten declining yields and permanent deterioration of the soils. Long ago Jean-Paul Harroy[11] sounded the alarm that African lands were dying. There is great danger that dense African populations will make them die faster. Improved methods in agriculture are clearly imperative, but we know from considerable study and painful experience that they are not easy to find and put into practice. A great amount of research and experimentation will be needed; equally, receptivity and openness on the part of the African cultivator will be necessary. Prescriptions for African rural development now call for resettlement, new crops, new farming practices, new forms of land tenure and co-operative organizations. To achieve these changes will require knowledge, will and administrative strength which villagers themselves cannot supply. But these changes will be of little effect unless they have the intelligent co-operation of the ordinary African working his land, or assessing a new opportunity.

For education to make a real contribution in this urgent African need for rural transformation, it must cease to alienate its products from the land, and it must give them something useful towards a life on the land. There is hope that this change may come about, and not only from changes in the character of education. A natural, if painful, social evolution promises a new compatibility of education and a rural existence. Young Africans are gradually coming to accept that their future may lie on the land. The break of continuity that is implied by the opening of perspectives of a new life can be applied to a rural existence as well as to an urban one. Perhaps the important thing is that a conception of new possibilities has been opened up. It may be vague and shapeless, but it at least provides a bed for the seeds of new development.

The forms of education imported from Europe, being at first strange to African cultures, could only be received in a half-comprehended formalized way. As long as education is seen as a somewhat mysterious acquisition, it naturally has the effect of setting apart its products as people of different and special status. It cannot be accepted unselfconsciously and "naturally" to become a part of the normal equipment for everyday life. One of the best effects of universal education must surely be that its mere acquisition is no longer dazzling. The possibility is then opened up of making education an effective aid in coping with everyday problems of life.

The content and character of education must be altered to realize these potentialities. Common prescriptions are that it must become "more practical" and have a strong "rural bias". René Dumont[12] has called for a revival of the "farm school". But there has been ample experience in trying to include practical agriculture in primary school curricula and it does not encourage optimism about the effect of this approach. The danger is always that too much time will be spent in purely traditional practices and uncreative drudgery. If new things are to happen in African rural life, they are unlikely to be adequately anticipated in what can be reproduced in the schools at any given time. Much more important would seem to be the preparation of young people for a creative, pragmatic approach to new conditions and new problems. The qualities necessary for this practical flexibility are naturally generalized ones. They depend upon the acquisition of fundamental skills in analysis and observation. The sort of education which firmly relates the elementary skills of language and calculation to the interpretation and manipulation of the world around is certainly the kind to be sought. Hope that it will be found is nourished by the prominent demands that education be given a strongly African character. The teaching of African history, geography, and culture will help to make education seem less exotic; but this sort of Africanization is only the obvious part of the necessary development. In a much less explicit way the basic operations of education must be "domesticated" to African life. The techniques of reading, writing and calculating, and elementary ideas of science and the arts must be taught and displayed in ways that suggest their normal use by ordinary people. Obviously this must be done with African teachers who have themselves some everyday use for their own education.

These prescriptions have the apparent defects of vagueness. But one must be suspicious of more definite prescriptions. The realization of a better future for more rural Africans involves a multiplicity of new situations and new problems which cannot be anticipated in a school. The important thing is for Africans to emerge with a problem-solving capacity. Their agenda of future problems is vague and only the apparent vagueness of general accomplishment can hope to prepare them for these.

Education by itself cannot produce the changes that must come in rural Africa. There will have to be opportunities which education can help people to find and use, but cannot in itself provide. New methods of cultivation, new farm settlements, co-operatives, and marketing systems, will have to be planned and guided by highly trained specialists with resources provided by governments. Too often the meaning of a "return to the land" has been repugnant to school leavers because, having seen beyond the old traditional ways, they could not go back to them. Without programmes of rural development widespread education promises mere discontent. But development plans are now allocating heavy resources to rural development and there is perhaps at least as great a danger that people will be unprepared for opportunities offered them, as that there will be no opportunities.

These arguments suggest that elementary education can make important contributions to economic development other than as preparation for wage employment. They may have important application in urban as well as rural settings. How substantial self-employment may become in African towns will depend in part on the resourcefulness of the people themselves. A population given confidence in their capacities for problem-solving by an effective form of education promises to have some measure of the initiative that African societies need. The total effect of improved education for those who find employment only on their own rural holdings or by entrepreneurship in the towns looks extremely difficult to assess in terms that could satisfy planners. But effects that are hard to measure are not necessarily insignificant. In this case they could make the difference between success and failure in new African states.

THE EDUCATION OF MEN TO MAKE MODERN STATES

The dearth of people to fill jobs requiring higher levels of education is the basis of African policies that emphasize secondary, technical and higher education. These policies are often nowadays based on good professional assessments of the supply and demand for trained people. Basic manpower surveys have been made in Ghana, Uganda, Tanzania and elsewhere, and continuing organizations for manpower planning have been established in Ghana, Nigeria and Tanzania. Some uncertainties inevitably exist in projections of future needs, but in general the growing use of manpower planning has made possible much clearer targets in educational development. Techniques for assessing manpower have essentially to give careful attention to the distribution of need among various types of jobs. It is obviously not enough that African countries should have sufficient gross numbers of people with secondary and post-secondary education. Their trained manpower must be properly distributed among the needs for engineers, doctors, agricultural specialists, teachers, etc. The danger that the arts, social sciences and law will attract relatively too many students is known from other parts of the world, and great emphasis is being placed on technical and scientific education. Measures are being taken to direct student populations towards types of training and specialization that will be particularly needed. There are ample administrative problems to be solved in directing the educational choices of young people without undue coercion or the abundant production of misfits. But good progress is being made towards solving these problems.

All of this offers encouragement that African resources will be well directed towards producing trained people in the numbers and types that will be needed for African development. But planning does not ensure execution, and degrees and certificates do not ensure future performance. Manpower planning inevitably depends on judgments that a certain level of education is the minimum requirement for performance in a given job; but if the education is not very good, it may not be enough. Moreover, a great part of the work of the world depends on qualities which are not easy to develop by formal education. Judgment, assiduity, initiative, integrity—one can readily make a list of virtues for which there is no obvious curriculum.

A concern that educated Africans will not serve their countries as effectively and devotedly as they might has been a frequent theme of African leaders. Reminders to students, like the one by President Nyerere that I have mentioned, have been common. Those who go on to secondary and higher education are still a privileged few, and the fear that they may become a self-centred élite, unprepared for hard and humble work, certainly has some substance, if only because education has been such an important avenue to advancement in Africa. With exceptions in political life, striking social rise has been dependent on first acquiring education—perhaps more so in Africa than anywhere else in the world. The lack of opportunities during the colonial era for Africans to advance through occupational achievement from a low educational base has cut away a competing ladder of advancement that is important in other parts of the world. In such circumstances it would be most unlikely for educational attainments to avoid having an intrinsic value as a mark of status. It must seem important to be a university graduate whether or not the degree has made one capable of doing great things. The *formalization* of educational attainment, however natural, threatens to focus the values of the educated on the wrong things. It is not easy for young university graduates to regard their talents humbly or to appreciate that they may not yet be of much use to society. Careful scrutiny of what they have learned from the point of view of its increasing their practical effectiveness is not encouraged by their élite status.

These tendencies are well known, as irate speeches by African leaders attest, but they should not be credited to some exceptional corruptibility among young African students. I hope I have indicated that they are a normal consequence of the social changes that have come recently in Africa. They nevertheless pose urgent problems about the orientation and character of education at secondary and higher levels.

As in primary education, the most promising way of making African education at these higher levels a genuine preparation for African need seems to lie through a broadly conceived kind of Africanization. Without such Africanization there is danger that education will lack relevance and deteriorate in quality. As long as the system of education is seen as an importation in which Africans are trying to conform to somebody else's ideas and standards there must be artificiality and formalism in educational attainment. In the old days of colonial rule, the character and standards of the colonial powers' education could have some meaning for Africans. But African independence brings a rejection of the standards as well as the political authority of the colonial power. Africans have perceived that in much of their education they were doing things that were artificial to them. Feeling the impact of unjust discrimination in other spheres of life, they could not remain uncritical of the sorting and screening which are inseparable from any system of education. From accepting received forms of education as facts of life, Africans turn to be critical of them, often with bitterness over past acquiescence.

There is both promise and danger in this critical posture. The danger is that in rejecting the content and standards of European education that seem irrelevant, new ones that Africans believe in will not be promptly put in their place. Delay could encourage evasive and cynical attitudes towards educational systems and cause damage hard to repair. The egalitarian spirit that now pervades Africa makes criticism of the rigours and selectivity of the old system easy; it does not clearly encourage substitutes for them. The promise in current African criticism of educational systems is that changes are being urgently sought and many of them are in promising directions. The emphases on Africanization of teaching materials in as many fields as possible and on the sciences and technologies clearly respond to African need. As I emphasized in speaking of primary education, these shifts in the content of education are important, but they are not enough in themselves. Scientific education can be pedantically academic, technological education out-of-date, and Africanization superficial. More important than filling students with particular forms of knowledge, is the development of their competence in disciplined study of problems, in judicious analysis, and in the perception of values. It is not so much the content of education that matters for these things as the quality with which it is imparted. These principles are, I think, applicable in secondary schools, technical schools and universities. They will be attainable only with a combination of good staff in these institutions and with the kind of African guidance and acceptance which makes them a normal part of the new education in Africa.

Adapting a set of educational institutions derived from the Western world to African conditions will require immense creative effort. It must be done largely by Africans, and it will have to have the sensitive and loyal co-operation of teachers and researchers who come from elsewhere. I hope that my remarks have shown that this task is no mere courtesy to African national feeling. It is absolutely essential to the provision of the competent manpower that African countries will need to develop as they want and must.

I will not attempt to cap this analysis of need with specific prescriptions for action. The general direction of effort seems sufficiently clear: there must be intelligent and persisting reference of educational facilities to manpower needs; there must be abundant consideration and discussion of the character and aims of education by African leaders; there must be, for a considerable period ahead, much help in staffing by educators and professional men from elsewhere. These things are already being done. Let us do what we can to keep them vigorous and effective in the critical period that lies ahead. Educational systems in African countries could become a burdensome source of economic and social problems as much as a fountainhead of skills and power. To avoid such evils we must study deeply what it means that education be adapted to African conditions and needs.

Appendix

Let r be the annual rate at which employment grows, p the rate of population growth, and $e = r - p$. Then if one assumes that households dependent on those in employment are of the same size and grow at the same rate as households in the subsistence sector, the population in the modern wage sector E_n and the total population P_n, n years after a starting date, are related as follows:

$$\frac{E_n}{P_n} = \frac{E_o}{P_o}\left(\frac{1+r}{1+p}\right)^n = \frac{E_o}{P_o}\left(1 + \frac{e}{1+p}\right)^n$$

Calculations showing the increase in the fraction of the total population dependent on wage employment after 10, 20 and 30 years follow:

r	p	e	$\dfrac{E_{10}/E_0}{P_{10}/P_0}$	$\dfrac{E_{20}/E_0}{P_{20}/P_0}$	$\dfrac{E_{30}/E_0}{P_{30}/P_0}$
3	2	1	1·10	1·21	1·34
4	2	2	1·21	1·47	1·79
5	2	3	1·33	1·78	2·37
4	3	1	1·10	1·21	1·33
5	3	2	1·21	1·47	1·77
6	2	4	1·47	2·16	3·17

DISCUSSION

Lambo: May I congratulate you on a very comprehensive paper, Dr. Sutton. You have however raised a number of questions which seem rather formidable at the present time. For example, in 1957–58 we carried out a survey of the health and social problems of Nigerian students in Great Britain, especially the social problems related to academic difficulties, and our impression was that specific improvements were needed if the education programmes in Africa were to be geared to the needs of Africa.

There should be some form of basic selection right through the education system, even at university level. This particular factor of guidance has been lacking in the African countries; nowhere in Africa today is there any well-integrated, scientific scheme for selecting students for any form of training programme. I feel that this gap should be filled if we are to preserve and economize our human and other resources.

Sutton: A tremendous need for improved selection certainly exists. The critical point is, of course, at completion of primary school when students are selected for secondary schools and specialized technical schools. I know of large sections of Africa where people no longer have much faith in the examination systems at this level. Educational achievement is very important to people in Africa, and if they do not believe the system is an honest one which gives valid results, then the seeds of real social dissatisfaction are sown.

Goody: You have excellently pointed out the main problems in the rural field, Dr. Sutton. There has to be a transformation in the curricula of rural schools so that they are much more adapted to the current needs of the population. I recently heard a rural school teacher instructing his pupils on the seven wonders of the world: the hanging gardens of Babylon are completely outside the experience of the village youth and the incident brought home to me the artificiality of much of their learning. There should be a stronger emphasis on health education and on elementary science, as a basis for agricultural development.

Ghana is contributing to this change by the establishment of a University of Science Education at Cape Coast. But it will take some time for this programme to begin feeding back into the rural schools. As a short-term measure, one ought at least to consider the possibility of a transformation of the agricultural scene through the use of auxiliary techniques, such as mass education by means of the ubiquitous transistor. Another possibility in many African countries today is education through some party organization or other body; here ideological commitment may produce more immediate results than any purely academic approach.

One danger I see here, from the point of view of continental unity, is the increased emphasis on the national aspects of education. Geography tends to get taught around countries (especially one's own) rather than regions. And we have national histories, national literatures, etc., all of which lead to a restriction in the outlook of the pupils. This is happening at university level too, where African studies, for example, tend to become the study of the country concerned.

Sutton: A great effort is being made to develop better elementary school curricula in Africa. There is some particularly interesting work on science education, and I think one does not need to be over-romantic to feel that the acquisition of a scientific perspective by whole African populations may open up all kinds of development possibilities.

Adult education can be an important step towards rural transformation, but it is perfectly obvious that the transformations we are seeking are not going to take place in a few years. Hence, it is important to plan education not only for the people who are farming now, but also for the young people who will carry through the transformations during the next generation.

Acock: You have illustrated very clearly the importance of the sixth major policy approach of the expert meeting to which I shall refer in my paper (Chapter 11, ref. 2). For instance, when measures have been taken to make agriculture a more respected and agreeable way of life, this will help to attract more efficient types of workers to farming. It would seem that, given the right kinds of pragmatic education (of the type you described), plus rural development programmes, there may be some possibility of regulating the chaotic scramble from the rural areas to the urban areas.

Last: Dr. Sutton's review was to me a rather horrid reminder of the problems which I personally have to return to after this symposium. He has pinpointed the major areas, starting with the reform of curricula, because after all it is no use putting money into education unless it is going to bring results, and the results are achieved through what is actually taught and put over in the classroom. With regard to that, however, there are many areas in which we do not know and cannot identify the problems; we cannot really justify some of the things we would like to put into the curricula, and this implies a great deal of research, which is not yet taking place. It also implies a very strong link between the universities and the education authorities in general, and I very much appreciated Dr. Goody's remarks about regional formulation of curricula, which has not yet taken place. Most countries are working in isolation, and any steps which bodies like U.N.E.S.C.O. can take to bring together countries in the creation of a common approach within a region, rather than a national approach, would be a good thing.

When we turn to the practical problem of implementing programmes for the expansion and development of education, we immediately think of money. By and large, the capital costs of an expanding education programme do not present the same problems as the recurrent expenditure. We can often find the capital needed for expansion of education from some source or other, but most countries are faced with a weighty bill for recurrent expenditure, largely for teachers' salaries. The financial difficulties implicit in the targets outlined in the Addis Ababa Plan[13] are enormous. For example, to achieve something like 85 per cent enrolment in Ethiopia would require a gross national product of something like $17\frac{1}{2}$ billion* Ethiopian dollars as compared with just over $2 billion at the moment. It would require an expansion

---

* Billion = 1,000,000,000.

of the education budget from its present level of something like Ethiopian $30 million to something like $700 million if education is to be organized along traditional lines.

It seems that we need some radical change in thought if we are ever going to get the expansion which we need. At elementary school level perhaps we should establish very much closer links between community and administration. If there is direct responsibility, not only is there local supervision of education but the community is at the same time invited to establish its own balance between the money required for education and the amount of education which is to be provided.

I am interested in René Dumont's suggestions for self-supporting rural farm schools[12]. Apart from the financial advantages, they may represent nuclear points at which rural transformation can take place. Perhaps Dr. Sutton could comment on this?

At secondary school level the great difficulty is not only the recurrent cost of teachers' salaries but also the difficulty in obtaining and retaining teachers. I think the point was made earlier in this symposium that one of the ways in which we can solve this particular problem is to spread the high cost of teachers over the maximum number of pupils, making full use of radio, television, and programmed learning. By these means one can put the job in the hands of a few relatively highly paid people and counteract all the tendency in expanding education to a lowering of standards.

The problem of teachers is an enormous one in the African continent, firstly because of the lack of candidates coming forward from the secondary school systems for training as teachers; secondly because of the alternative professions and jobs which are open to graduates from the school systems; thirdly, the social and financial unattractiveness of the teaching profession; and lastly, the difficulty of obtaining instructors for teacher training centres.

To return to a more general question, would I be right in

thinking that a uniform expansion of education over the whole territory of a country is not possible or desirable at this time, and that we must put our ''educational eggs'' in the basket that is going to produce results? Should we give emphasis to the development of education in those parts of the country which can be termed development regions, because these are the areas which are going to produce the revenues which will enable the next stage to be undertaken—the more general expansion of education?

It is difficult not to feel that a massive expansion of basic education is the first step towards building a nation, but when one comes up against the money problem, it just cannot be done. We are forced to relate the development of education, at this particular moment, directly to those sectors of the economy where wealth is being produced.

Sutton: I agree with nearly all that Mr. Last has said; he speaks from real experience in coping with these problems. There are enormous practical difficulties in achieving the levels of education which are now eagerly desired not only by the leaders of countries but by the masses of the population in Africa. The problem is, I think, to achieve an adequate response to the need for concentrating available resources at points which will be significant for growth in those countries, and at the same time to move towards a gratification of the general desire for education.

The importance of the provision of good teachers can hardly be exaggerated. The kind of education I have suggested is only possible if there are teachers who exemplify the uses of education in their own lives, and who relate their education to the situation around them. One of the most disturbing things in Africa recently has been the decline in the prestige of teachers —of elementary school teachers particularly. This trend must be reversed, and as an impromptu recommendation I would suggest that the most promising line of development is to get more women teachers.

I did not have time to discuss the question of farm schools fully in my paper, but I want to sound a note of warning against the simple notion that if agricultural practices are introduced in school, this will somehow make boys want to stay on the farms. This idea has been thoroughly tested, and it just does not work. Dumont's idea is a little more sophisticated in that it links the alleged educational advantages to the problem of supporting the schools. But anything the school does in production may well compete directly with the market possibilities of other people. In sum, I am not very enthusiastic about farm schools.

I would agree that the only hope for the universalization of African education is the maintenance of strong local contributions to education. These contributions are well established in some places. The local contributions to the primary schools of Kenya, for example, cover about 60 per cent of the total costs; they are made through school fees and local rates. This is a considerable achievement, and if this sort of thing can be done it is possible to maintain a fairly broad educational system without undue drain on central government revenues. Widespread cash income through the sale of cash crops or employment is of course a necessary condition. This is in fact the situation in many parts of Africa now, and the development plans for rural areas typically envisage growth towards more cash income. Emphasis on local contributions gives only an indication of a solution to the problem of finance, but it does seem promising.

Mancini: The responsibility for primary and secondary education lies, of course, with governments. However, it may become remarkably difficult to train good technicians, good chemists, good engineers, and good doctors in good universities by good professors if all the African countries intend to have their own universities. I would suggest that African governments should try to establish sub-regional universities, which might help to cut down the cost of higher education and at the same time make it possible to achieve integration of curricula on a sub-regional or regional basis.

Sutton: We all strive manfully in this direction—it is not easy to achieve, but I think there has been some real progress. We have a regional university in East Africa; substantial efforts are being made towards the establishment of other universities serving whole regions; and there is now an embryonic Association of African Universities, which may very well help national universities to co-operate and avoid the multiplication of expensive professional faculties. Medicine is perhaps the most difficult problem, because of the urgent need for more doctors, the extreme costliness of medical education, and the desire of people in each country to have their own medical school.

Mancini: There is an advantage in having a medical department at university level in a country, because it also provides certain medical services; but it is expensive, and it is one of the cases where I would advocate the setting up of a regional centre where there would be professors, laboratories, libraries, a research centre, etc. This is a good example of the real need for regional co-operation in Africa in order to cut down the cost, yet it is probably the field in which regional co-operation is the most difficult.

Brown: I agree with Mr. Mancini and Dr. Sutton on the costliness of medical education and the desirability of regional institutions.

Countries need to realize also that student health services are important at the university level. The number of graduates is very small in relation to the needs and every one represents a very big capital investment. These students are also subjected to quite big cultural transition problems, and perhaps Professor Lambo could comment on his personal experience in this respect. There is some evidence that failure to pass examinations—in some cases resulting in the mere prolongation of studies, but in others in the actual loss of students who start their university training but do not complete it— could to some extent be prevented by more adequate student health services than exist at present. I am thinking of student health services in quite a wide sense, i.e. not just curing overt disease, but also preventive physical and mental health services.

Sutton: I applaud your point here: if a thousand pounds per annum per student is being spent, one really ought not to risk losing these people through illness; they deserve to be carefully guarded as national assets.

Lambo: After our survey on students in England, we conducted a similar survey in Nigeria and we also obtained figures from three other universities in Africa. At the present time, wastage through failure due to illness alone is about 5 per cent at home and 35 per cent abroad. The percentage of students who change their courses because of severe emotional problems is about 20 per cent at home and 45 per cent abroad. Some of those returning from abroad are even unable to work for two or three years afterwards. We feel that these figures are unduly high. The greatest wastage was found among the private students as opposed to the government scholars. Within the private students' group there was no selection of any kind; they often rely entirely on their families for financial help and tend to choose their courses arbitrarily.

Brown: Dr. Sutton, is it known to what extent literacy is lost in the rural areas? I have heard it said that many people learn to read and write at school and then subsequently, for lack of opportunity to practise, lose these arts.

Sutton: It is a common observation that literacy is typically lost by children who go to school for one to five years and remain in rural areas. But I don't think there has ever been a serious study of the effects of education and whether or not literacy is completely lost; we need research to check the impressions of people who have lived in these areas. The standard indictment of brief primary education is that it leads to the expensive production of illiterates and is of no positive use at all. This needs re-examination. People with a very few years of primary education and without a great deal of use for literacy may still have acquired a new grasp of the world and a new approach to problems. Such acquisitions could be very important for the practical transformation of rural life.

For some years everybody has been trying to extend the period at primary schools from four to six or eight years. Now there is a tendency to review the whole situation, and in order to review it intelligently, a great deal of educational research is needed.

Patel: Often more than half the high cost of teaching university students goes on almost palatial dormitories. Do you see any desirability for an extension of university facilities on the present elaborate scale, and need there be so high a proportion of residential accommodation?

Sutton: Certainly there will be a considerable decrease in the cost per student per annum as the universities get larger—they are uneconomically small at present. The possibilities of getting away from residential requirements seem to me much more uncertain. Due to the lack of satisfactory private housing for students in African cities, it is very difficult to envisage students having a serious chance of doing well in their university studies without residential facilities. Lack of good housing has even been the cause of trouble at secondary school level, and has made day secondary schools look like a doubtful economy. In Ghana four or five years ago the residential schools were getting about 85 per cent of their pupils through the School Certificate examination, while the non-residential schools were only getting about 50–55 per cent through. In other words, if education is made cheaper in this way, half the students fail. So we will probably have to provide residential facilities for a considerable time to come.

Lambo: The cost of maintaining such universities is extremely high in Africa, and one of the greatest dangers in perpetuating this particular foreign heritage is that the intellectual group is separated from the general population. There is a great risk here, as Dr. Sutton pointed out, of building up an élite group which may be irresponsive to the national needs and insensitive to the general feelings of society. In Nigeria we think the answer may be found in what we call "halfway houses"—the building of houses and flats (with supervision) among the general population in towns—which may thus achieve a compromise between a purely residential university and one which does not make any provision for residence at all.

Habte-Ab: What kind of education must we concentrate on in order to produce a critical minority of fully competent managers?

Sutton: It is perfectly clear that creative managers are indispensable to development, and we must emphasize the kind of education which might produce such people. But it is obviously not easy to produce competent managers through an educational system. Clearly, the qualities that go into the making of a good manager are acquired to a considerable extent outside school.

Habte-Ab: Assuming that the main problems are the great shortage of good teachers and the scarcity of financial resources, would you advocate the closing of certain secondary schools in order to concentrate on fewer but better schools?

Sutton: The situation is being reached in West Africa now where one might consider this a real problem, but in Africa as a whole we have typically been in the situation where almost any secondary school graduate was better than none. This situation will change very rapidly over the continent in the next few years. For example, in Tanzania forecasts show that the supply of secondary school pupils will be in balance with the demand for them by 1970, which is not very far off. We could very shortly in East Africa have the kind of excess of secondary school leavers which may already exist in Nigeria.

Bourgeois-Pichat: Your paper points out the real difficulty of economic development, Dr. Sutton. For a given country at a given time, there are at least three possible populations to be regarded as economically active: first, that forecast by the economic planners; second, that corresponding to the educational knowledge provided in the country; and third, the one which the people themselves have in mind, and which depends on their desires and the prestige of different professions, etc. The trouble comes from the fact that the three economically active populations do not coincide, and if one wants to achieve economic development without producing social disorder, these three have to be reconciled with each other.

Apeadu: Dr. Sutton, please would you evaluate some of the methods that are being used in African countries to accelerate the pace of educational development? You very rightly pointed to the danger that standards might be lowered and you also said that there was a reaction on the part of the leaders of these countries against the type of education that had been given under the former colonial governments. Another complication is the limitation of financial resources for all kinds of development, and governments have reacted in a variety of ways. For instance, in some countries there has been a tendency to put school leavers who have just completed their primary education straight back into schools to teach others; the authorities could not wait to go through the tedious process of teaching these young people how to teach. In some cases they have organized brief occasional vacation courses of training for these new teachers. Other countries have found that not good enough, and have decided to provide two years' continuous training instead of the usual four years. In many countries children finish school without being able to spell and all the evidence points towards a low standard of teaching arising from causes such as these.

The tendency has been to compare this lower standard of teaching with the training given to medical assistants, the argument being that if you can get hold of someone to cure your simple ailments, you may often be better served than waiting a whole six years for a doctor. Also, in an effort to push as many children as possible through the school system, some countries have insisted on automatic promotion for every child at the end of the school year. This is meant to avoid wastage, but it only results in a lot of dead wood being carried, and so far it has not been very profitable.

At some of the universities, too, one gets a clear illustration of an attempt to break away from the old traditions which still exist in some overseas countries. For instance, some African governments seek to discourage the teaching of classics, ancient and mediaeval European history, etc., and in some cases they also try to reduce the content of a particular course. These are just a few examples of the methods adopted in the anxiety to get on quickly and to break away from whatever traditions they regard as unacceptable. How does all this strike you?

Sutton: Some of it is inevitable, I think. You have filled in points that I could only suggest very briefly in my paper. The picture you give of the changes in Africa is certainly very much in accordance with my own observations. The effects of these changes are very difficult to assess; there is a very diffuse effect of education of a not very high standard which may be valuable for African development, and the great expansion that has occurred with the use of under-qualified teachers may have provided a base which is necessary for further development. But it is certainly clear that the present trends open up dangers as well as showing promise. There can be a tremendous amount of waste in ineffective education and one of the major problems which must now be faced in Africa is the improvement of schools which have been built rapidly and staffed with under-qualified teachers.

The emphasis on changing the character of the curricula is on the whole healthy; there will undoubtedly be some excesses at first, but I think such excesses are inseparable from attempts to achieve the needed results. As I emphasized before, African teachers, professors and leaders don't believe in much they have inherited and there is just no use in having an educational system which people don't believe in. At the lower levels it probably is important to have an easing of the system, but I am not sure that this is so at university level; there is a great waste of expenditure in ineffective university education.

Lambo: We have come to the conclusion after many years of observation that if education is really going to go forward in Africa, all sections of life must be covered; in other words, some form of education should start at home. To take a simple example, the use of educational toys is not encouraged in many African homes. By the time the children reach primary or secondary school level most of them have failed to acquire any basic knowledge of simple mechanical items, and manual dexterity is much worse than it need be. Therefore a boy who plans to study, say, engineering or physics, later on may be severely handicapped. We must think not only in terms of institutions, but also in terms of basic family conditions and what can be done to stimulate the interest of a child from infancy in the directions which may prepare him for a scientific world.

Goody: Perhaps educational efficiency could be increased without any additional expenditure by the more intensive use of equipment, possibly by instituting a shift system, or possibly by reconsidering the school holidays. This of course links up with a more intensive use of teachers' time. There does not seem to be any reason why teachers should necessarily have longer holidays than economic planners or any other category of persons engaged on research or administration. But I am thinking mainly of a more intensive use of time of the school population itself. Very often in a village one sees schoolboys on holiday sitting around in apathetic idleness. If you have compulsory school, why not compulsory holiday activities? Why not make farming or similar activities compulsory during holidays, as one makes school compulsory during term time?

IO

BIOLOGICAL RESEARCH IN DEVELOPING COUNTRIES

J. B. S. HALDANE *

THIS communication is based on my experiences in India, that is to say visits from 1951 to 1956, and nearly continuous residence with active direction of research since 1957. I have been an Indian citizen since 1961. India differs from most African countries except Egypt in several respects. It has a longer cultural history, and has made more serious contributions to world science, such as the distinction between monocotyledons and dicotyledons, and the invention of sines and cosines. It has had universities of a European type for a century, and it has taken over intact from its European rulers not only a highly trained administrative personnel but also a set of rules presumably designed to check initiative of subordinates and certainly acting to do so. However, I think much of my experience in India is directly applicable to Africa.

Biological research falls into three main categories: agricultural research, medical research, and what may be called fundamental or "pure" research. Agricultural research generally demands a good deal of land and labour, but not much imported apparatus; medical research usually demands expensive imported equipment; pure research may be expensive, but need not be so. Students going abroad are too often given problems requiring expensive

---

* Professor Haldane was prevented by illness from presenting this paper in person and it was read for him by Dr. Wolstenholme.

It was with great regret that news of Professor Haldane's death on 1st December 1964 was received while this book was being prepared for publication.

apparatus, and do not learn to carry out simple experiments or observations. On their return they are incapable of research. Nor do they learn statistics, which can largely take the place of apparatus.

In India I have directed some medium-scale agricultural research, but mainly cheap pure research. By cheap I mean that in my first year my group here cost Rs. 64,064 (£4,800). My own salary is Rs. 1,000 (£75) per month. Yet in that first year we published 19 scientific papers, besides numerous reviews, popular articles, lectures and so on. I want this to be an example of what can be done in poor countries.

Our principles are as follows:

(1) We should only tackle problems which can better be tackled in India than elsewhere. As a general rule no research should be done in an undeveloped country which can more easily be done in a developed one.

(2) We should choose problems which need the minimum of apparatus.

(3) We should hope in at least a third of our work to be ahead of the rest of the world.

(4) We should attempt to inflict no pain on animals, and to kill as few as possible. This is a concession to Indian sentiments which I share. I do not ask Africans to accept it.

(5) Any worker should be free to observe whatever he wishes, and to devote a little time to it from his main assignment. The director should be prepared to let him abandon his assignment for a more profitable line.

The last principle is perhaps the most important of all if you hope to leap ahead of the rest of the world. Let me give you two examples from our own work. I gave Dronamraju a dull problem in plant genetics, to which however he could be reasonably certain of finding an answer. He noticed that a pink and an orange variety of the same plant species were being visited by different butterfly species. More accurately some species visited both, some only one, some only the other. This had not been observed in the 170 years since insect fertilization of flowers was discovered. It is the analogy in plants of Darwinian sexual selection. I gave Ray an equally dull problem in human genetics. In his first three weeks he discovered a hereditary abnormality unknown in Europe and very rare in Japan. It happens to be of very great genetical interest. If you do not give your young men and women this kind of freedom, there is little hope of Africa taking the lead in any branch of biology. However, it should be emphasized that unless the worker is a statistician or has a good statistical colleague, he will be overwhelmed by the bulk of his data.

Naturally I cannot suggest problems of this kind for Africa as I often failed to do so in India. But I am going to suggest three problems which could be tackled in almost all African states, and two which could be tackled in many.

(1) What dry weight of earth is brought up by earthworms per hectare per year? You need a coarse balance, an oven drying at 100°c, and a number of plots of about one square metre, if possible on different types of soil, some shaded and others exposed.

(2) How many persons with short fourth toes on one or both feet can you find in a sample of, say, ten thousand, in your area? If you find them, in how many parents, children, brothers, and sisters of each is the condition found? I have oral information that it is not rare among the Batutsi, of the Congo. For this task an ordinary camera is useful but not essential.

(3) Are total crop yields improved by species mixture, for example by growing a cereal and a legume together? Quite small plots are needed for this. This problem has been neglected in countries where harvesting is mechanical and in colonial countries because attention was mainly paid to cash crops. To my mind an important question of this type is "What crops, if any, can be grown under a primary crop of fruit trees, e.g. coconut or oil palms, mangoes, etc.,

without diminishing the yield of the trees, while raising the total yield per hectare per year?''

(4) Coconut palms have their leaves arranged in a right-handed or left-handed spiral. The two are equally common, but in India and Ceylon one produces, on an average, more fruits and more copra than the other. Is this true in your district? If the difference is as large as in India you can raise your coconut yield 20 years hence by 10 per cent or so without manuring or selective breeding.

(5) Are rice yields improved by growing two varieties in alternate rows? Roy finds increased yields up to 30 per cent with a few pairs. Other pairs give a lowered yield.

You will see that three of these problems have immediate applications to agriculture, while two are ''pure'', that is to say I cannot foresee their applications. I have no objection to applied research, provided the workers are occasionally allowed to escape from it. On the contrary I think a man who has done no applied research has missed a great deal. But one who has done nothing else has probably always worked as a member of a team, and may turn out to be sadly lacking in initiative.

To my mind a very promising field is the study of animal behaviour. Unfortunately this demands an accurate watch or clock, and for some species, including most birds, field glasses, or a small mounted telescope. Moreau worked on the nesting behaviour of some African bird species. Most of the observations were made by African observers, and he was thoroughly satisfied with their work. Similar work with slightly more up-to-date methods could be undertaken. Extremely little has been done on the behaviour of African bees and wasps, at least since Roubaud's pioneering work over 40 years ago. In both these cases the work of my colleagues Jayakar and Spurway* could serve as an example. Their methods are original but cheap. I believe them to be fairly

---

* Present address: Dr. Helen Spurway (Mrs. J. B. S. Haldane), Genetics and Biometry Laboratory, Government of Orissa, Bhubaneswar 3, Orissa, India.

applicable to the more stable African states. This work, on both birds and wasps, solitary and social, is of a type new not only to India, but to the world. These workers also have data on the genetics of wasps and tortoises, which might be harder to follow up in Africa. Perhaps I should add that it has been stated that African bees are likely to be more valuable than the Asian species as a source of honey in the countries of Southern Asia, but this statement is based on rather slight evidence.

No doubt many Africans, like many Europeans, are incapable of independent work of this kind. But in India I have had no difficulty in finding men who can do so after a few hours' training. If, as I suppose, they are equally frequent in Africa, it should be possible to produce a cadre of original African biologists.

DISCUSSION

Lambo: People who are not connected technically with scientific development tend to misunderstand when we talk of this artificial division between fundamental, pure research and applied research. Some national leaders in Africa, especially those who have to supply funds for university development, often state that they are not interested in fundamental research, since funds could be used for the next twenty years without any tangible results. Consequently, they are only interested in applied research. We should state here that the line between the two is not well defined and in practice there is a great deal of interaction between the two.

It is very difficult to defend such a view when the type of report we have just heard gets into the hands of some of the national leaders and administrators, because it is this artificial division which is talked about all the time. It may encourage the tendency to think that fundamental research is entirely esoteric and vague and that it interests "rather cranky" investigators, in contrast to applied research, which such people say is much more relevant to the urgent needs of the developing countries.

Gille: This question was discussed at length during the International Conference on the Organization of Research and Training in Africa in relation to the Study, Conservation and Utilization of Natural Resources, organized by U.N.E.S.C.O. in association with the Economic Commission for Africa in Lagos from 28th July to 6th August, 1964, to which reference was made earlier. Delegates were expected to express the views of their governments, and I am glad to say that many showed how conscious they were of the importance of fundamental research. At the closing session, the Conference unanimously adopted a number of decisions and recommendations which constitute, as it was said, a blueprint for the development of scientific research in Africa, now known as the ''Lagos Plan''. The first resolution of the Plan, considered as the most important, constitutes a real declaration of faith in scientific research. It recommends, among other things, that: '' . . . . the governments should devote continued and very large-scale efforts to the promotion of scientific and technical research''. This is followed by a list of the ten imperatives of national science policy established by the Conference, of which I would like to quote three:

''Recognition by the African governments of the need to establish scientific research and industrial research programmes, both short-term and long-term'';

''Recognition by the governments of their responsibility for the organization of scientific research and the encouragement of research by creating an atmosphere favourable to it'';

''Recognition of the need to establish a proper balance between fundamental and applied research. The African countries are aware of the importance of fundamental research and oriented research, knowing that their development is indispensable to progress in applied research and that they constitute the base of the pyramid of research activities''.

Michaelis: Perhaps I might be allowed to repeat what I said after Mr. Gayer's paper. If the questions raised by the last two speakers were regularly discussed every year at different African universities during meetings of an African Association for the Advancement of Science, then these would soon persuade politicians and scientists that the right balance between pure and applied research could only come from experience.

I understand that this year the Organization of African Unity has made special provision for scientific and technical research. Possibly one might make the suggestion that they should work through an African Association for the Advancement of Science rather than with individual universities, and so follow the lines which have proved so useful in India, Pakistan, Australia, New Zealand and elsewhere, wherever an Association for the Advancement of Science exists.

Gille: I think that this is very important because of the rôle that science associations have to play in the growth of national scientific communities in developing countries, such as the African countries. Regardless of the institution to which they belong, one must encourage among African scientists working on similar problems the strengthening of the bonds that unite members with the same interests.

One way of encouraging this development is to catalyse the creation of scientific and technical associations and societies open to a wide range of disciplines, such as the natural sciences. I am glad to say that a number of such organizations already exist in Africa, such as, for instance, the Ghana Science Association, the Science Association of Nigeria and the Sierra Leone Science Association, which are themselves members of the West African Science Association, the Association pour l'avancement des sciences naturelles du Sénégal, the Société Congolaise des sciences naturelles, the East African Academy, the Société des sciences naturelles de Tunisie, etc.

Wolstenholme: I am a little afraid that the suggestion made by Dr. Michaelis is running, like the Awash river in Ethiopia, into the sand. It is one thing to have national organizations called ''for the advancement of science'' or learned and scientific societies for the study of this or that. These give opportunities for scientists to communicate with each other. However, Dr. Michaelis, in citing the example of the British Association, was very much more concerned that scientists of all the different disciplines should have an annual forum at which they could bring to the notice and understanding of the public at large, and politicians in particular, the implications of their work. And further, that since in Africa research in any one country is necessarily very restricted, such a forum, to be properly useful, should be at a pan-African or continental level. I am not quite clear from what has been said whether anything of this kind is in fact being done in Africa now.

Lambo: Professor Monod, being the President of the Scientific Council for Africa, is in the best position to answer this question.

Monod: Professor Lambo is himself the Vice-President of the Council!

The West African Science Association is at present trying to extend its scope to scientific associations in French-speaking territories, and to become decisively bilingual. Its meetings are convened every two years; the last one was in Kumasi in 1963, and the next one will be in Freetown. Whether or not these meetings attract a sufficiently large public audience, I don't know, but scientists are meeting together and discussing their problems on many different subjects. It is exactly like the Association for the Advancement of Science in Britain or the equivalent body in France in that it covers many subjects in separate sections.

Probably the system could be improved if more attention was given to these scientific meetings by the press and by government officials, or at least by the government departments interested in research.

The West African Science Association could form a nucleus for regional research, and I think there is a better case for regional development on these lines instead of enormous pan-African institutions. Regional development is what is happening at present: for the last two or three years there has been an Academy of Science in East Africa; there are of course a number of institutions in North Africa, and now West Africa is beginning to form its own regional organizations. Of course, now that the Organization of African Unity is to have its own scientific commission and its own technical commissions, it will cover the whole of Africa. There may be room for both types of organization, the regional body and also the scientific advisers to the scientific and technical commissions for co-operation within the pan-African organization.

Michaelis: I could not possibly argue with you on the issue of regional versus pan-African development, but I am quite sure that the real point to be stressed here is the efficient communication of scientific information to people outside the laboratories.

As I mentioned earlier, the British Association particularly has learned this lesson and, as you probably know, its meetings are very fully reported in the press, on radio and on television. Almost a page is devoted to the meeting each day in the national daily newspapers. This came about because the press persuaded a reasonable number of scientists that they had something interesting to say. It was a very long struggle; in its early history the British Association was very strongly attacked by "The Times", and Charles Dickens made fun of it. I think it was only because scientists felt very deeply that they had to make a case for themselves that the British Association achieved its object of acting as an instrument to further general knowledge and understanding of science.

With due respect to what has been said here about the Lagos meeting, I feel strongly that much depends on scientists themselves making their own case to their respective governments and showing that their results are useful to the community, to their own nation, and to their own continent. Only if this can be proposed in very strong terms will science in Africa get the same respect as science is now getting in Europe and in

America. There it has been a really long struggle, and I think a study of the history of science in the European countries might have some relevance for Africa.

Lambo: I endorse whole-heartedly what Dr. Michaelis has just said. It is important for young scientists in developing countries to make a very strong case for science, and we shall have to define how they should do this—that is equally important.

There was a mention in Professor Haldane's paper regarding adaptability—being able to use the minimum of apparatus to achieve great ends—and he warned us against one of the great dangers we have to face when he pointed out that most of the young scientists who return to African countries after being trained overseas have got used to expensive, sensitive, and complex equipment, and therefore expect this type of equipment to be provided by African governments. Some people will not or cannot work with less than they have been familiar with in Europe or America. Probably the only way to make a very strong case for research is to be as selective as possible in relation to one's facilities in the initial stages and always try to produce results which will stimulate the interest of the public, in the long run gaining its sympathy and support for work which needs expensive instruments. We may have to wait patiently for another fifty years in Africa to get all the things we need. But we cannot afford to wait; we have to improvise in the meantime.

Gille: I would like to raise a point of terminology. During the last twelve years or so U.N.E.S.C.O. has been engaged in a survey of scientific organizations existing in the world, and about ten years ago we published the first edition of a directory of scientific organizations, covering about 20 countries. It is intended to publish shortly another issue covering about 82 countries. In making this survey we compared the types of organization existing in different countries, and we soon came to the conclusion that the name given to an organization in one country had a completely different meaning in another country. For instance, the Academy of Sciences in Ghana is completely different from the East African Academy. The one in Ghana was built on the Soviet pattern and is a government-run body which has powers to direct scientific research and responsibility in orientating research in Ghana. The one in East Africa is more a learned society than a body which directs research. As already mentioned, U.N.E.S.C.O. attaches great importance to this question and it tries to encourage the creation or the development of such organizations. It may, for this purpose, provide assistance to countries requesting its help. For example, at the request of Kenya a specialist is being put this month at the disposal of the East African Academy within the framework of the Technical Assistance programme for that country. One may mention also the French Academy of Sciences as being built on a completely different pattern from that in Ghana. There is a question of semantic differences and we must be sure in U.N.E.S.C.O. of the terminology we are using.

Apeadu: In many African countries a fair amount of research has been going on for a number of years, but also a lot of work has been lost in the files or somewhere in the offices. On one agricultural research station, for example, it was discovered that over a period of about ten years research into a certain problem was carried to completion on three occasions, yielding the same answer. A new man coming to the station after another has been transferred hasn't really had access to a full record of what has been done; some of the records are bundled up away at headquarters and he is not told about them, so he goes through the same motions again and his subordinates may not have the courage or imagination to tell him that they have already done the same thing.

What is even more significant is that extension services for applying the results of research have not been taken seriously in Africa, and this is why it is so often believed that, whatever the subject of study, the aim of research is just to satisfy the curiosity of the scientist, and that the life of the man in the street is not immediately affected. This applies to research in practically all fields. This is not to say that the research workers are always at fault, but I believe all the institutions and the individuals working in a country should show interest in the extension services which try to apply the results of research. If this is done in a sufficiently impressive way, governments would see more of the effects of research and their understandable prejudice against all research would be lessened.

Young: Could you expand a little on what you think might be done? What should the people whose research has been pigeon-holed somewhere do about it, in practice?

Apeadu: I suppose in their small way they could impress on governments and the entire country the fact that when the results of their research have been published or made known in some other way, the work is not completely finished, but must be carried on by a different kind of service altogether. In some places there is a misapprehension that whoever carries out the research and gets thc results, should himself see that the results are put into effect. This is probably not exactly the duty of the researcher.

Young: An analogy, as I understand it, is that large industrial organizations have research laboratories, and also a research and development department as a separate organization; the latter receives results from the research laboratory and develops them for industrial purposes, maybe then doing the research which is needed to put a proposed new process on a practical basis. Is this the type of research and development that you feel is lacking in Africa?

Apeadu: I think so.

Acock: The importance of extending education and research, especially in agriculture, was brought out very strongly by the experts who met in Addis Ababa in April-May this year (F.A.O./ E.C.A. Expert Meeting on Government Measures to Promote the Transition from Subsistence to Market Agriculture in Africa; 1964). In their report these experts considered that the extension services were a vital factor in promoting agricultural growth.

Gille: This question was also discussed during the Lagos Conference on the organization of research to which I have referred. It was recommended that, in each African country, national research organizations be set up to co-ordinate the elaboration and implementation of programmes of research and that effective links be instituted between national research organizations on the one hand, and planning commissions and establishments making use of the results of scientific research on the other hand. Neighbouring countries must co-ordinate their research policies in matters of common interest, exchange information on their work, and co-ordinate efforts with a view to the implementation of joint projects and joint use of research institutes. African countries have limited budgets and the part that they can devote to research is usually small. It is, therefore, the responsibility of governments to make sure that every franc or shilling invested in research produces some result.

Brown: In my years with the World Health Organization, I have seen a great change in the Organization's attitude towards research as a whole. When the first World Health Assembly took place in 1948, the general attitude taken by the member governments at that time was that we already knew a lot and the main thing was to get some of this knowledge applied. Research did not really come into the general picture of the Organization's activities at all. Over the years this situation has gradually changed, and we now have an increasingly important research division.

In one particular case, when the member governments decided in 1955 that there should be a world campaign to eradicate malaria, and the Organization was given responsibility for providing technical guidance to governments in this matter, the question of research very soon came up. One of W.H.O.'s main functions here has been, through its expert committees, to define the gaps in our knowledge, and to get some kind of publicity for these gaps, in the hope that various institutions can pick them up and get to work on them. We began like that, and now we are going further and attempting by contact with various institutions all over the world, but without any kind of direction, to bring about some co-ordination of effort and the best use of the research facilities which are available. We are even undertaking research work on our own account.

I was thinking of this when Dr. Wolstenholme was reading the first part of Professor Haldane's paper, when he pointed out that if research work is planned in a country where funds are short, it should be research that can best be done in that country; I would like to add also that it should be research work which relates to the filling of a gap in world knowledge. We have had so many examples of duplicated effort, and now we are finding that the institutions available are still insufficient to cope with all that has to be done. Therefore, at world level, it is helpful to indicate to institutions where the needs really lie, and to build up some kind of balanced knowledge. The World Health Organization is certainly showing a very much greater interest in co-ordination and stimulation of research. I would like to hear whether our sister organizations, U.N.E.S.C.O. and F.A.O., have had this same experience.

Gille: U.N.E.S.C.O. has indeed always been interested in research and in science in general. However, the space given to science in this programme is becoming more and more important. For the last 18 years science has been dealt with by the Department of Natural Sciences, the social sciences being the responsibility of another department. Because governments are every day becoming more conscious of the rôle of science and technology in economic and social development, it was decided last year to establish two science departments in U.N.E.S.C.O., one responsible for the programme concerning the advancement of science and the other for the programme concerning the application of science to development. This decision can be considered to be a consequence of the Conference on the Application of Science and Technology for the Benefit of Less-Developed Areas, organized by the United Nations in Geneva in February, 1963.

As you know, in the past the emphasis in U.N.E.S.C.O.'s programme has always been on education. One could say some kind of mutation took place last year, when for the first time it was decided that scientific and educational matters would have an equal importance in the programme and budget of the Organization. This shows that the 117 member governments of U.N.E.S.C.O. are now realizing that science is of fundamental importance for the development of their countries.

Acock: I am a little out of touch with F.A.O.'s recent development, after five years in Africa. In general I would point out that F.A.O. has never conducted technical research itself through its own organization. The secretariat services meetings of the member governments. It also assembles technical information, but to an ever-increasing extent it has become engaged with administration and operational problems. There is an extensive technical assistance programme to governments and a large number of projects are operated under the United Nations Special Fund, under the Freedom from Hunger Campaign and through the World Food Programme. Under this ever-growing mass of operational and administrative activities, I am afraid that fundamental research has been very much pushed into the background.

In F.A.O. there are, of course, individual officers in the Technical Department dealing with fishing, plant industry, animal diseases, and so on, who keep up their interest in research, and administratively they support research by governments, but my general impression has been that interest in research, as such, has declined rather than increased over the years in F.A.O.

Now that some of these field programmes that I mentioned have been planned, such as the Freedom from Hunger Campaign, there has been some opportunity for F.A.O. to take part in specific fields of research, usually of an applied character. I have in mind the fertilizer trials which are being conducted in Africa— in Nigeria, Ghana, and in several other countries in West Africa.

F.A.O. has recently established a small unit in the Rural Institutions and Services Division which deals with the organization of agricultural research at a national and regional level, but it does not do research itself.

Habte-Ab: In African countries, as you know, the sad tale is that there is no money for all the projects that we wish to undertake or for industries to make themselves more efficient. Recently the Ethiopian Government asked the Technical Agency to organize a survey, on behalf of a British company, in regard to fisheries (i.e. to conduct an investigation of the Red Sea for fish), oil seeds and raisins. Part of the cost would be borne by the British Department of Technical Co-operation and the local costs by us. When suitable investigators were being selected I suggested that scientists from the university here, provided they were of the necessary calibre, could be asked to help. The British representatives immediately agreed, and they said they would need biologists, marine biologists, and other experts. This made the President of the University very happy. The company then made a grant to the University through the Ford Foundation for this work. Although the company was not able to use these experts full-time in the survey, because they had teaching commitments, yet as the scientists knew the country so well, they could estimate the time it would take to conduct the survey and they also knew what by-products of such a survey would help them in their own research. So I think it is desirable that whenever consultants are engaged to make a survey, the scientists resident in the country, whether nationals of the country or not, should be associated with them.

Sutton: We in the Ford Foundation have become more and more concerned with research because we have become more and more aware of fundamental gaps in our knowledge. We recently gave several million dollars to establish an International Rice Research Institute in the Philippines and I think this pattern may be followed on other problems. One example in Africa is the difficult business of managing tropical soils under more intensive rotations than long bush fallows. The dearth of information on this subject is such that Professor Mohammed Nour once said to me in the Sudan: ''If you had a better extension service, you wouldn't know what to tell the people through it, because in many places there is just no well-tested information on how to improve the techniques of cultivation''.

At a time when there is growing awareness of the need for research, it is my overall impression that the research organizations on this continent are running down rather than building up. With the coming of independence there has been a tendency for some of the old organizations to decline and a natural lag before new ones develop.

I I

AGRICULTURAL POTENTIALITIES IN AFRICA

A. M. ACOCK

COMPARISONS WITH THE REST OF THE WORLD

I T is a somewhat irresponsible exercise to speculate on economic magnitudes in Africa, largely because no one can prove that the figures are wrong and, similarly, one cannot prove that they are right, because they are incomplete and unreliable in most instances. A serious and careful worker might prefer to avoid speculation under these circumstances, but available statistics do permit broad comparisons and conclusions, so I intend to be very irresponsible and to deal with some rather rough comparisons and, on the basis of these, to advance conclusions of quite a sweeping character.

First let us look at African population and agriculture in relation to world population and production. About 8 per cent of the world's population is in Africa and about 12 per cent of the world's farmers are African farmers. These African farmers produce about 4 per cent of the value of world agricultural production, less than 1 per cent of total world production and about 40 per cent of total African production. These figures indicate immediately that the African farmer is only one-third as productive as the average farmer in the world and, as one would expect, even less productive in relation to non-farmers.

When we turn to the resources, we learn from the F.A.O. Production Yearbook (1962)[1] that Africa has 17 per cent of the world's arable land and land under permanent crops, 23 per cent of its permanent meadows and pastures, 27 per cent of the unused and potentially productive area and 18 per cent of the forested land. It also has 12 per cent of the cattle, 14 per cent of the sheep and 29 per cent of the goats in the world.

In all cases these percentages of the world's resources greatly exceed the meagre 4 per cent of world agricultural production ascribed to the African farmer. In every case recorded the figure is at least three times the production level of 4 per cent. Now, as was stressed at the outset, figures of these broad magnitudes are subject to wide errors, particularly as in many countries not even the human population is known, but the errors cannot be of an order exceeding threefold. We are also told that African soils are often poor: leached and unstable in the forest area, dry and hard to work in the savannah zones. There are, however, many other parts of the world which also have soils which are naturally poor or have been impoverished by centuries of use and by erosion, but their farmers achieve higher levels of productivity than does the African farmer. Pests and diseases of man, other animals and crops are also not confined to Africa. The African plague locusts have largely been controlled, trypanosomiasis in man seems to be under control. Africa also has many rivers and lakes whose potential is untapped or only partially utilized for irrigation, fishing and power, and there is a reserve of 27 per cent of the world's unused land, which does not include deserts and other unusable areas.

I could go on much longer recounting figures to indicate that, at the present stage in history, the agricultural sector in most African economies is an unproductive sector. This is the case despite an abundance of resources in relation to population, and natural obstacles which are formidable, but not unique or insuperable. Although the title of this paper is "agricultural potentialities" it would be rash and unrewarding to attempt to assess what levels of production could be achieved. But sufficient information has been presented to show that very much more could be produced and to suggest that it is not Africa but Man who is limiting the realization of much higher levels of agricultural production in this continent.

A key factor in the very low levels of productivity, both of land and labour, in African agriculture is the high proportion of the population which is on the land, deriving its livelihood from subsistence farming. F.A.O. lists agricultural populations for only a few countries, but it appears that at least two-thirds of the African population is, on the average, on the land. In some countries the figure exceeds 90 per cent of the total population.

Under these circumstances, in the absence of massive agricultural exports, it is inevitable that a high proportion of agricultural production will be for subsistence. About 15 per cent of production is exported and the domestic market demand depends on one-third or less of the population who are living in the towns and cities. Such estimates of national accounts as are available confirm that in most countries of Africa, and in the continent as a whole, production for subsistence accounts for more than half of the total estimated value of agricultural production. Each farm family supports itself and less than one non-farm family, whereas in the wealthy industrialized countries each farm family supports 10, 15 or more non-farm families and has a correspondingly high income.

A main reason, therefore, for the low productivity of agriculture has been the lack of demand. But this is not a complete explanation. In such countries as Ghana, Kenya, Liberia, Libya, Nigeria and the United Arab Republic the value of food imports has at least doubled in the last decade. These imports have included livestock products, rice, sugar and other commodities that can be, and often are, produced domestically, but local agriculture has been too slow to respond or does not meet the quality standards needed. Meanwhile there is evidence of rising food prices in many countries of the region, yet despite this stimulus adequate supplies are not forthcoming to meet the demand which already exists.

Reasons must also be sought, therefore, in other factors apart from market demand, such as attitudes, lack of incentive, lack of knowledge, inadequate technical skills and technical inputs including fertilizers, rigid tenure arrangements, poor communications and a host of others. This evidence of inertia is indeed very disturbing in view of the current trends which appear to require more dynamic qualities on the part of the agricultural sector if it is not to be a serious brake on general economic growth.

TRENDS AND PROSPECTS AFFECTING AGRICULTURE

It seems that the population of Africa is increasing at an average rate of about $2\frac{1}{2}$ per cent per annum. But urban population is increasing at a rate variously estimated at between 5 and 10 per cent, according to the lower size limit of towns considered to be "urban", i.e. it is growing at more than twice the rate of growth of the agricultural population. If this trend continues it is clear that there will be relatively more and more non-agricultural producers to be supported by fewer and fewer agriculturalists. As has been seen, food production is already lagging behind demand.

From the point of view of economic growth this trend towards urbanization can be a very healthy one, because in African countries urban incomes from industry and services are supposed to be three or four times as high as those in the rural sector. In this high productivity lies the key to rapid economic growth, but only if city populations are well fed and productively employed in industries supported by capital, raw materials and labour. Furthermore, there must be a market for the products of industry. A few African countries have mineral resources from which industrialization can be financed, but it is to agriculture that most of the countries must look for food, raw materials, investment, foreign exchange and labour needed for healthy industrial growth. With the great bulk of the population in agriculture it is also to the rural areas that the new industries must look for much of their markets. It is quite clear that powerful stimulation may be needed to bring the largely uneducated, often undernourished and perhaps disinterested rural peoples of Africa into a more commercial frame of mind. How can they be induced to produce more, market more both for domestic use and export, introduce new crops, sell their cherished cattle for money and buy more clothes, shoes, furniture, tools, fertilizers, etc., etc.?

The previous paragraph is quoted almost verbatim from the address of the Executive Secretary of the Economic Commission for Africa (E.C.A.) when opening the E.C.A.-F.A.O. Expert Meeting on Government Measures to Promote the Transition from Subsistence to Market Agriculture in Africa, held in Addis Ababa, Ethiopia, from 27 April to 7 May 1964[2]. The problem of raising agricultural productivity becomes even more pressing in view of the apparent tendency for urbanization to accelerate rather than slacken. If the anticipated industrialization takes place even in moderate measure, it will be accompanied by rising incomes and growing and changing demands, both per head and aggregate, for more and different kinds of food, clothing, fibres, wood and other materials. Unless the import bill is to become an intolerable burden, it is local agriculture which must supply to urban markets these growing and changing needs of the right quality, at the right time and place and at the right price. All this will require a much more modern and sophisticated agriculture than exists in most African countries today. And it is needed now. Little reference has been made to exports, but these must also continue to expand through larger and more efficient production to help earn the foreign exchange needed for industrial growth.

HOW PRODUCTIVITY CAN BE IMPROVED

An accelerated transition from subsistence to market agriculture is only a part of the growth process needed in African agriculture, but it is a very important part and provides an appropriate central theme for general agricultural development.

It is ultimately the investment of the hard work, accumulated experience and savings of millions of individual farmers, both small and large, upon which progress and growth will depend. But in order to stimulate, organize and direct this great, largely latent, force there must be wise central initiative. The E.C.A.-F.A.O. expert meeting on the transition to market agriculture[2] considered, therefore, that the rapid advances needed in African agriculture require a large measure of government action. Although they did not specifically say so, the experts implied that they did not, however, see a "socialist" solution. They clearly considered that most governments do not possess the managerial experience and technical skills to operate agriculture as a state enterprise. They looked to governments rather to remove obstacles which have hampered progress in the past and to create favourable conditions for progress, both through improvements in small-scale production and through intensive schemes requiring large capital investment.

The expert meeting did not attempt to propose a universal recipe for the 60 countries and territories in Africa, but concluded that the solution to a rapid increase in marketed supplies of agricultural produce lay in varying combinations of the following main approaches by governments:

(a) A comprehensive national development plan including agriculture so that policy would be directed towards a consistent set of objectives rather than being haphazard and possibly contradictory.

(b) Specially close attention to government services for extension to individual producers, backed by research and credit. It was recognized that these services, in the light of limited resources, could not be spread over all farmers in all areas, but should be concentrated at least initially on more efficient farmers and in more productive areas. Such services must of course also be backed by adequate supplies of fertilizers, pesticides, improved varieties of plants and animals and access to other improved inputs. In this connexion we find, for example, that Africa applies about 2 per cent of the world's chemical fertilizer production to 17 per cent of the world's arable land; and most of that is used in the U.A.R. and South Africa. Much the same is true of pesticides and farm machinery.

(c) An integrated national training and recruiting programme for professional and technical workers required throughout the economy including agriculture. Lack of trained technicians and skilled manpower was considered to be, in most African countries, the major bottleneck to progress. Agriculture lacked economists, technicians, research and particularly extension workers.

(d) A recognition by governments, in the light of (a), (b) and (c) above, that agricultural development in Africa calls for increase in skills rather than for fixed capital. This requires an expansion of the current expenditure share of the budget for agriculture.

(e) Large capital intensive agricultural projects can give quick specific results, e.g. for import substitution, but they need careful scrutiny, as resources allocated to them might with better advantage be applied to manufacturing industry. Governments can attract foreign capital, including private capital, by creating favourable conditions for investment.

(f) Measures to make agriculture a more respected and attractive way of life and to enlist the support of farmers in order to retain and attract more efficient types both on the land and in government agricultural services. Removal of discrimination between different branches of the government services, subsidies, and promotion of small rural industries were among the measures proposed.

(g) A broad programme of studies and surveys to fill strategic gaps in the information upon which development policy can be founded. Government services, universities and foreign aid agencies should be enlisted and existing material re-examined.

Foreign aid, it was concluded, should also be channelled to the seven main priorities set out above.

In the view of the meeting these seven major approaches have wide applicability in many African countries. They need to be backed by various specific measures which will vary, in the light of local needs and circumstances, from country to country. Among these, some of the most universally necessary would appear to be provision of roads and other infrastructure, improved marketing facilities and services, reform of land tenure and other rural structures, soil conservation and measures to raise fertility, education including nutrition education[3], improved farming practices including mixed farming and use of fertilizers and the organization of co-operatives for marketing credit and production. This list could be almost indefinitely extended, but the experts realized the futility of advising governments to do everything.

A criticism that can well be levelled at the expert report is that it is too general. The planning authority in a country might feel that, like so many other surveys and seminars, this one draws attention to the well-known general deficiencies of African agricultural organization and proposes well-known remedies. An alternative would have been to be much more dogmatic, and to propose limited campaigns against selected weaknesses. For example it has been estimated that storage losses of grain on the farms in an East African country range from 25 up to 100 per cent from season to season. A "crash" programme to reduce or eliminate these losses could have an immediate and probably lasting effect at relatively little cost. Attention and resources could then be concentrated on another objective, perhaps the increased use of chemical fertilizer. When this had been achieved another specific bottleneck would be attacked. This kind of "giant killing" operation might work in some countries, but the experts were more impressed by the benefits of a strategic rather than *ad hoc* tactical approach. An argument quite widely used was the political one that the African people expect some tangible results from their newly gained independence and no government can afford to neglect major sections of the community, even though this may involve spreading limited resources too thinly to have maximum effectiveness.

The experts' conclusions were adopted and commended to the attention of the governments of the Region by the Third Regional Conference for Africa held in Addis Ababa in September 1964. In a sense, therefore, they may be regarded as providing a policy for integrated action by the various departments and agencies and national governments.

CONCLUSIONS

On the basis of some rather rough statistics and ratios it has been argued that Africa, compared with other parts of the world, has a relative abundance of land, soils, water, forests, cattle and other resources. At the same time it has a relatively small population, mainly composed of farmers. Yet, despite all these farmers well endowed with resources, diets are poor[3], the continent is a net importer of meat[4] and wood[5] and a growing importer of other foodstuffs and raw materials. The region does not even support itself with its present small population and low levels of living. But population is doubling itself every 30 years; non-farmers in towns are increasing at more than twice this rate. How can all these new people be fed, clothed and housed? How can their levels of living be raised? How can the existing potentialities be more fully realized?

An answer is sought through industrialization of urban areas and stimulation of the big, largely subsistence rural sector, encumbered with tradition and ignorance, and often producing too little even to feed itself adequately[3]. In considering measures to raise the agricultural potential, emphasis is placed on ways to bring agriculture to an increasing extent into the monetary sector of the economy. It is food and raw materials delivered to urban and export markets that are needed most urgently. A solution is not sought in heavy injections of capital into agriculture. Most of the available capital will be needed for industrialization. Agriculture already has heavily committed resources of land and labour. The aim is to utilize these more efficiently by greatly stepped-up extension services to producers together with advisory services and organizations for marketing. Some capital will clearly be needed in the form of installations and communications and there will be justification for some large schemes to achieve, for example, rapid import substitution. All these competing claims will call for integrated national development plans to avoid waste and confusion.

The emphasis throughout this paper is on making man in Africa more productive, more efficient, better fed and better integrated into an expanding economy. The approach proposed is through training, advice, education, improved farming and marketing methods, and changes in attitudes. A big question is whether there is time for this approach in depth, or whether more dramatic emergency measures may not be needed to grow food in a hurry.

DISCUSSION

Brown: You said that what is required is hard work from millions of individual farmers, Dr. Acock. But how can one expect hard work out of millions of individuals who are carrying around parasites, who are suffering from one or more diseases, who are periodically attacked by communicable diseases, and on top of that have mental problems as well? Maybe your association with a sister organization has led you to leave out any reference to health in the seven major policies listed in your paper; but we start with the individual, and I don't see how one can expect anything except inertia and disinterest from people who feel rather like we feel when we have a bad cold—we just don't feel very much like going to the office. Most of the African rural population is chronically in this state.

Acock: I agree with you, Dr. Brown, but my emphasis has been on making man more efficient, by better productivity, for example through use of fertilizers, with the same input of labour.

My whole emphasis is on raising incomes so that one can afford to have the necessary health services. One could then even afford to introduce Professor Lambo's psychiatric services and those kinds of things.

Brown: But do you feel that it is going to do any good to train people who are laden with these health burdens?

Acock: Yes, sir, a man laden with parasites and training is better off than a man laden with parasites only.

Habte-Ab: I think it was the Minister of Commerce of Nigeria who made the headlines at a recent conference at Geneva on world trade. He said that Nigerians had been told to work harder and they had worked harder, but they are growing poorer in proportion to the production of cocoa. Between 1952 and 1962 production was higher but world prices were much lower. Nigeria, in order to buy the same amount of manufactured goods, will have to double its production to maintain the same standard of living. The relative value of primary products is therefore of vital importance.

Acock: The Economic Commission for Africa spent a number of its sessions deploring the declining terms of trade of the primary producing countries. I am not sure that the picture is quite the way it is presented. Some people, who put forward this view very strongly, usually choose a convenient starting point, for example the Korean war when agricultural prices were extremely high, and they point to the decline in prices since 1951 or 1952, whereas the prices of manufactured goods have continued to remain at the same level or to rise, which means that the primary producing countries earn less for a bigger quantity of exports.

It is a complicated economic issue. The richer countries tend to use substitutes: synthetic rubber, synthetic fibres and so on. The long-term outlook for commodity demand is not a favourable one—I agree with you there. But quite a lot can be done. Again, I hark back to my old point about efficiency: if prices of these things could be brought a little lower by more efficient production techniques, without increased labour input, they would command better markets and would discourage the search for substitutes. We come constantly back to the same factor of labour efficiency.

Bourgeois-Pichat: I think that the argument can be reversed. If the price of cocoa is low, this is an incentive to build local factories to prepare chocolate. If it is the same for every primary product, the incentive to industrialize the country is obvious.

Dekker: Dr. Acock, one of the points you mentioned is an improvement of extension services in order to increase agricultural production. Now, isn't the heart of the matter a political concern? Is there not a need for more rural education, for the rural areas in Africa to be made more self-conscious, to stress the importance of being a farmer, of living in rural areas, with their traditions and culture—in short, for making the rural inhabitants more conscious of being appreciated by the government, of having a great value to the whole of the country? Governments need to engage the inhabitants of rural areas as full members of the political life of the country. Africa has perhaps not yet had its revolution and the man in rural areas, being self-contained in his small community, is not being given the chance to be a proud member of his country. I think here lies a very large responsibility of African governments.

Acock: I don't agree with you when you say Africa hasn't had its revolution. I think that is what we have been going through in the last five years or so. When the Economic Commission for Africa began its work some six years ago there were, I think, seven independent countries and now there are about 34. There has been a very considerable revolution, mostly a peaceful one, but the psychological impact must have been considerable.

However, although the changes have been considerable, I have the impression that there is still a very strong family-tribal orientation on the part of many African people, and there is not a full sense of nationalism. Whether we want to engender a sense of nationalism or not, I don't know; it is perhaps more a pan-Africanism we need, like the spirit of this symposium, but I think you are right about the importance of projecting the aspirations of the people beyond the extended family and the tribe. And your idea of making agriculture a more attractive way of life constitutes the sixth major policy agreed upon by the experts. I am sorry to say they weren't very explicit on how they proposed to go about it, but perhaps there may be ideas around here on how such planning could be more explicit.

One point I mentioned was the unification of pay rates in the government service; another was the extension to the rural areas of political party movements and co-operative movements, to bring about what I think the French call ''rural animation''.

Gille: Could we have a few more details on the activities of F.A.O. in Africa? For instance, how many Special Fund Projects has F.A.O. in Africa as compared with the rest of the world?

Also, how great a problem do you think the question of land tenure is in Africa?

Acock: About one-fifth of F.A.O.'s resources are devoted to Africa in the Expanded Technical Assistance Programme. In the World Food Programme, which is still in the preliminary stage, the proportion is rather higher—I think about one-third of the budget is spent on Africa. And as far as the Special Fund is concerned, about a third of F.A.O.'s share is devoted to Africa.

However, the F.A.O. programme for Africa is a drop in the ocean, and the bilateral programmes of, for example, the U.S.A. and U.K. are very much greater than any multilateral programmes, although the bilateral programmes put more into non-agricultural projects than they do into agriculture. But all the foreign aid and all the U.N. aid is again only a small proportion of the total investment that is necessary to develop the potential of Africa's internal resources. All that foreign aid and U.N. aid can do is to stimulate and assist by surveys, studies, and some investment.

Regarding your second point, land tenure in Africa has baffled many experts. I believe that so much can be done with the existing structures that it is better not to start monkeying around initially. There are people who say that without land reform you can't do anything; that where there are peasants who have to give two-thirds of their product to the landlord it is hopeless to start any improvement programme without a reorientation of the land tenure laws; or that where there is tribal, communal ownership of land, that is an evil thing, and nothing can be done until it is removed and individual tenure is introduced. I don't think there is a great deal of substance in these arguments. The initial impact to raise yields can be within the existing structure to a large extent, and the system will adapt itself as agriculture becomes more commercialized and more efficient.

It would be fairly easy at this stage to grant small rigid peasant holdings, but it may be very much more difficult 20, 30 or 50 years hence to get rid of those small farmers if this should be necessary in the interests of more production or more economic holdings. It is often better to wait before rushing into land reform.

Lambo: You mentioned national training and recruiting programmes for professional agricultural technicians. I wonder whether international or regional training programmes would not be much more effective than national programmes?

Acock: The point is, how far is it feasible? In theory it certainly seems desirable, and the various U.N. agencies are concentrating on regional and sub-regional training programmes. F.A.O. has just held a training programme in Nairobi on the marketing of staple foodstuffs, in which trainees from virtually all the African countries participated. A few years ago we held an agricultural credit seminar for the English-speaking countries of Africa and next year F.A.O. will have one for the French-speaking countries, so that is another form of regional division. U.N.E.S.C.O. and the I.L.O. have, I understand, similar regional and sub-regional training projects which are directed not only geographically, but also at a particular level in the various professions.

A lot depends on the extent to which the governments are prepared to go in for this sort of thing. The Economic Commission for Africa lays great emphasis on this regionalization, on projects which have one training centre for a region, one factory, one iron and steel works, one cement works for a complete area; they would like to create a general pattern to conserve scarce resources. But usually, when it comes down to brass tacks, governments aren't so willing to surrender their sovereignty—they want their own iron and steel works, their own university, their own medical training centre, their own psychiatric workers.

Mesfin: I would like to see this programme in a general world context. Africa has such a great potential and a comparatively small population still, though with a high rate of growth, yet you mentioned that imports of food are increasing, and the prices of food products are rising. In the world as a whole, the population is soaring, and the food problem is becoming more and more acute. But Africa, which could have contributed to a certain extent to the relief of this general world problem, is itself rapidly becoming a problem area.

I personally disagree with your statement that land reform is not an urgent priority. The most important incentive for the farmers themselves is the enjoyment of the fruits of their own labour. Take Ethiopia, for instance: there is definitely a very big difference in the productivity of farmers in the northern part of Ethiopia where they farm their own land, compared with those in the southern parts of Ethiopia where they are mostly tenants.

This is not to say that the farmer who has his own land will necessarily produce more, or that land reform necessarily means giving small plots of land to individual farmers. There are places in Ethiopia where individual farmers have plots of land that are no bigger than these two tables we are sitting at. This breaking up of these small plots for the children and great-grandchildren and so forth must be stopped, as with successive generations it becomes absolutely useless economically whatever the size of the original estate. In some parts of Ethiopia this has become such a problem that slopes of about 70° are being farmed; the farmer ties himself by the waist with a rope attached to a tree or a big stone, then, held by the rope, he cultivates a small plot of land.

The farmer is becoming more and more inferior to the traditionally less respectable trades, such as, for instance, the blacksmith, or the potter or the weaver. Although 30 or 50 years ago he was not considered a human being, the blacksmith in Ethiopia today has more money than the farmer, and he can marry a farmer's daughter, which he couldn't do 50 years ago. Respectability and pride depend on cash, which the poor farmer cannot get or of which he has very little.

Acock: The land tenure system in Ethiopia is not quite characteristic of that of Africa to the south or the west. Ethiopian institutions, I think, are much more closely related to the Middle East than they are to Africa, and the fragmentation of the holdings to which you refer is undoubtedly a very bad thing, but over a large part of East and Central Africa, and in Western Africa too, the man who has a holding is still relatively rare. Most land is held in communal tenure; it is owned by the tribe, sometimes identified with the chief. And I don't think a high value is set on land in many parts of Africa. Often the valuable thing is cattle rather than land, and there are many unproductive cattle in the continent which don't improve the erosion situation. My own instinct is that there are good reasons for not worrying too much about individual tenure, and for holding back a little bit to see how institutions can be evolved which will fit in with the economic requirements. Perhaps in parts of Ethiopia land reform should be given top priority. It is a problem for the individual government.

Howard-Goldsmith: We have heard something about land reform and other long-term measures to make better use of the agricultural potential. But, apart from potential wealth, isn't there in livestock an actual wealth which does not require any long-term planning, and which could be used at once? We saw from your figures that there is a great deal of livestock on this continent, and yet meat is being imported, and I suppose in most countries there is a deficiency of protein. Isn't that the first thing to tackle, to eat that livestock and thus improve the diet? Isn't this surplus wealth which is already there and which doesn't have to be developed?

Acock: Livestock and cattle represent money in large parts of the African continent. Cattle are also a sign of prestige. But there is the big problem of disease, and also of productivity. There are a lot of cattle in Africa, but the regeneration rate—not the birth rate but the number of young cattle coming on—is often very small.

Ethiopia has about 20 million cattle, but all they can produce for the meat industry is a maximum of about half-a-million cattle a year. The whole livestock industry is extremely inefficient—inefficient in the Western sense, but not so inefficient from the point of view of its function as a form of saving, a form of wealth, in the African economy. We tend to look at these things only from an economic and monetary point of view.

Monod: The word ''fisheries'' has hardly been mentioned up to now, in spite of their importance to food production in Africa. A good deal is going on in fisheries development in Africa. Trawling, for instance, is developing in certain parts, and a trawling survey is going on now in Guinea under the auspices of the Scientific Council for Africa with a grant from A.I.D. But the main answer might be either coastal fishing for clupeids, through cast-nets, drift-nets and beach seines, or high seas fishing for tuna, which are already exploited, and even over-exploited, by many countries, including of course Japan and the U.S.S.R. Besides the marine fisheries there are the inland fisheries, savannah rivers, lakes, fishponds, and so on. Again, there are many other aquatic resources besides fish, for example

255

spring lobsters, shrimps and prawns. A few months ago the Scientific Council for Africa convened a specialist meeting on marine crustaceans.

Acock: Thank you very much for stressing this point, Professor Monod. The word ''fisheries'' does occur just once in my paper, but it is certainly worthy of very much greater emphasis, if only because of the protein shortage.

I should like to add a word in general, that Africa has an excellent opportunity of learning from experiences elsewhere; African countries can catch up very rapidly, they don't have to go through the long, painful process of finding things out for themselves, which, for instance, the Americans had to go through. A lot of that information can be transported and applied, no matter what the special circumstances in Africa may be.

Gayer: I have pushed a plough myself. In Eastern Nebraska we had about 200 acres, and first we had to cut down the trees where corn and other things now grow wonderfully. We did everything ourselves: we set aside little plots of land where vegetables were grown, we had our own bacon, we lived off the farm—we didn't have to buy very much. But now such farms have been combined. Three or four farms are working together; production is very high in a specialized field.

When I was on the farm we did not order fertilizers, we used the by-products of the farm; my father, a graduate of the University of Nebraska, at that time, 1918, did not even learn about fertilizers. We had a number of cows but they were all different types; they were not very productive. The same is true in Ethiopia today. However, now in Nebraska we have selected productive breeds. A calf is assured each year. I am sure the same thing is possible here and the problem is how to attain such progress in the minimum time.

Acock: I think Mr. Gayer has the answer to the question. By improved breeding, improved techniques, improvement in feeding, improved machinery, a miracle was achieved in the

United States. From 1918 to the present time, which is less than 50 years, a tremendous amount has happened.

Sutton: It is very striking that in the United States there was almost no increase in productivity per acre until the late 1930's. Scientific agriculture, which started at least a hundred years ago, really didn't make itself felt until just before the last war. Since that time there has been such a spectacular increase in productivity that the surplus crops have become a major problem to the United States. Perhaps this kind of sudden increase in productivity may occur elsewhere and we may end this discussion on a note of hope.

12

CONSERVATION OF NATURAL RESOURCES IN AFRICA

TH. MONOD

THE programme of a symposium on "Man and Africa" would be neglecting an essential aspect of its theme if it did not give its proper place to the question of the relationship of man to nature and its resources. The question is, of course, not only an African one; it also has implications for the whole world. But we are concerned here with the African side of the picture, and therefore with a regional survey of a world-wide problem: what should be the proper use of natural resources, and what are man's duties in changing the face of the earth? What should be his right attitude towards nature and the living world?

What are "natural resources"? Broadly speaking they are, of course, anything within the universe which man can use to his own profit, be it solar energy, wind, waterfalls, soil, animals, vegetation, or anything else. If a classification of some kind is needed, an elementary one would distinguish inorganic (minerals, etc.) from animal and vegetable resources; often the distinction is made between renewable and non-renewable resources, the first being the organic resources plus water and soil, and the second inorganic, like coal, oil, ores and so on. Again, one could try to distinguish between "raw" and "modified" resources, according to the degree of human intervention involved. A more refined classification has recently been worked out by Worthington[1], who enumerates the following types:

(A) *Inorganic resources*

      (1) The land's surface (physiography, landscape, land use, National Parks and other types of protected areas)

(2) Rocks and minerals
(3) Air (climate, etc.)

(B) *Semi-inorganic and semi-organic resources*

(4) Water
(5) Soil

(C) *Flora*

(6) Wild flora (phytogeography, ecology, etc.)
(7) Forests
(8) Agriculture

(D) *Fauna*

(9) Wildlife (taxonomy, distribution, ecology, etc.)
(10) Animal husbandry
(11) Invertebrates
(12) Fish

Each of these topics is, in Dr. Worthington's classification, considered under three different approaches: research, conservation, utilization.

However, in using exclusively the word "resources", are we not arbitrarily and perhaps dangerously limiting to their practical uses the wealth of riches nature can—and does—offer to man? Are there no other natural "resources" than those which can be thought of in terms of material profit? A few years ago, the biologist and philosopher Sir Julian Huxley[2, 3] strongly insisted that modern man seemed more concerned with means— technology and quantity—than with ends—creativity and quality; that quantitative productivity could not be an end in itself but only a means towards some higher end; that the satisfaction of man's mental and spiritual needs is no less important than catering for his material and physiological requirements; and that in any modern planning the usual concept of *utility* should give way to the more general concept of *value*, a concept which, besides utility, also embodies others—psychological, social, scientific, aesthetic, ethical or spiritual values.

Therefore, although the conservation of natural resources will have its legitimate utilitarian aspects, the question arises whether effective, permanent conservation can be securely based on the promises of mere material gain. If practical considerations only are invoked, these may prove temporary and transient—true today, perhaps, but disproved tomorrow. If forests, for instance, are protected only because of their economic potentialities, what will remain of our reasons for having forests at all if some substitute for wood becomes of general use?

In a recent and very important book, "The Population Crisis and the Use of World Resources"[4], Professor Farnes, who teaches planning at Michigan State University, strongly underlines the necessity of rejecting and pushing beyond a "reductive, quantitative notion of natural resources", according to the "narrow utilitarian concept" which views nature only "as a set of commodities completely subverted to the price system and human consumption". But Professor Farnes adds wisely that "whether we do this or not is an ethical choice".

Therefore, I see much to commend in Marston Bates' threefold vindication of conservation[5]: "Ethical, esthetic and utilitarian reasons all support the attempt to conserve the diversity of nature. It is morally the right thing to do; it will provide, for future generations, a richer and more satisfying experience than would otherwise be possible; and it provides a much-needed insurance against ecological catastrophe". (p. 202.)

Conservation is basically and necessarily a many-sided business, being the integrated expression of interactions between man and nature. One of the fathers of modern ecology, Charles Elton, once remarked[6]: "Unless one merely thinks man was intended to be an all-conquering and sterilizing power in the world, there must be some general basis for understanding what it is best to do. This means looking for some wise principle of co-existence between man and nature, even if it be a modified kind of man and a modified kind of nature. This is what I understand by *conservation*."

DAMAGES AND THREATS

In spite of the fact that Africa has only recently begun to experience the dubious blessings of the predatory and destructive economy so often linked with the development of the industrial era, the situation is already deteriorating by reason of the natural vulnerability of tropical communities, the general population growth and also an increased exploitation of natural resources under the influence of colonization.

Even if the situation in Africa is not—or not yet—what it has become in other parts of the world, the continent will not be spared the problems of overpopulation: as Elspeth Huxley says[7], "the most terrifying phenomenon in Africa today is the insect-like hatching of millions and millions of babies: the unchecked, mounting, crushing explosion of a fecund population for the first time preserved from famine and disease. This has got out of hand. While effort, money and skill are poured into the top of the tank in the form of education and health and welfare services, an unchecked birth-rate blows a great hole in the bottom and out it all pours."

The misuse by man of African nature is a complex story, only a few aspects of which can be touched on in the present summary. Besides, Africa is such a diversified continent that generalizations are exceedingly dangerous where regional or local situations remain the only concrete realities.

In certain parts of tropical Africa the population density can reach or even exceed 300 per square kilometre, with 1,000,000 cattle for 1,550,000 hectares of pasture, i.e. about $1\frac{1}{2}$ hectares per animal when six to ten hectares seem necessary—a typical example of overstocking and overgrazing[8]. Elsewhere, however, the situation is quite different. Brasseur[9] observes that in regions of low population density (e.g. $10/km.^2$) the traditional system of shifting cultivation still holds good, but that with a population of $25/km.^2$ a field can lie fallow for only one year in ten, and with $50/km.^2$ the danger to nature *might* begin. However, population growth does not always lead to disastrous consequences, for instance, where some kind of tree is deliberately protected and then multiplies—for example *Acacia albida* or the oil palm.

It is well known that African soils when mismanaged are readily vulnerable to both mechanical and chemical deterioration: examples of erosion and degradation of soils are generously scattered all over tropical Africa, with a marked predominance of certain aspects in the three main climatic zones, desert, savannah (in the broad sense) and rain forest. The various mechanisms or reactions involved have been carefully described, and data are accumulating. A very informative map of "erodibility" has been produced[10], and methods are being devised to protect the integrity and fertility of soil threatened by so many factors, both natural and human (including of course the still very common ignorance of manure and fertilizers), in a regional environment where irreversible alterations like lateritic hard-pans are by no means rare.

The amount of top soil displaced by erosion depends of course largely on the type of run-off locally active, and thence on the rainfall. Together with the soil, water is the very foundation of life, and like the soil it is frequently subject to abuse or misuse. Here again unfavourable modifications may be either natural or man-made, the distinction being sometimes difficult. Africa is, on the whole, a thirsty continent, and careful management of existing water resources becomes more and more essential. In many parts of Africa, over enormous areas, scarcity of water remains the prime factor limiting agriculture to strictly seasonal operations, restricting permanent pastures and even, in extreme cases, preventing human settlement. In the Western Sahara, an enormous empty quarter, the Majâbat al-Koubrâ, has not a single well for about 250,000 km.^{2}. Besides its quantity, the quality of the water must also be carefully maintained, as sooner or later pollution may occur, even in Africa.

One of the most spectacular and omnipresent examples of wanton destruction is de-afforestation, with its all too frequent influence on the economy of river basins, soil erosion, scarcity of fire-wood around settlements, etc. Within historical times—and documented history is here very young—forested areas in many regions have dwindled enormously. Serious as the present situation may be, it should not be forgotten that "the suffering planet has immense power of natural rehabilitation if given its chance"[11]. As long as real climatic changes, as opposed to brief fluctuations, do not occur, then however severe the wounds there is still a hope of healing, provided reasonable measures of protection are agreed and (what is much more difficult in Africa) enforced—I know of a gnarled population of desert trees, reduced to mere stumps by overgrazing, but restored to normal shape by just a few years of fencing.

If the plant-cover is exposed to multifarious attack, the onslaught on wildlife is no less pitiless, human action being both direct, by sheer killing, and indirect, since destruction of habitat implies that of the animal species ecologically linked to it. There is no better-known or sadder story than that of the decimation or extinction of species in Africa within the last century: anyone interested may discover the present situation through the "Red Book" of the Survival Service Commission of the International Union for the Conservation of Nature (I.U.C.N.), which describes the status of every endangered species—our modern "living fossils", some of them depleted beyond recovery, others still ready to regain their former strength if appropriate measures are taken in time. But will they be taken? Will *Homo* so-called *sapiens* put an end to the merciless slaughtering of Africa's wildlife? Will there be anything left in the next century? As Elspeth Huxley puts it[7], "We've done our best to exterminate, in Africa, the world's most prodigal collection of creatures. In whole countries and regions we have, indeed, succeeded apart from a handful of mice, snakes and birds; and every year survivors dwindle as men, white and black regardless, pursue them with arrow, pit, snare, musket and rifle." When will the extermination of a living species be deemed as heinous a crime as murder, or the destruction of some priceless work of art? Till then, man will have no right to call himself "civilized".

Even if politicians or the general public are still ignorant of the facts, man's intervention in the ecological network of nature has created enormous dangers by upsetting a delicately adjusted balance. Technology has not yet learned to think ecologically and biologists are still too seldom associated with the planning of big engineering or land reclamation projects.

The results are obvious: "The corridors of time", says George Kimble[12a], "are littered with the debris of human folly: with the discarded stubs of unnumbered mines and oil fields; with the ashes of a thousand forest fires, the dust of a dozen man-made deserts, and the cast-off clouts of as many thriftless societies. Nor is all the debris of great antiquity. On the contrary: ever since the days of Noah there have been floods, but I will wager that the Kansas floods of 1951 killed more animals and destroyed more homes than any that devastated Mesopotamia."

The impact of western exploitation on African nature has been tremendous, with dubious benefits as far as conservation is concerned. A specialist in African agronomy, Professor Portères[12b], flatly declares that the development of export crops proved more harmful than centuries of traditional agriculture, and that devastations had never taken place so rapidly and on such a scale. And everybody knows the significant title of J.-P. Harroy's classical book[13]: "Afrique, terre qui meurt".

The dangers threatening Africa's natural resources are many: I have mentioned only some of them; more could be added (e.g. the introduction or spread of noxious species), and others may soon enter the field: for instance, indiscriminate use of pesticides may well mean that "silent springs" will begin to invade Africa too.

ECONOMIC ASPECTS

This particular facet of the problem is by far the most widely recognized. For most of us it is probably the only legitimate argument in favour of conservation. If natural resources must not be wantonly wasted, if forests, soils, water, and wildlife must be wisely and carefully husbanded, it is because of their immediate or potential profitable use. Modern Africa is, quite legitimately, preoccupied with the welfare of its inhabitants and therefore is tempted to view the problem of its natural resources and their conservation in the light of economic necessities.

So long as the improvement of man's conditions of life is really at stake, so long as the battle is against hunger or disease, well and good: the physical needs of men, although these are not their only needs, must be met—if not as absolute ends at least as necessary means towards some higher purpose.

There is, therefore, ample reason to consider a wise exploitation of natural resources as a sound economical procedure. The point is so obvious that it needs little explanation, and everybody acknowledges—in theory at least—that destruction or loss of fertility of soils, heedless de-afforestation, disregard of ecological realities, and disobedience to nature's laws may entail disaster.

Utilitarian arguments can be found even for the protection of wildlife; for instance, the profits of tourism in National Parks, or the new methods of game cropping or game farming may well prove the most profitable type of land use in many habitats unsuitable for successful cattle-breeding: "You never see a thin zebra", writes Elspeth Huxley[7], "even on the poorest scrub. Exterminate the zebras, replace them by cattle and you see a lot of walking, and often dying, scarecrows after a drought."

PALLIATIVES

Even if man in the past has too often proved a senseless predator, he may at last be becoming conscious of his responsibilities towards nature, aware that he is after all no more than its temporary tenant, answerable to his descendants for it. Nature's power of resilience is such that, in spite of all the damage already done, recovery is, over vast regions, still possible. Much can still be saved, if man is willing to act accordingly, but such a change in his traditional and deep-rooted instinctive behaviour will involve acceptance of a certain number of basic principles.

Firstly, the findings of biological sciences and, principally, of ecology must be listened to, understood, and accepted. Actions having undesirable consequences could then be avoided. Ecology, being what has been termed "the physiology of communities", is able not only to describe the actual patchwork of interactions within a given habitat or biocenosis, but to foresee the changes to be brought about by a given outside intervention. Henceforward, therefore, man can and must think on a sufficiently vast and far-reaching scale and plan efficiently for a distant future, instead of floundering about in the well-worn tracks of short-sighted empiricism.

But if the future must be thoughtfully prepared, much in the world of today has to be rapidly and definitively saved; tomorrow it may be too late, for the pace of destruction never slackens. It is therefore urgent to set aside, for definitive protection, well-chosen types of various habitats which will thereby be permanently preserved for science, enjoyment or recreation. National Parks and various types of natural reserves are consequently of utmost importance: a certain number of these protected areas—some of them justly world-famous—already exist in Africa, but many more are needed.

No measure of conservation, however right and wise, will prove successful for long without the support of public opinion; and men in general, and in Africa more than elsewhere, are utterly ignorant, the great majority of them still regarding nature as a profitable prey to be remorselessly plundered. A large-scale effort of education, beginning in the schools, is needed before the customary misconceptions can be replaced by a more enlightened outlook.

Lastly, it must be emphasized that nothing really efficient will ever be done in Africa as regards conservation, until (1) every country has its own specialized conservation agency, both scientific and technical (Dekeyser[14], pp. 289–290), and (2) the training of conservation personnel, at all levels, is seriously organized (a good beginning has already been made for wildlife management and National Parks by the Mweka School in Tanzania).

THE AFRICAN SITUATION

Before I try to summarize the present situation and the prospects for conservation in Africa, now that the new African states are fully responsible for their policy, it is only fair to mention some of the international aspects of the question.

As early as 1933 an international "Convention relative to the preservation of fauna and flora in their natural state", was signed in London between Great Britain, France, Italy, Portugal, Spain and the Anglo-Egyptian Sudan. Its importance cannot be over-emphasized, as it is still, in fact, the code underlying every national policy. The London Convention contains an official definition of "National Parks" and "Strict Nature Reserves" and lists the species granted total or partial protection. Twenty years later, it was felt desirable to bring in some amendments and in Bukavu in 1953, at the instigation of the Commission for Technical Co-operation in Africa, the Belgian Government convened the Third International Conference for the Protection of the Fauna and Flora of Africa, whose recommendations, some of them perhaps of doubtful advisability, were never implemented. Therefore the question, not of drastic transformation but of bringing the convention up to date, after being raised again a few years ago by the Scientific Council for Africa (C.S.A.) and the Commission for Technical Co-operation in Africa (C.C.T.A.), was handed over to I.U.C.N. before going back for discussion and action to the African governmental organizations.

During recent years I.U.C.N. has devoted much of its attention to Africa. The "African Special Project", whose Phase II was the Arusha Conference (1961), was jointly convened by C.C.T.A./ C.S.A. and I.U.C.N., and Phase III of the Project, subsidized by

F.A.O., consisted in the assistance given by two specialists to a number of African states. At the 1961 Conference, the Tanganyika Government made the solemn Declaration now known as the Arusha Manifesto.

The Commission for Technical Co-operation in Africa and the Scientific Council for Africa always regarded conservation as one of the regular items of their programme; hence their participation in the Bukavu Conference (1953) and the Arusha Conference (1961), and the adoption by member states at Dar-es-Salaam (1963) of an "African Charter for the Protection and Conservation of Nature", in which the general principles which must guide conservation policy in Africa are formulated in eight points.

One of the groups of states, the Union Africaine et Malgache, adopted in 1962 four resolutions which, like the Arusha Manifesto of 1961 and the Kenya Declaration of 1963, show a very gratifying and hopeful attitude among a number of African statesmen.

Two of the Specialized Agencies of the United Nations, namely U.N.E.S.C.O. and F.A.O., are each in their own field strongly and efficiently supporting all African endeavours in the realm of conservation. At its 12th General Assembly (1962) U.N.E.S.C.O. adopted two important texts, one a resolution on economic development and the conservation of natural resources, fauna and flora, the other a recommendation on the protection of landscapes and natural sites. Very recently (August, 1964), U.N.E.S.C.O. convened in Lagos an important conference on natural resources in Africa.

Through the official list of National Parks and Equivalent Reserves whose establishment has been prescribed by the U.N. Economic and Social Council, many African protected areas will receive international recognition and status, a measure which will undoubtedly prove an incentive to countries which have not yet established any areas of that type. The General Assembly of the United Nations Organization in its 17th session (1962) passed a resolution on economic development and conservation, strongly backing the basic principles involved.

Besides inter-African organizations and the United Nations agencies, private organizations are also at work in Africa, e.g. the World Wildlife Fund (which prepared a World Wildlife Charter) and the African Wildlife Leadership, both of which are generously helping Africa to save—where still possible—its unique wildlife.

International action and help is all very well, but nothing lasting will be achieved without decisions being made—and enforced—at the national level. Where do we stand here? What are the prospects? Is there any hope of seeing African local policies wholeheartedly devoted to the great cause? It must be honestly admitted that the prospects are not too bright. Do not misunderstand me : there are a few countries in the world where the conservation of nature and the protection of wildlife have become the earnest concern of the state, most of them being in Central or Eastern Europe, but in industrialized, over-civilized regions there is not much left to protect, wildlife has largely gone, and gone for ever. In Africa, on the contrary, there is still something to preserve; intelligent action *could* be taken, much of the unrivalled African wildlife *could* be saved if appropriate measures are taken in time. But, the question is, will they be taken?

Let us be outspoken.

A fruitful policy of conservation would, as J.-P. Harroy has reminded us[15], require a government, *firstly*, to be fully aware of the problem and well informed by scientific advisers, *secondly*, to be able to devote appropriate funds to efficient action, and *thirdly*, to be willing to enforce unpopular measures unfalteringly and to possess the means to do so.

Without these conditions, there seems to be very little hope of drastic changes in the situation, in spite of some local improvements to already existing systems of National Parks. Such a view might appear somewhat pessimistic, but are we not here to say, not what may be pleasant to hear but what we think is the truth? And, however dark the picture, there is no need for discouragement: even rearguard actions have to be gallantly fought, if only for honour's sake.

In September, 1963, a U.N.E.S.C.O. mission composed of Sir Julian Huxley, A. Gille, L. Swift, E. B. Worthington and myself was able to spend a few days in Ethiopia and was given a very hearty welcome by the Ethiopian authorities, who are well aware of the issues at stake and eager to launch out into vigorous action.

Ethiopia is undoubtedly a privileged country from many points of view, thanks to its geographical situation, physiography and cultural history. A double series of differentiations—vertical, with altitudinal zonation, and horizontal, with an intricate admixture of palaearctic and tropical elements—makes Ethiopia a fascinating country of astonishing diversity, where the plant cover ranges from lowland desert *Acacia* to alpine vegetation, and which may have been an active centre of speciation and dispersion.

Five species of mammals are both endemic to Ethiopia and at present very rare: the Walia goat (*Capra walia*), the mountain nyala (*Tragelaphus buxtoni*), the Somali wild ass (*Equus somaliensis*), the dibitag (*Ammodorcas clarkei*) and the simien fox (*Simenia simensis*), other rare species being *Giraffa reticulata* and Grevy's zebra (*Equus grevyi*).

Culturally also, Ethiopia is a very rich country, with a wealth of archaeological sites and ancient monuments, a strong artistic tradition, and a number of interesting customs.

The natural sites, the scenery and picturesque beauty of Ethiopia remain unequalled anywhere. Lakes, waterfalls, volcanoes, plateaux, rugged peaks, deep gorges, coral islands, swamps, lava or salt deserts—the diversity of landscapes has no limit, and the Blue Nile canyon can bear comparison with its Colorado counterpart, although one is green, the other red.

Unfortunately, as in all other African countries, wildlife is dwindling rapidly, being actively, if illegally, hunted for either meat or hide. The situation has become very serious and only energetic measures will be able to cope with it. Among them are the following:

(1) *National Parks:* Extension of Managasha National Park (forest), creation of National Parks in the Awash plain (Matahara) (mammals), on Lake Abidjata (birds), farther south in the Rift Valley (fauna and scenery), and on the Upper Blue Nile (scenery).

(2) *Protected areas for wildlife:* Lake Stephanie—Lower Omo region, Sudan boundary regions (Madji and Dinder).

(3) *Sanctuaries for endangered species:* The organization necessary for the various aspects of conservation (legislation, research, education, trained personnel, etc.) is at present under careful study by the appropriate Ethiopian authorities and there is every hope that this beautiful country will in the not too distant future have its own conservation agency, ready to act courageously not only for the benefit of the country, but for Africa and, in fact, for mankind as a whole.

THE CORE OF THE PROBLEM

To many these concluding remarks may seem superfluous, as they sincerely believe there is no ''core'' and even perhaps no ''problem''. For them the only justification for conservation lies in its practical, utilitarian aspect: we will fight erosion but only because it may lower yields, we will refrain from excessive de-afforestation but only to protect a watershed, or keep springs running, we will stop hunting giraffes but only because people coming from abroad will pay to take snapshots of them, our factory will cease polluting that stream only if the fine exceeds the cost of a purification system.

This is a simple, realistic, matter-of-fact attitude. Profit remains the golden rule of man's activity. Nature becomes something to be freely, unscrupulously exploited for the material benefit of man.

Even amongst the conservationists, a growing tendency is developing which, either for basic or for strategic opportunist reasons, insists strongly on the utilitarian aspect of conservation. For such a school of thought, the very term "nature protection" must be condemned, as nature has no intrinsic rights of any kind and can only be "managed", they say. Such words as "philosophy" or even "ethics" will smell of heresy: in a technical scientific age what need can men still have of such outdated, nebulous considerations?

The supporters of what they, at least, call "realism" condemn "philosophy", but are they, in fact, shunning philosophy as such or only a philosophy different from their own? Because, in reality, their attitude *also* implies a philosophy, and votaries of progress follow, if unconsciously, what must even appear sometimes to the impartial observer as a genuine religion, with its full array of paraphernalia, dogmas, creeds, orthodoxies, and the like.

So basically the cleavage appears to be not between a philosophy and a practical view but between two philosophies: that which refuses the exclusively anthropocentric outlook and thinks in terms of unity and therefore of sympathy, and that which holds man to be the "Lord of creation", and entitled, in this capacity, to exploit nature for his own sole benefit, largely material, though sometimes, as a concession perhaps, aesthetic.

It is clear that as man is physically part of nature, even though he is no longer inside his original ecosystem and drawing out from it the basic necessities for his material sustenance, he has to avoid any abuse or misuse, if only in his own obvious interests. Nobody questions this. But, going one step further, some believe that nature must and can be rightfully transformed, where needed, to suit man's requirements and needs. But nature must also be respected by man.

Conservation, therefore, as I have come to understand it, must rest not on one but on three distinct pillars, ably described by Marston Bates—after Charles Elton—in a delightful and clever little book, "The Forest and the Sea: A Look at the Economy of

Nature and the Ecology of Man''[5]. I could not devise myself a better formulation than that offered by Marston Bates' own words.

The first pillar is *ethical:* the philosophy we need "will have to consider not only the problems of man's conduct with his fellow man, but also of man's conduct toward nature. Life is a unity: the biosphere is a complex network of interrelations among all the host of living things. Man, in gaining the godlike quality of awareness, has also acquired a godlike responsibility. The questions of the nature of his relationships with the birds and the beasts, with the trees of the forests and the fish of the seas, become ethical questions: questions of what is good and right not only for man himself, but for the living world as a whole.'' (p. 198.)

The second pillar is *aesthetic:* "Nature is beautiful, therefore it should not be wantonly destroyed.'' But "ugliness—by any aesthetic standard—remains the predominant characteristic of development of urbanization, of industrialization. We talk about regional planning, diversification, working with the landscape— and we build vast stretches of the new suburbia. . . . The Romantic Movement, despite its 200-year history, has not yet reached our city councils or our highway engineers.'' (pp. 199–200.)

The third pillar is *utilitarian,* but Marston Bates does not, even here, quite agree with the current technocratic creed and sounds a note of warning: "Utility,'' he says, "at first thought, requires man to concentrate selfishly and arrogantly on his own immediate needs and convenience, to regard nature purely as a subject for exploitation. A little *further* thought,'' (italics mine) "however, shows the fallacy of this. The danger of complete man-centred-ness in relation to nature is like the danger of immediate and thoughtless selfishness everywhere: the momentary gain results in ultimate loss and defeat.'' (pp. 200–201.) And he goes on explaining how the logical aim of biological simplification versus diversification ''would be the removal of all competing forms of life—with the planet left inhabited by man alone, growing his food in the form of algal soup cultivated in vast tanks. . . . Efficient, perhaps; dismal, certainly; and also dangerous. . . . It is man working against nature: an artificial system with the uncertainties of artifacts." (p. 201.) For "the simple crop system is always in precarious equilibrium", when stability in nature means diversity and complexity, to say nothing of the kind of social and political structure necessary to enforce such a pattern of life.

However unpalatable it may prove, let us face the fact that in spite of his mechanical achievements, man has not yet emerged from prehistory, and is still wavering on the threshold of humanization: the Bronze Age has its enticements, war its secret spell, but the right thing to do would obviously be to act henceforward both rationally and morally, to have done with violence and killing, to learn to breed more thoughtfully than rabbits and to stop defying and destroying nature.

Only through a kind of re-integration into an ecologically conscious system of interrelations between living beings, purposely maintaining and respecting original diversities and complexities—in other words only through the three-pillared type of conservation just outlined—will man be able, if he *really* wants it, to build the post-Bronze Age world of tomorrow.

This applies to mankind as a whole including, of course, its African section.

DISCUSSION

Young: I suppose that the process of the civilization of man has depended to some extent on his upsetting the balance of nature in those areas of the world which he inhabits, but if it is true that man's happiness in the widest sense is the object of the process of civilization, in the long run the proper evolution of civilization should involve the preservation of many aspects of nature, as Professor Monod has so ably pointed out.

Bourgeois-Pichat: Professor Monod has depicted the future of a world where man is alone. We can also reverse the prediction and think of a world where man is absent, because for the first time in the evolution of life on earth there is one species, the human species, which is on the point of being able to suppress itself. Apart from nuclear annihilation, in relatively few years man will have complete power to reproduce himself or not to reproduce himself. He can have children, or not, at his will. So, for the first time a living species will have the power of continuing evolution, or of ending it.

Monod: The fact is that man is henceforward responsible not only for his own evolution, but also for the evolution of all living beings on the earth, and even their very existence and that of this planet can now be wrecked.

Young: Many years ago Professor C. H. Waddington discussed a definition of ''good'' which suggested that one might define ''good'' as what assists the evolutionary process. But this idea was opposed by some who said: ''How does one know that in the long run man is the highest form of life that will result from the evolutionary process?'' Crustaceans might in fact be destined to rule the earth.

Monod: No, I don't think the crustaceans have any chance! The main group which will probably take the lead after the mammals and the primates will be the cephalopods, a kind of aquatic mollusc; they are already a long way ahead of their kin, their brain is highly developed, and their sense organs also, *but* they are aquatic animals.

Michaelis: What about insects?

Monod: No; they have put their skeleton on the outside; it is not a good arrangement. It is a blind alley.

Sutton: Can you tell us of an instance in which there has been joint planning of land use in Africa by people concerned with the conservation of wild life and those concerned with pastoral or agricultural uses?

Monod: There have been experiments, of course.

Apeadu: You gave three broad justifications for supporting conservation measures: the ethical, the aesthetic and the utilitarian reasons. I suspect that though African countries will realize the importance of all three aspects, they are likely to concentrate on the third—the utilitarian. This is not because these countries do not appreciate things ethical or aesthetic, but because the pressure on development resources is so great for them. It would be useful for them to set up agencies and also set aside resources for carrying out these conservation measures, but I believe that this should be regarded more as a world responsibility. We should not expect much from African governments, who in the last analysis are likely to go to the same world sources for funds for doing other things they consider more important. So we must expect much more from the world community who, after all, have to see to it that this should be done for the benefit of all mankind. Would you agree that the entire world community has an obligation here, not only in the sense of drawing attention to the problem through discussion and resolutions, but also really applying funds and human resources to it wherever the areas of importance exist?

Monod: Yes, of course. But already we have good examples of help coming from outside. Mr. Gille could give us examples of what the international agencies are doing in the present situation.

Gille: I agree that everybody, all mankind, is responsible for conservation, but everybody has responsibility at his own level. Among international organizations, U.N.E.S.C.O. has been engaged in conservation activities since its very beginning in 1946. It was under the auspices of U.N.E.S.C.O. that the International Union for Conservation of Nature and Natural Resources was created in 1948 at an international conference convened jointly by the French Government and U.N.E.S.C.O. in Fontainebleau. This Union is a non-governmental organization enjoying a consultative status with U.N.E.S.C.O., which utilizes its services as scientific and technical adviser on conservation matters or in the execution of a number of projects in education or in research. For instance, U.N.E.S.C.O. has produced, in collaboration with I.U.C.N., a large amount of teaching material such as manuals, film strips and posters for teaching conservation, either in or out of schools. I would like to mention here the manual called "Our Mother Nature", prepared by I.U.C.N. at the request of U.N.E.S.C.O. for teaching conservation in the primary and secondary schools of the Sudan-Sahel zone of Africa. Several thousand copies of this manual were printed in English and in French, and U.N.E.S.C.O. can provide copies, free of charge, for distribution to school teachers and to governments wishing to introduce conservation items in school curricula.

U.N.E.S.C.O. can also help by organizing or sponsoring conferences, such as the Symposium on Conservation of Nature and Natural Resources in Modern African States held in Arusha which was mentioned by Professor Monod, and by financing the publication of the reports of such conferences. U.N.E.S.C.O. can also send experts to gather reports on the situation of wild life and natural habitats in regions where these important resources are in danger. It was on such a mission that the great English biologist, Sir Julian Huxley, was sent four years ago to East and Central Africa to advise on the measures to be taken for preserving this heritage of world-wide significance. Professor Monod has already mentioned the U.N.E.S.C.O. mission of five specialists, again including Sir Julian Huxley, which at the request of the Ethiopian authorities toured Ethiopia in 1963 to study the possibilities of developing national parks with a view to protecting the unique wild life and archaeological sites. The recommendations made by the mission have now been approved by the Government of Ethiopia, which has requested U.N.E.S.C.O.'s assistance, within the framework of its Technical Assistance Programme, to implement them.

I would also call your attention to an important suggestion made by a number of scientists, including Professor Bourlière, the President of the International Union for Conservation of

Nature and Natural Resources. This is for the use of marginal lands, where no agriculture or animal husbandry can be done, for game cropping—African diets are deficient in proteins, and game meat, if well utilized, could constitute an important source of protein. Furthermore, the creation of national parks may be of great economic value to African countries. In Kenya, for instance, tourism, mainly due to the attraction of the national parks, constituted the second largest source of income of the country three years ago (£4 million). Last year it became the highest source of income with some £8 million.

Monod: It might be useful to emphasize the fact that Ethiopia is undoubtedly a very privileged country from many points of view, thanks to its geographical situation and also of course its social history. The special interest of Ethiopia lies in the differentiation which we have in this country, both vertical with the mountains, and horizontal, with an admixture of both palaearctic and tropical elements. That makes Ethiopia a very fascinating country of astonishing diversity, where the plant cover ranges from lowland desert to alpine vegetation. Also, Ethiopia may have been a centre of dispersion: for instance, we know of certain botanical genera which in Ethiopia have a great number of species; in Senegal the genus *Commiphora* is represented only by two species, and in Ethiopia there are 30 or 40 of them; they probably originated somewhere here in Africa, and from here they spread elsewhere. We all know, of course, of the few mammals endangered here at present, which can still be found in Ethiopia but which require urgent, permanent and efficient protection.

The conclusions of our short mission were put in a report which was submitted by Mr. Gille to the Ethiopian Government. We enumerated a certain number of places where we wish to see local sites of protected wild life—new ones might be created. Protected areas for wild life, other than in the national parks, might be created, and also some local sanctuaries for conservation of fish. The Ethiopian Government is said to be greatly impressed with the report and they are now beginning, with the help of U.N.E.S.C.O., to improve their system of conservation.

Wolstenholme: Are W.H.O. and F.A.O. adequately represented, as well as U.N.E.S.C.O., in the work of conservation? When there are such problems as the decimation of animals in the attempted control of sleeping sickness, or if, as seems likely, we discover that some of the monkeys are important reservoirs for some of the more serious virological disorders of humanity, it seems to me essential that both these organizations should be very closely concerned in any work done by the I.U.C.N.

Brown: I cannot give you any very clear indication of W.H.O.'s policy in this matter. But in some of our projects we have already come up against this kind of problem. In one area where we were assisting in a malaria eradication campaign, the use of D.D.T. exterminated many cats, and we had complaints from the local population. I only hope that as time goes on our philosophy in these things will get a little nearer to the level of Professor Monod's excellent exposition.

I have been in a good many parts of the world, and have lived in countries where wild life has been drastically depleted. When recently I had the pleasure of driving through the Albert Park, I was struck by seeing a different kind of nature from that which I had ever seen before. I felt much as Professor Monod himself has said, that man has some sort of responsibility, which I had never really realized before until I saw these animals secure in the park in large numbers. The park represents some kind of refuge for these animals.

Also it is surely worth observing that in the course of all the troubles in the Congo, most of the staff of the park stayed on, even though some of them were not paid for eight or nine months. A few even gave their lives protecting the animals in the park from hunters.

I hope we may take it that all the people round this table accept the philosophical position taken by Professor Monod in his paper.

Monod: It is interesting that the parks are refuges for fauna from elsewhere. Sometimes there are even too many animals in one park, which is a great problem. For instance, in the Murchison Park in Uganda there are far too many elephants; and in the Tsavo Park in Kenya if the elephants breed freely they destroy too great a proportion of vegetation, and their numbers will have to be reduced for their own benefit.

Young: I wish to thank Professor Monod for emphasizing the whole question of man in his environment in Africa; it has been an interesting and valuable discussion.

13

THE RÔLE OF MINERALS IN AFRICAN DEVELOPMENT

R. C. HOWARD-GOLDSMITH

WHEN the word "mineral" is mentioned, most of us think of industry, large machinery and furnaces: yet minerals play a preponderant part in our everyday life, not just in its more sophisticated aspects. Man cannot exist without salt or iron, and there would be no plant life on this earth without calcium or phosphorus. Minerals not only constitute the earth's surface, they are also a prerequisite of most forms of life. At present we only extract a minute proportion from the earth's crust, where there are excessive concentrations. As technology advances we shall make use of a far greater percentage of material which at the moment appears to be of no economic interest. While it is true that minerals do not reproduce themselves like vegetables or other living matter, it is surely correct to visualize the total mineral reserves on this globe as being of such magnitude as to be virtually inexhaustible. The crust of the earth, for a depth of about 10 miles, carries over 7 per cent aluminium, 4 per cent iron and 3 per cent calcium, to mention but a few of the 1,500 different chemical combinations known as minerals. It may well be that some of the richer concentrations as we know them today will become exhausted, but they only represent an insignificant amount of the reserves available for our use if the need arises.

Like agriculture, mineral production can be traced back to the early years of history. Suitable rock minerals helped to arm our ancestors just as they do today: the quartzite arrowhead has been

281

replaced by a titanium-built supersonic warplane. The earliest graves contained mineral products used for ornamental and practical purposes. It is also probable that salt production, be it from sea water or from rock salt deposits, was known and practised by the very first human beings.

The association of man and minerals applies particularly to Africa, which may be truly described as a treasure house of mineral resources. The limestone pyramids of Egypt and the bronzes of Beni and Ife, as well as the constructions of Zimbabwe, all bear witness to the close relationship between African life and African minerals. Yet this continent's sub-soil resources were not recognized by the outside world until recently. Unlike Latin America, to which the conquistadores were attracted by its mineral wealth, Africa has, until recent times, mainly been considered as a source of vegetable and animal products; Libya, for example, served as a granary for Rome. Farming in South Africa preceded gold mining by centuries, and Liberia produced rubber long before the first shipment of iron ore was made. It is only during the last 50 years that Africa has been recognized as a continent richly endowed with a wide range of minerals. Many important and easily accessible mineral concentrations or mineral deposits, as they are more commonly called, have been discovered in this part of the world, and by now the continent supplies an important percentage of the total world production of a great number of minerals. Without going into detailed figures it may be sufficient to mention that minerals and metals accounted for over one-third of the total exports from Africa in 1963.

There can be little doubt that mineral production will continue to provide most of the developing countries on this continent with much of the income they need to raise the general standard of living and improve the daily life of their people. This is particularly striking in countries like Zambia, Gabon, the Republic of South Africa, and especially Libya, where the Government's annual oil revenues alone already exceed 100 U.S. dollars per head of population.

It is popular nowadays to equate the production and export of raw materials with the status of an underdeveloped country. The extraction of minerals and their bulk shipment to foreign manufacturing centres has often been described as a survival of colonial practice and abuse. Many governments in Africa aim to transform the mineral riches found on their territories into finished consumer products by means of large-scale industrialization. It is, of course, quite true that one pound of aluminium metal worth 24 U.S. cents at today's prices is a far more desirable export product than a pound of aluminium ore, i.e. bauxite, valued at about half a cent. This illustration is applicable to most mineral resources; the difference in value between the original raw material and the final metal or product varies considerably depending on the amount of work and material required to effect its transformation. It would seem logical and wise for countries to channel their efforts into what they can produce most economically. They should not attempt to engage in work for which conditions are not suitable. The final processed product is not always the most profitable although it is the most costly. Some countries in this world have few or no mineral resources, and live entirely on the transformation and finishing of imported raw materials; Switzerland is an example. Others have a large surplus of certain mineral resources in world-wide demand and are natural suppliers of these commodities. The processing and transformation of mineral production in its country of origin should be based as a rule on economical and technical reasoning and not on political expediency. There is no more stigma attached to the export of copper metal from Zambia or phosphate rock from Morocco than to the sales of wheat, rather than flour or biscuits, by the United States and Canada.

In many countries there are favourable conditions for the economic up-grading of mineral production with a consequent increase in export earnings. A good example is the manufacture of fertilizers in North Africa, based on that region's phosphate rock resources. On the other hand, it is difficult to visualize the transformation of bauxite into aluminium metal in a country like Guinea, where the supply of cheap electric power is problematical. Similarly, the transformation of iron ore into steel is likely to be uneconomical in those countries which possess neither the fuel resources nor the additional materials required for the process.

The above remarks are meant for individual countries which aim to extract and process their mineral resources on a national scale. A sub-regional approach, on the other hand, can often provide the answer to the up-grading and industrial processing of minerals. The manufacture in Cameroon, where cheap electric power is available, of aluminium metal from Guinean ore is a good example of industrial co-ordination. Similar processing of this same ore could be done in due course in neighbouring Ghana when the Volta hydroelectric power scheme is completed. The proposed steel plant for Nigeria would be best served by using the high-grade iron ore from Liberia or Sierra Leone. Bechuanaland's brine resources could meet South Africa's requirements for salt and soda-ash. There are many more examples where co-ordinated planning of industrial projects would be of mutual benefit to a group of neighbouring countries. Such a sub-regional approach, which is sponsored by the Secretariat of the Economic Commission for Africa (E.C.A.) and by other United Nations agencies, is often the only economic way of furthering the industrial use of African mineral production.

It is logical that the African countries would want to retain the greatest possible share of the intrinsic value of their mineral exports. Transportation costs are included in the final value at the point of delivery: for iron ore sold overseas, the shipping costs can amount to 50 per cent of the product value at the manufacturing centre. If African producers were themselves to handle the freight and insurance of their bulk shipments, they would retain a larger share of the export product's final price.

It is surely in the interest of African governments to encourage the efficient extraction of mineral resources and the sale of surplus production to foreign consumers. The revenues resulting from taxes, export duties and the like, could contribute towards national development projects. It is immaterial to the technician whether mineral production is undertaken by foreign or national, state or private organizations. The important criterion is efficient and rational production. In the past this has been more easily achieved by private enterprise than by government agencies which have frequently had to fall back on the taxpayers to cover up industrial inefficiency. This applies to quite a few of the present nationalized mining industries in Africa. Undoubtedly, the interests of private organizations do not always coincide with national plans and projects. On the other hand, governments can assist development in the right direction by suitable legislation and fiscal policies.

Several African countries have struck a happy and fruitful compromise between private and governmental operations. State agencies concern themselves with the exploration and development of mineral resources which at first sight do not attract private capital. Once the economic feasibility of these resources has been established, private enterprise is given the opportunity of managing and exploiting the new ventures. Compensation for the pioneering work by the government may take the form of a share in the operations or of an outright refund in cash or kind. Such an arrangement favours the detailed study of all possible mineral resources. Their eventual exploitation is left to established organizations with operational and marketing experience; and this is, in the last analysis, to the benefit of the national economy: Togo's phosphate operation, Gabon's manganese production and Swaziland's iron ore mine are the direct result of governmental exploration, followed by private exploitation.

Minerals can also provide the raw materials for domestic industries. Under present-day African conditions where most national markets are below the scope of efficient industrial units, these should frequently be planned on a sub-regional basis. Industrialization is the foremost aim of most developing countries;

if well planned it provides a powerful impetus towards raising the standard of living. However, an ill-conceived industrial venture will sap a country's economic strength, raise the cost rather than the standard of living, and act as a deterrent to potential investors in other projects. Mineral deposits are a help towards industrialization, but usually many other factors have to be taken into account. It was indicated earlier that the aluminium content in bauxite amounts to less than one-fortieth of the final metal product value. Similarly, the iron in iron ore becomes about five times as valuable when it is transformed into pig iron, and this is only worth one-third of the same amount of steel. Modern manufacturing methods require such a variety of different materials that the local existence of any one important constituent is not necessarily a decisive factor.

The African continent as a whole has most of the necessary raw materials and fuels for almost any kind of industrial undertaking. However, transportation costs and facilities will remain an important consideration: it is difficult to imagine, for instance, that Tunisia would buy coal from Southern Rhodesia rather than a Mediterranean neighbour, or that Somalia's oil supplies would come from Libya rather than the Persian Gulf. Geographical and economic realities therefore recommend industrial co-ordination on a sub-regional and not on a continental level.

Most African industrial projects are based on the more glamorous sub-soil resources such as iron, copper, aluminium, petroleum, coal or phosphate. These are traded daily in the world markets and costs and profits connected with projects based on them can easily be evaluated. The effect on the gross national product and on the balance of payments position can be estimated and projected into the future. The average citizen in Africa would get more immediate personal benefits from the development of some of the more humble substances which also abound in the African sub-soil: the sands, gravels, rocks and clays suitable for building, pottery and other aspects of everyday life. Practically every one of the developing countries has sufficient resources of construction material to provide proper dwellings instead of mud huts, and all-weather roads instead of dirt tracks. Such improvements in the standard of living do not require the capital, time and skills usually associated with large industrialization projects. Most citizens would contribute their own efforts if suitable material were made available to them. Furthermore such projects can be developed on a national or even local basis, and would not require sub-regional co-ordination.

Africa has been generously endowed by nature with mineral resources of all types. A rough calculation shows that present mineral production amounts to approximately 80 U.S. dollars per square kilometre of continental surface. This is a low figure when compared with 260 U.S. dollars for Canada or an estimated 500 dollars per square kilometre in the U.S.S.R. For the sake of comparison, mineral output in the U.S.A. in 1962 was valued at 2,000 dollars per square kilometre. There can be little doubt that Africa's mineral and fuel production should be expanded to accelerate the continent's economic development much faster than is the case at present. The bottleneck is not so much a shortage of resources or funds but of human skill and application.

The lack of technical personnel for the development and utilization of mineral resources is one of the most important problems of the African countries. Contrary to the general belief, this is not just due to the lack of training facilities; some 20 institutions in Africa give instruction at university level in geology and mining engineering. A similar number of institutes provide technical training courses for prospectors, drillers and mine foremen. Nearly every one of the above-mentioned establishments has yet to attain an output of qualified men corresponding to the existing facilities. Quite apart from African institutions, foreign training is also open to African candidates at some of the foremost institutions in the world, but up to the present the vacancies and available scholarships far outnumber the applicants. It is true that the value of foreign training facilities is easily over-rated. They cannot be a substitute for national or regional establishments which train the students in their own language and environment. Education at the basic technical or professional level should be acquired within the boundaries of Africa. The use of foreign seats of learning should be limited to advanced studies and research in specialized fields.

An academic training course is an important and usually essential first step towards the formation of a member of a profession, but it takes many years of practical experience to acquire competence. It is a short-sighted policy in many developing countries to fill responsible technical posts with recent graduates. This is particularly dangerous in the field of mineral resources, where a little knowledge and no experience can result in very costly mistakes. It is unlikely that any African leader would allow himself to be operated upon by a student fresh from the medical school. For the same reason the development of the mineral resources of a country, which may have a decisive bearing on its economic life, should not be left in the hands of a recent graduate from a foreign university.

Technical training programmes must provide not only theoretical knowledge, but also practical experience. In the advanced countries the bigger organizations give on-the-job training to their new professional staff for one or several years before entrusting them with positions of responsibility. This is not always possible for an African graduate in his country of origin. Arrangements should be made between the governments to give short-term employment to young professionals from countries adjacent or further afield so as to widen their experience and make them more competent technicians or administrators.

Private enterprise also plays an important rôle in the field of technical training, especially at lower levels. As a rule the smaller operators are rather more prepared to train indigenous personnel because they cannot afford imported skills. With the bigger organizations governmental pressure is sometimes necessary to persuade them to introduce training programmes. On the other hand, conditions vary much from one country to another. In some territories only a minority of national personnel are at present keen to increase their knowledge and skills, and an operator can only spend so much time and money on a general education campaign. Whilst the employment and technical training of national personnel should have an important part in any enterprise, the latter's main purpose is efficient operation. This should not be prejudiced by unrealistic legislation which imposes employment and training policies without regard to costs.

There is as yet a general disinclination in Africa to take up a professional career in the field of mineral resources. One of the most advanced countries, the Federal Republic of Nigeria, can serve as an example: in a speech made on 3 November 1963, the Federal Minister of Information stated that there were more than 1,500 indigenous lawyers. On the same date the number of mining engineers and geologists was about 20. Even with that number, Nigeria is amongst the most favoured countries in this respect. Quite a few African states have not yet a single qualified citizen in the field of mineral resources, whilst most of the remainder have less than half a dozen, even though in some instances their mineral production may have a value in excess of $100 million per year.

It is an urgent task for the national authorities to arouse interest in careers devoted to the development of mineral resources. In most of the developed countries the main attraction of this profession is the glittering reward awaiting the successful prospector or operator. Many of the new African governments prefer policies of collective development which do not offer outstanding rewards for the successful individual. In these circumstances, the remuneration and career prospects must compensate for the physical risks and hardships inherent in the development of mineral resources. A career in this field usually involves living in temporary quarters in isolated regions: normal family life is often impossible. There is more likelihood of accidental injury on a prospecting campaign or in mine workings, open pit or underground, than in a city office. The disadvantages of a career in mining or geology have to be compensated in a concrete manner, otherwise the profession will continue to be ignored by potential candidates.

In summing up these observations it may be stated that mineral and fuel resources are amongst Africa's biggest assets and play a vital part in her development. The outside world is glad to use African petroleum and natural gas, iron ore and manganese, bauxite and copper, gold and diamonds. Known reserves and production of these and other sub-soil resources are such that there will be, for many years to come, a large surplus available for sale abroad. The export products should be processed and shipped in such a manner as to provide the maximum economic benefit to the producers. Government revenues from these exports can contribute substantially towards national development projects.

Apart from earning foreign exchange by direct export, mineral resources also provide the raw material for national and especially sub-regional industrialization projects. These should be based on economic reasoning: if well planned, they will provide large incomes. Industrialization is, however, not a cure for the unemployment which casts its shadow over most of the developing countries: modern industries rely on automated equipment and a minimum of labour, otherwise they cannot be competitive. A poorly-planned project will delay the country's development if the initial heavy capital investment is succeeded by permanent subsidies for the manufacture of inferior products.

The lack of export value has retarded the development of those mineral resources which can improve everyday living conditions. There is much scope for employing local construction material for housing, road building, irrigation, drainage and other projects which are of immediate benefit to community development.

Further progress in the development of African mineral resources will depend largely on a supply of national professionals and technicians, since foreign personnel is likely to become increasingly scarce. Better use should be made of existing training facilities. New standards of persuasion and new incentives are required to attract promising candidates towards careers in the exploitation of sub-soil resources. Otherwise the developing countries in Africa will neglect what is for many of them the biggest known asset of their national heritage.

DISCUSSION

Michaelis: Is there any particular reason why uranium was not mentioned—it is surely one of Africa's most important export minerals?

Howard-Goldsmith: No. At this moment uranium is not an important export mineral. It may be that in 10 or 15 years' time atomic power plants will prove to be economical and competitive, but at this stage far more uranium can be produced all around the world than can possibly be consumed. The only active uranium mine in Africa at the moment is the one in Gabon. On the other hand, South Africa's uranium production, which is a by-product of gold production, is being reduced gradually; it may come to a complete standstill in another three or four years' time according to present arrangements.

Sutton: There is a somewhat disappointing lull in the development of world demand for the mineral resources of Africa. Do you foresee a profitable early expansion of copper and iron production?

Howard-Goldsmith: Some fairly big projects are now being studied. They include one of the world's biggest iron ore deposits in Gabon. It takes ten years or more to get ore deposits into production and this was started five years ago; at the very earliest it would only start operating in another five. The scheme there calls for a ten-million-tons-a-year project, for which a port is required, a railroad, and other facilities.

Michaelis: What about Fort Gouraud?

Howard-Goldsmith: Fort Gouraud has been operating since last year, and is now in full production.

Monod: There is a small historical problem about the origin of the copper which has been used for West African bronzes—not only from Benin, of course, but also from many other West African countries. Most of these bronzes are probably not very old; there is practically no trace of a copper age between the latest stone age and the iron age in western Africa. About a dozen specimens of early copper implements are as much as we have at present. I know of only two places in western Africa where there is an indication of ancient copper mining and copper working, the first being in Mauritania, and the second in the Niger Republic. Since the second half of the 15th century copper and brass have been imported by sea, but for probably an extremely long time they have been brought into West Africa from the north, through trans-Saharan trade. We have already found a number of copper ingots in the western Sahara, and we have been looking for some years for the wreck of a Moroccan mediaeval caravan in the western Empty Quarter. I hope to reach the place in December this year. It is a rather difficult region, but there are great quantities of copper ingots there, and also cowrie shells which were imported from the Indian Ocean, but came from the north through the caravans*.

Howard-Goldsmith: I have no comment to make, except that copper is not found in West Africa with the exception of the Akjouit deposit in Mauritania; the nearest other known copper is in Congo (Brazzaville), which can hardly be described as part of West Africa.

Monod: What about the mine west of the Aïr mountains, near Teguidda-n-Tesemt. There are ancient workings of copper there, at Agelik, 25 km. north of Teguidda; the copper is in recent sedimentary deposits (''calcaires hamadicus''), and the place has been found where the copper was worked.

---

* The site has since been reached and I found there about 2,000 brass rods, large amounts of cowries, and enough organic matter for a radiocarbon dating.— Th. Monod.

Howard-Goldsmith: It is quite true that the Bureau de Recherches Géologiques et Minières studied an area just west of the Aïr mountains in Niger three years ago and found some copper, but it was of too low a grade to be called a deposit.

Mineral traces are found frequently but economic deposits are more scarce. Naturally countries would like to study the possibility of processing the mineral themselves, and therefore, if a new deposit is found, the first reaction of the government is: Can we make that the basis of a new industry? That takes a lot longer to study and decide than just to mine and ship it abroad. If there are sound economic conditions for local manufacture, why send all Guinean bauxite abroad, when perhaps in ten years' time you could have aluminium smelters in West Africa, treating that bauxite and sending out pure metal? I think many African countries now have a certain reticence in giving new mineral concessions with the sole purpose of allowing straight export.

Michaelis: Another point of development is the transformation of crude petroleum and oil into petrochemicals. Has that occurred yet in Africa? Are any petrochemical refineries in operation?

Howard-Goldsmith: The refining capacity in North Africa is at present in excess of consumption needs. This is not, strictly speaking, petrochemicals, but just straightforward oil refining. One petrochemical project is being studied in Tunisia, using Algerian oil; another one is in Algeria itself, at the Arzew terminal, where they are now going to ship liquid gas to England; lastly, Morocco has petrochemicals on its second list of priorities, the first priority being fertilizer manufacture.

It is a bit difficult under African conditions to try to adopt the policy followed by countries like Switzerland, namely, to process imported raw materials—labour in Africa is still very expensive. You could not import oil, convert it into petrochemicals, and hope to compete with the re-exports in the world market. Labour costs in Africa are extremely high, because the labour is unskilled. What you have to start with is your own raw material, and you have to try to treat that as economically as possible.

Wolstenholme: You referred to the exploitation of humbler materials, such as clays. Do you see any big future for the provision of cheaper and effective building materials, which ought to be so very much in demand?

Howard-Goldsmith: Yes, I could visualize that small crushing plants could be set up all over the continent to produce gravel; bricks could be produced locally, in suitable places. I think all the housing could be improved by a very small effort. Even today many African countries are still importing building materials from abroad. There should be a determined effort to find local substitutes. This is getting a bit out of my field, as this is civil engineering we are talking about now, but I have noticed often that everybody wants gold and diamonds, copper, lead and zinc, and looks down on a small brick plant or on a small crushing plant to produce building material which seems to be unworthy of being incorporated in national programmes, or even local programmes.

Michaelis: What about cement?

Howard-Goldsmith: There is an overall deficiency of cement in Africa at this moment, but cement plants are going up fairly rapidly. Dr. Patel could perhaps answer that. The raw material is available, but not in every corner of Africa. North Africa has plenty of limestone—on the other hand, some parts of West Africa have practically none. It is again a question of sub-regional projects, of having a cement plant in one country to supply one or more neighbouring countries too. Theoretically, there is no reason why Africa shouldn't be practically self-sufficient in cement, and as far as I know at the moment the continent produces about 50 per cent of its needs.

Young: Can you give us some concrete figures, Dr. Patel?

Patel: The North produces considerable amounts of cement. East Africa is self-sufficient, and in fact some of the cement plants are not working at full capacity. Central Africa, including the Congo, is producing at a very low level. The data on cement output in various sub-regions of Africa are easily available in studies by the Economic Commission for Africa.

Dekker: Nigeria is at the moment constructing its third cement factory, and I expect in four or five years' time it will produce sufficient cement for the internal market.

Apeadu: Some of the Nigerian factories are based on imported clinker, and not on local raw material.

Dekker: There are two cement plants working on local raw material; it is only because the construction of the Kainji dam on the Niger river suddenly required such a big increase in the amount of cement that it was decided temporarily to import clinker.

Lambo: In view of what is known now of the distribution of mineral resources in Africa, and in view of the limited mineral surveys which have been undertaken, is it possible to predict the extent and distribution of future exploration?

Howard-Goldsmith: One difficulty in answering your question is that what is useless today may be valuable tomorrow. For example, bauxite is a clearly defined mineral, yet in the Aswan region there are some aluminous clays—a few hundred million tons of them—which until a few months ago were considered quite useless; but now, with cheap power becoming available, it is thought they might be a source of future aluminium production. In the same way, I wouldn't like to say whether the sands of the Sahara contain anything valuable or not, because technologically so much progress has been made that suddenly substances become of great importance which 10 or 20 years ago we hadn't heard anything about. Africa has many minerals, and mineral production will without doubt go on increasing, but I wouldn't like to say where and by how much.

Michaelis: Now that hydroelectric power is available in Africa, is it not likely to promote the local development of raw materials, for instance in the production of fertilizers here in Africa, instead of having them imported from abroad?

Howard-Goldsmith: There are some odd ideas about hydro-electric power. It is not necessarily cheap, in fact it is usually very expensive—in Africa especially. In the Republic of South Africa power is produced from coal much more cheaply than from any hydroelectric plant in the rest of Africa, including the Zambezi dam; similarly Algeria is already producing electric power from natural gas at about half the cost that neighbouring Morocco is producing it from water. Hydroelectric power alone is not such a rosy prospect as people often imagine; it must go together with irrigation.

The fossil fuel resources in Africa, in both coal and in natural gas, justify production of nitrogen fertilizers in Africa. The North African countries which have the largest fuel resources have not been primarily interested in nitrogen fertilizers because they are already producing phosphate fertilizers for which they have the required raw materials. However, an ammonia-manufacturing plant is being discussed in Algeria. Morocco has also been talking about one, and the Economic Commission for Africa has recommended that there should be one large ammonia plant for the whole of the North African region, using Algerian natural gas.

Young: I am most surprised at the relative costs of power from hydroelectric sources and from coal which were cited. I should have expected that with hydroelectric power the capital costs would have been substantial, but that running costs would have been relatively small, and that with coal there would be much higher running costs. What is the basis of your comparison?

Howard-Goldsmith: The capital costs of a hydroelectric scheme can be enormous, perhaps 30,000 dollars per kilowatt of power installed, and afterwards the interest on that money has to be paid.

Gayer: Power projects are long-term, ten years or more. The cost of the dam and all associated with it must be considered.

We are trying to achieve an adequate return not only for power, but for irrigation projects, etc., so that one must be very careful when comparing the costs only to the production of electricity. If electricity is considered as a *by-product of an irrigation scheme*, then hydroelectric power is very low-priced. Naturally, in Switzerland for example, this aspect is not important, but in such areas as the Tennessee valley in the United States, where water is required under controlled conditions, the provision of power is simply part of a greater complex.

Dekker: I am amazed at the idea that the cost of power should be paid for by the people who apply irrigation. I can assure you that agricultural people usually say the opposite; in fact, it is the returns on sale of energy which should pay for our irrigation water.

Howard-Goldsmith: In Morocco the hydroelectric power costs are of the order of 15 mils per unit, which is three or four times the price in the United States. I have tried to get at the reason and I just couldn't; I was told it was all the accountants' fault! On the other hand, in the Republic of South Africa, they are producing power at something like 2d. a unit—2–3 mils, which is fantastically low. The power stations are built on top of the coal mines, and conveyor belts run the coal, as mined, straight into the boilers. That produces very cheap power.

Gille: I would like to bring to your attention some maps produced by U.N.E.S.C.O. which are relevant to this subject. In 1959 we published, in collaboration with the Association pour l'étude taxonomique de la flore de l'Afrique tropicale, a vegetation map of Africa south of the Tropic of Cancer, scale 1 : 10,000,000. In 1963, in collaboration with the Association of African Geological Surveys (A.S.G.A.), a map indicating the location of the chief mineral resources of Africa, also on a scale of 1 : 10,000,000, was produced; and in collaboration with F.A.O. a bioclimatic map, scale 1 : 5,000,000, was published which covered the northern part of Africa down to the south of the Sahara. This year we have published, also in collaboration with

A.S.G.A., a geological map of Africa in nine sheets, scale
1 : 5,000,000. A tectonic map and a mineral map, on the same
scale, are now being prepared.

Howard-Goldsmith: I might add in conclusion that unlike the
previous very interesting papers we heard today on conservation
of natural resources and on agricultural production, the picture
for minerals is not so gloomy; it is really rather promising.
Both present and future prospects for the development of
minerals in Africa are really bright, and, as far as one can judge,
are being taken care of quite well, with the exception that there
is a great shortage of trained local personnel.

I4

PERSPECTIVES FOR
INDUSTRIALIZATION IN AFRICA

A. F. EWING AND S. J. PATEL

IN the last few years the importance of industrialization in the development process has been widely, indeed generally accepted. The earlier notion has been exploded that whatever pattern of specialization emerged from the free play of world market forces should be followed—because, in practice, this left the under-developed world to produce agricultural goods and raw materials and, for the same reason, ensured that the rich grew richer and the poor poorer. At the same time, it is widely recognized that industrial and agricultural development must go hand in hand and are not in opposition to one another. There is also a growing realization that while industrialization must start with the further processing of raw materials and with the substitution of imported consumer goods, the point is soon reached when basic industries making capital goods must be set up.

Except in a limited number of countries which are better endowed and achieved early independence, serious thinking about industrialization in Africa began at about the time when the Economic Commission for Africa became fully established, that is, in about 1961. A study was prepared in 1962 which presented, in what was regarded at the time as a somewhat dramatic form, the argument that for the economic transformation of Africa to reach broadly the present levels of Western Europe, an approximate doubling of agricultural output per head and a 25-fold increase in industrial production per head would be required and that this was feasible by the end of the present century.[1,2]

E.C.A. has subsequently, of course, set its sights primarily on what can be done in the present decade. It has established a possible industrial map of Africa in the early 1970's and is now actively involved in helping African governments in their negotiations with a view to trying to make this map, or something like it, a reality. The present paper describes briefly what might be achieved industrially in the next few years*, but its main purpose is to look further ahead and examine what could be the industrial picture in 1980 and in 2000. Such an exercise is bound to be somewhat speculative, yet there are good reasons for believing that what is suggested here could be achieved if the will exists and the right policies are pursued.

OUTLOOK FOR THE SIXTIES

There are 23 countries in Africa with a population of four million or less each. There are 12 with less than two million and seven with less than one million. Since, in addition, incomes per head are very low, it is evident that basic industry is inconceivable without sharing of production and grouping of markets. There are two basic economic principles which have to be observed: international specialization in the African context, and economies of scale. This is not the place to examine in detail what are the economic sizes of plants in different industries, even after making full allowance for the fact that plants in many industries can operate efficiently at lower scales of output than are now customary in the developed world. Some illustrations only can be given.

A modern integrated iron and steel works, even if it concentrates on light steel products, requires a minimum output of about 500,000 ingot tons. Ammonia can be produced reasonably economically at a minimum of 50,000 tons. But there are great savings if the level can be substantially raised. The figures for the

---

* For an account of both the general philosophy underlying the thinking of E.C.A. on industrialization and work done so far, see Ewing, 1964[3].

basic acids and alkalis are much lower but still considerable in relation to North African markets, i.e. from 5,000 to 10,000 tons for sulphuric, nitric, hydrochloric and caustic acids. Furthermore, basic chemicals and fertilizers, normally the first objectives of a chemical industry in a developing country, require combinations or complexes. Surpluses arise in relation to a given purpose, or there are by-products which require proper outlets for the whole plant to be economic. The generally accepted minimum scale of output for an integrated pulp and paper mill is about 40,000 tons; that for flat glass is of the order of 10,000 tons. Cement can be produced on a comparatively small scale owing to the protection offered by high transport costs, although there are marked economies as capacity rises. Textiles can also be produced quite cheaply on a fairly small scale, except viscous rayon which demands a minimum output of 20,000 to 30,000 tons.

In the light of these basic considerations the E.C.A., in the second half of 1963 and the beginning of 1964, sent three industrial co-ordination missions to West, East and Central, and North Africa with a view to establishing a basis for the co-ordinated industrial development of these three sub-regions of Africa. The emphasis throughout was on industry of a sufficient scale to require grouping of markets. It was assumed everywhere that each country would be pressing forward with the development of industry appropriate on a national scale. Some of the main conclusions are summarized here, since if it proves possible to proceed in the light of the missions' recommendations, the new industrial map of Africa in the early 1970's will begin to take shape. More intensive studies have since been carried out, and a series of sub-regional meetings is planned, with a negotiating purpose.

An integrated 500,000-ton iron and steel works is being constructed in Algeria. Unfortunately Tunisia is also laying down a small integrated works of 70,000 tons capacity and Morocco is considering a small electric works of about the same capacity.

Negotiations for the co-ordination of these enterprises, which are of course urgent, have now started. In East and Central Africa a picture is emerging of two 80,000 to 100,000-ton electric steel works—one in Uganda and one in Zambia—supplementing the integrated works in Southern Rhodesia which produce 350,000 tons of iron, and with plans for a marked expansion and with a crude steel capacity of 150,000 tons. These three countries could cover the steel requirements of the East and Central African sub-region for the next decade. West Africa is on the threshold of decisions. A 400,000 to 500,000-ton coastal plant is envisaged, probably in Liberia or Nigeria, supplemented by a 100,000 to 150,000-ton electric steel works probably in Mali. These two works would largely meet the needs of the West African sub-region in products capable of being manufactured economically in Africa at the present stage.

Suggestions for a pattern of development in basic chemicals and fertilizers have also emerged in the light of raw materials available and also the heavy demands made by this group of industries on cheap and abundant electric power or natural gas. In West Africa the main elements are a nitrogen complex in Nigeria with ammonium sulphate fertilizer and industrial explosives as principal end-products; single superphosphate in Togo and triple superphosphate in Senegal; a salt electrolysis complex in Ghana; polyvinyl chloride in the Ivory Coast; and calcium carbide in Dahomey and Ghana. In East and Central Africa a nitrogen complex should be set up in Zambia; phosphatic fertilizers in Southern Rhodesia and Uganda; and Ethiopia should be the supplier of potassium sulphate, potentially for much of the African region. Kenya is the logical location in the sub-region for a salt electrolysis complex, with a second complex perhaps in Zambia or perhaps Bechuanaland; a coal distillation chemical complex might be feasible for the whole sub-region in Tanzania.

In the Mahgreb, Algeria, Morocco and Tunisia not only can supply their own needs in phosphatic fertilizers but can compete in overseas markets. There would, however, be a real advantage in having a single ammonia plant to supply the three countries, located in Algeria and based on its abundant and cheap natural gas and low-cost power. It would be logical to supply the three countries with ammonium nitrate fertilizers manufactured at the same location. Algeria is also a natural place to set up a petro-chemical industry with, in the first instance, synthetic rubber and raw materials as the main products for a growing range of plastics.

Regional as well as sub-regional markets could be tapped. For non-ferrous metals, regional rather than sub-regional specialization can be aimed at. There are two major copper producers, Zambia and Congo (Leopoldville). In the former, at least, there is a good case for starting to manufacture extruded copper products. The bauxite in Guinea should be transformed progressively into alumina. Ghana will soon have ample cheap power and a logical joint venture would be to transform alumina from Guinea into metal and aluminium manufactures in Ghana for the African market.

More investigation is required into the possibilities in the engineering field, but metal working and light engineering are beginning to appear at what have been called the growing points throughout Africa. The time has come for a conscious effort to co-ordinate and share out plants. Some possibilities can be indicated: Kenya specializing in light machinery, electric equipment and agricultural tools; Tanzania in machine tools, light and medium agricultural machinery, assembly of commercial vehicles, railway rolling stock and aluminium rolled products; Uganda in electric transmission equipment, tractor assembly and portable gas containers; Zambia in electrical equipment, certain types of mining machinery and some of the equipment for oil refining and manufacture of fertilizers; and Southern Rhodesia in agricultural tractors, motor vehicle assembly, bicycles and domestic durables. West Africa is at a lower stage of development in this group of industries, but the need for a co-ordinated approach to, for example, vehicle assembly including bicycles, is already apparent, with the existing facilities in Senegal, Ivory

Coast and Nigeria, and those in the course of construction in Upper Volta.

In the Mahgreb losses have already been incurred through failure to co-ordinate assembly of motor vehicles—private and commercial—and also tractors. A high degree of standardization and also co-ordination of types would facilitate cost reduction in the manufacture of different parts—engines, axles, gear boxes, pistons and valves; subsequently more advanced components could be made, e.g. parts of the chassis. The range of products manufactured in the Mahgreb could be steadily increased so that up to 80 to 85 per cent of the work could be done there, taking into account also the contribution of the expanding textile, chemical, tyres, gas, and electrical accessories industries.

There are immense possibilities for increased production of building materials and components. Virtual self-sufficiency could be attained by about 1970 in cement, sawn wood, wood-based products, clay and ceramic products, sheet glass, paint, concrete products and domestic electrical components.

The textile industry is another where there are advantages in co-ordinating specialization, although there are also immense possibilities for development at the national level. More than 70 per cent of Africa's present consumption (excluding South Africa) is imported. Economies of scale become significant in the case of rayon fibre. A viscous rayon complex of 20,000 tons capacity in Nigeria, to serve much of the needs of the West African sub-region, would seem to be viable. In the Mahgreb, requirements of fibre rayon amount to 30,000 tons. One plant, probably in Morocco, could serve the three markets.

One of the difficulties in sub-regional industrial development schemes of the kind outlined is that the industrial plums tend to go to the relatively more advanced countries. A way of offsetting this is to encourage the poorer countries to specialize in smaller-scale industries producing not only for their own consumption but also for export to their neighbours, who should themselves to some degree abstain from constructing these plants. Examples are the production of textiles in the inland countries in West Africa, and also meat and meat products.

It goes without saying that an essential condition for the realization of sub-regional schemes of industrial development on a co-ordinated basis is the creation of free trade areas for the products of the plants set up to serve more than one country.

Such then is the picture of Africa in the early 1970's in the industrial field which is seriously within the realm of possibilities.

PERSPECTIVES FOR 1980 AND 2000

(a) Development of total output

The next step is to consider what could happen by 1980 and then by the end of the century. Reference has already been made to an E.C.A. study[1] which indicated the gap between Africa and present levels in Western Europe and how it was within the bounds of practical possibility to close this gap. The required growth rate of national output would be about 6 per cent for 1960–1980 and rather over 7 per cent for 1980–2000. Africa now has a population of about 270 million and produces goods and services valued at about 32 billion* U.S. dollars, of which almost one-quarter comes from the Republic of South Africa and South-West Africa†. Africa's present income per head is a little more than 110 U.S. dollars.

A century ago the average income per person in Western Europe, the United States, Canada and Australia was about 170 U.S. dollars. The comparative picture in Africa today, with one-third more population and 10 per cent less output, is not significantly different. In the last century the population in these now industrialized countries has increased 2·7 times and output 19 times.

---

* Billion = 1,000,000,000.

† In the discussion of industrial development possibilities so far in this paper, the Republic of South Africa has been excluded. From now on it is included in all the estimates, since it is assumed that by 1980 the Republic will have an African government.

These averages are, however, somewhat misleading since many of the countries concerned began the phase of sustained development comparatively recently. There has in fact been a marked tendency for per head and total growth rates to rise progressively as a new country entered on the path of industrialization. The growth rates which have been assumed for Africa are not unduly optimistic. The U.N. resolution on the Development Decade urges an annual growth rate of at least 5 per cent by the end of the 60's. A number of countries have already set significantly higher targets. But it would be Utopian to believe that these growth rates can be achieved automatically. At this stage they are no more than an indication of what can be done with proper planning and serious and sustained efforts towards execution.

An outline of the overall development possibilities in Africa until the end of the century is shown in Table I.

It will be seen that the gross development product for the continent is projected to rise from 32 billion U.S. dollars in 1960 to 100 billion in 1980 and 400 billion in 2000. Population projections are in three categories. The low estimate is 442 million in 1980 and 620 million in 2000. The medium estimate is 457 million in 1980 and 737 million in 2000. The highest estimate is 473 million in 1980 and 879 million in 2000. The rate of growth of population in Africa, while less alarming than in other developing continents, is already giving rise to concern. It should be remembered, however, that a decline in fertility is usually associated with a growth of incomes and education. Furthermore, increasingly rapid progress towards cheaper and more effective methods of birth control can be expected.

If the forecasts in Table I are applied to the medium population forecast, incomes in Africa would rise to 545 U.S. dollars per head in 2000; on the lower assumption it would rise to 645 U.S. dollars or about the same as the average in the O.E.E.C. countries during the 1950's.

A further point should be made here. The output of agriculture and services is normally seriously undervalued in all poor countries. This is particularly true of agriculture in Africa. It follows that the real income in Africa by 2000 could well be more than 645 U.S. dollars per head, or alternatively may attain this figure even if the medium forecast of population growth turns out to be correct or if a somewhat lower growth of output is realized.

Table I

AN OUTLINE OF THE POSSIBLE ECONOMIC DEVELOPMENT OF AFRICA, 1980–2000

Sector of origin	Net domestic product (billion U.S. $ [1960])			Structure (per cent)			Annual rate of growth (per cent)	
	1960	1980	2000	1960	1980	2000	1960–80	1980–2000
I Agriculture, etc.†	11	30	75	35	30	20	5·2	4·7
II Industry	6·6	30	165	20	30	40	7·9	8·9
Commodity output: total	18	60	240	55	60	60	6·2	7·2
III Other sectors	14	40	160	45	40	40	5·4	7·2
Total product	32	100	400	100	100	100	5·9	7·2
II *Industry*	6·6	30	165	20	30	40	7·9	8·9
Mining	2·2	7	25	7	7	6	6·0	6·6
Manufacturing:								
Light	2·9	10	55	9	10	14	6·4	8·9
Heavy	1·5	13	85	5	13	21	11·4	9·8

Note: These are estimates of order of magnitude, and not forecasts. Their realization depends on the adoption of some of the policies suggested here.

Sources and methods: Data for 1960 from United Nations *Yearbook of National Accounts Statistics* 1961 and 1962[4], and national statistics; some of the gaps in the data have been filled in by partial estimates. The estimates for 1980 and 2000 derived on the basis of the growth framework given in Table II.

† See text, which draws attention to the serious under-estimations of agricultural output. Owing to this, the real growth rates required to achieve these targets will in fact be lower than those shown here.

The outline of the growth framework can be shown more clearly in figures (see Table II).

The implications of the structural transformation of Africa can now be seen. The share of agriculture falls from 35 per cent in

1960 to 20 per cent in 2000, and that of industry rises from 20 per cent to 40 per cent.

(b) Outline of industrial transformation

Major expansion is in industry, including mining, and indeed as has been shown already this is necessarily so. The net value of industrial output will rise from 6·6 billion U.S. dollars in 1960 to 30 billion in 1980 and to 165 billion in 2000, or some 25 times.

Table II

THE GROWTH FRAMEWORK

(Total gross development product for 1960 = 100)

Sector of origin	1960	1980	2000
I Agriculture	35	95	235
II Industry	20	95	515
Commodity output	55	190	750
III Other sectors	45	125	500
Total product	100	315	1,250
IV Gross capital formation	13–14	63	250

To keep this apparently staggering increase in proportion it should be recalled that industrial production in the countries now already developed increased from 6 billion U.S. dollars in 1850 (measured at 1960 prices) to 265 billion U.S. dollars in 1960, or 44 times in 110 years.

The capital requirements for this economic transformation and, in particular, rapid increase in industrialization, are enormous. Massive foreign aid will be required for a long time and such aid will have to be better directed. But these considerations are outside the scope of the present paper. Similarly, and perhaps even more important, manpower will have to be trained at all levels on a very large scale and in the early stages at least will have to be supplemented by the loan of foreign personnel. This problem also cannot be discussed here.

The remainder of this paper is devoted to an examination of the industrial content of the industrial transformation envisaged, together with a necessarily speculative sketch of where in Africa these industries may grow. Some wide assumptions are of course made and have indeed already been made as part of the framework of negotiations in the first stages of the transformation which E.C.A. is attempting to promote by the early 1970's. Apart from the supply of capital and of skilled manpower at all levels, the transport system has to be developed. The present system of trade and payments has to be transformed. National development plans have to be progressively co-ordinated. Above all, there has to be determination on the part of African governments to integrate their economies. These efforts can best be made through sub-regional co-operation.

Turning now to a more detailed consideration of the industrial transformation of Africa, the estimates already given in this paper show that if the income of Africa is to rise to over 200 dollars a head in 1980 and to 645 dollars in 2000, and if industries are to account for 30 per cent of total output in 1980 and 40 per cent in 2000, then the net value of industrial output per head would increase to over 60 dollars in 1980 and over 200 dollars in 2000. This is no place to discuss in detail the methodological approach adopted. It may suffice to say that within the overall framework of growth envisaged, the level and structure of output have been derived from data for other groups of countries which have reached or passed through similar levels of development.

In a United Nations study countries have been divided, so far as industrialization is concerned, into four classes, based on the net value of industrial output per head of population[5]. On the basis of the projections made, Africa will approximate to class III in 1980 and to class I in 2000. The structure of industrial output for these two classes has been taken and applied to the total estimates of the net value of industrial output in Africa in 1980 and 2000. The results are shown in Table III.

The total industrial output is projected to increase at about

8 per cent from 1960 to 1980 and at 9 per cent from 1980 to 2000, with the rate of growth of mining somewhat lower and

Table III
ESTIMATES OF NET INDUSTRIAL OUTPUT IN AFRICA
from 1960–80 and from 1980–2000

Type of industry	Value in billion U.S. $ (1960 prices)			Annual rate of growth (per cent)	
	1960†	1980†	2000†	1960–80	1980–2000
Industrial output	6·6	30	165	7·9	3·9
Mining	2·2	7	25	6·0	6·6
Manufacturing	4·4	23	140	8·6	9·5
Light industry	2·9	10·0	55·0	6·4	8·9
Food, beverages and tobacco	1·0	3·1	16·7	5·8	8·8
Textiles		3·7	16·2	6·7	7·7
Clothing, footwear and made-up textiles	1·0				
Wood products and furniture	...	1·2	5·9	...	8·3
Printing and publishing	...	...	7·1	...	...
Heavy industry	1·5	13	85	11·4	9·8
Paper and paper products	0·1	0·7	5·6	10·2	10·6
Chemicals and chemical petroleum and coal products	0·6	3·6	16·4	9·4	7·9
Non-metallic Mineral products	0·3	1·2	5·2	7·2	7·6
Basic metals		2·4	9·0	13·2	6·8
Metal products	0·7	5·6	49·6	12·9	11·2

† Overall estimate of net industrial output distributed among the various sub-sectors on the basis of the structural pattern for class IV in 1960, class III in 1980 and class I in 2000.

that of manufacturing somewhat higher. Within the manufacturing industries, light industry expands significantly more slowly than heavy industry. These calculations show that the share of mining will fall from one-third to about 15 per cent by 2000.

This is still a high figure, accounted for by the fact that non-ferrous metals and crude petroleum will continue to play a major part in the African economy. The share of light manufacturing will also fall, although the absolute volume will be some 19 times higher than in 1960. Heavy manufacturing will rise from 1·5 billion U.S. dollars in 1960 to 85 billion in 2000, or 57 times. These figures are substantially in line with what has happened in the advanced countries in the last century. At this stage there seems no need to devote much space to the inevitability of a higher rate of growth of heavy compared with light industry. This is neither a socialist "invention" nor a capitalist "taboo" but simply the central feature of industrial development everywhere.

The next step is to translate these estimates into what can be expected in the major industries, an exercise which can be established on broad lines but is necessarily somewhat speculative, partly because the base-line statistics are inadequate, and partly because unforeseeable changes in technology constantly alter relationships. It is not possible, within the framework of the present paper, to demonstrate that the natural resources base for such an expansion of industrial output exists in Africa. Even on the basis of present knowledge, however, Africa appears to be well endowed with the appropriate natural resources, and one must recognize that present knowledge is inadequate and in addition that the accelerating development of science and technology is constantly opening up new possibilities of using resources at present regarded as of marginal value.

(c) Targets for key industries
The broad pattern of expansion of industry by selected key groupings derived on the basis already explained is shown in Table IV.

Energy: Africa is rich in energy resources apart from coal. It has 40 per cent of the world's hydro-power resources, almost limitless reserves of oil and natural gas in North Africa and probably elsewhere, and significant resources of natural gas in

Nigeria. Africa's energy output from all sources amounted to 70 million tons of coal equivalent in 1960 and is estimated to rise to 240 million tons of coal equivalent and to 0·8 tons per head by 1970. In comparison, the consumption of energy in Europe

Table IV

INDICATORS OF EXPANSION OF MAJOR INDUSTRIES IN AFRICA
(1960, 1980, 2000)

Industry and unit	1960	1980	2000	Index (1960 = 1)		Annual rate of growth (per cent)	
				1980	2000	1960–80	1980–2000
Energy (coal equivalent, million tons)	70	400	1,000	5·7	14·3	9·1	4·7
Electricity (billion kilowatt-hours)	40	240	700	6·0	17·5	9·4	5·5
Steel (million tons)	3	24	100	8·0	33·3	11·0	7·4
Cement (million tons)	9	40	100	4·4	11·1	7·8	4·7
Sulphuric acid (million tons)	0·5	...	15	—	30·1	...	8·9†
Nitro-fertilizers (million tons)	0·07	...	3	...	43·0	...	9·9†
Superphosphates (million tons)‡	1·1	...	20	...	18·2	...	7·5†
Cotton yarn (million tons)	0·2	0·6	1·0	3·0	5·0	5·7	2·6
Synthetic fibres (million tons)	0·02	0·1	1·0	5·0	50·0	8·4	12·2

Note: The indicators for 2000 apply broadly to a continental area with a gross development product of 400 billion U.S. dollars. They are estimated on the basis of present technology and the prevailing relationships between output and technological requirements.

† 1960 to 2000.
‡ Net phosphatic content of approximately one-sixth of gross weight.

in 1929 was about 1·4 tons a head. The efficiency of energy utilization is increasing steadily. It would seem that Africa would require about 400 million tons in 1980 and 1,000 million tons in 2000 (with a consumption of 1·6 tons a head). The growth rates involved are 9·1 per cent per annum from 1960 to 1980 and rather less than 5 per cent for the next 20 years. This would seem to be well within Africa's means.

Steel: The output of crude steel in Africa in 1963 was approximately three million tons. At a consumption of about 200 kilograms a head, equal to the average for the O.E.E.C. countries between 1950 and 1955, steel requirements in Africa by the end of the century would be about 120 million tons. This is likely to be an over-estimate since experience shows that there is a progressive increase in the efficiency of steel utilization, and also substitution of other products, particularly aluminium and plastics, for steel[6]. Within the general assumptions of this paper, steel requirements of about 100 million tons by the end of the century would seem reasonable. There is no reason why African production should not attain this level. Steel output in the United States increased from 1·3 million tons in 1880 to 42·8 million tons in 1920, i.e. by 33 times in 40 years, or by about the same order of expansion as is indicated for Africa. Japan's output, despite the lack of coal and iron ore, increased by 16 times in 14 years.

Cement: At present Africa produces nine million tons of cement, or about the same amount as was produced in all the O.E.E.C. countries in 1920, in India in 1960–62, and a little more than in the U.S.S.R. in 1949. In the latter country cement output increased to 60 million tons in 1963, i.e. $7\frac{1}{2}$ times in 14 years. The projections given suggest an increase of cement output in Africa to 40 million tons in 1980 and to 100 million tons by the end of the century, rates of growth of 8 and 5 per cent respectively for the two periods, and less than the 11 per cent growth rate in the first post-war decade.

At the present stage it is not feasible to provide even rough projections for *non-ferrous metals* or for the heterogeneous group of industries described as *engineering*. Africa is likely to be in a position to supply its requirements of copper manufactures and of aluminium metal and manufactures. The same could indeed well be true of most of the major non-ferrous metals, with which Africa is well endowed. The engineering industries are likely to be widely spread throughout Africa, including the whole range of metal manufacture, light engineering, a wide range of heavy

313

engineering and the manufacture of a wide range of vehicles. There is also likely to be large-scale production dispersed throughout Africa of both light and heavy electrical engineering.

The output of *sulphuric acid* is projected to increase from the half million tons at present to about 15 million tons by the end of the century. Comparable rates of expansion may be expected in the other *basic acids* and in *fertilizers*.

Output of *cotton yarn* and *synthetic fibres* at present amounts to about 220,000 tons. By the end of the century this total should rise to about two million tons. Expansion in synthetic fibres is likely to be faster than in cotton yarn. By the end of the century synthetic fibres may well account for half of total fibre consumption.

As a final stage in the argument, in the light of the foregoing projections and the resource endowment of Africa, a rough idea of the industrial map of Africa in 1980 and 2000 now emerges. By 1980, Africa as a continent could be largely self-sufficient in food, textiles (except some synthetic fibres) and other light industries, and building materials and components. The emergence of Africa as a producer of the general run of capital goods is likely to be clear towards the end of the century, though it should already be supplying nearly one-third of its requirements from domestic output by 1980. There will be large-scale production of iron and steel throughout northern Africa, in Mauritania, Senegal, Mali, Guinea, Sierra Leone, Liberia, Ivory Coast, Ghana, Nigeria, Gabon, Congo (Leopoldville), Zambia, Southern Rhodesia, Tanzania, Sudan and perhaps Kenya and Ethiopia. Some of these countries will be producing the whole range of steel products including heavy steel and wide strip, e.g. the United Arab Republic, Algeria, Liberia, Nigeria, Congo (Leopoldville) and Southern Rhodesia.

Zambia and Congo (Leopoldville) will be producing copper manufactures on a large scale. Guinea, Ghana and Cameroon will become major producers of aluminium, with aluminium manufactures widely dispersed throughout Africa.

Production of fertilizers will be widespread, with the countries which are in a position to start immediately probably still in the lead. Algeria, Senegal, Guinea, Mali, Ivory Coast, Ghana, Nigeria, Congo (Leopoldville), Zambia, Southern Rhodesia, Uganda, Kenya and Tanzania will be centres of large-scale chemical industry. Algeria and Nigeria will be major producers of petrochemicals and plastics.

Mechanical and electrical engineering industries will be located throughout Africa. The leaders are likely to be Morocco, Algeria, Tunisia, United Arab Republic, Senegal, Liberia, Ivory Coast, Ghana, Nigeria, Congo (Leopoldville), Sudan and most of East and Central Africa. Production of motor vehicles is likely to get under way first in North Africa, along much of the coast of West Africa, Congo (Leopoldville) and much of East and Central Africa.

South Africa is of course already well developed and its further pattern of development is likely to be along the same lines as in post-war Western Europe.

The picture which emerges is of an African continent with, taken as a whole, a high degree of self-sufficiency. Africa's traditional exports of agricultural products and raw materials will still be significant in absolute terms, with additional items such as aluminium, copper manufactures and petrochemicals. Africa might indeed become by the end of the century a significant exporter of certain iron and steel products. There will be significant trade between Africa and other parts of the world in manufactures of all kinds, in much the same way as there is a high level of intra-trade in Europe in manufactures. Africa will continue to import capital goods from the rest of the world, particularly more specialized kinds of equipment.

The outline of industrial transformation of Africa by the end of the century, as presented here, of course depends for its realization on the vision, wisdom and vigour with which the countries in the continent apply themselves to the task of accomplishing in half a century what took nearly a hundred years in the industrial countries. The task is immense, but so also are the benefits to be derived for its people. The economic transition could well form the rallying point for all its people in a firm determination to overcome the age-old afflictions of mankind—hunger, disease and ignorance.

DISCUSSION

Young: In 1950 I had to give a talk in America on the British National Health Service. I took up an attitude of the sort that you did, Dr. Patel. I thought it was important to trace the history of its development, and I started with a discussion of the ideas of utilitarian philosophy at the beginning of the nineteenth century in Great Britain. The innovators decided that what was to be worked for in Britain was the greatest happiness for the greatest numbers, and that the first moves to be made with this aim in mind were the emancipation of the slaves and the extension of the franchise. It became clear too that universal education was needed. It could be thought at that time that if men were free, given the vote, and educated, they would vote an ideal government into power. But it slowly became clear that for happiness not only must men have a vote, be educated and have work, but also that some degree of assistance to remain healthy and well-nourished was needed. In Britain a health service began with Lloyd George's National Insurance Act of 1911, and the National Health Service in 1947 was an inevitable outcome of 150 years of social development. If I understand correctly, you are suggesting that in Africa now it should be possible to telescope the developments that occurred in Britain, Europe and America within, say, 100 or 150 years, into 50 or 60 years, by studying the processes which occurred by blind evolutionary development in our part of the world.

I should like you now to expand a little on the question of management of the growth of output.

Patel: What I had in mind behind the phrase was some relatively simple economic concept. It is clear from the history of the growth of western Europe that rising capital formation has not always preceded a rise in output. As Dr. Acock pointed out, for example, if the maximum use is made of available knowledge and techniques, agricultural output could be raised fairly rapidly through an increase in yield on many acres of land. On such a scale yields can be raised by 30 or 40 or even 100 per cent in a relatively short period. Similarly, the unemployed labour force could be mobilized to create social capital. Many factories are working below capacity; some of them work only one shift, and many of them (though not necessarily all) could work two shifts. In the early phases of growth, such excess capacity can be used to raise the rate of growth; and when growth gathers momentum, investments in the economy can be raised by making sure that not all of the additional output goes into consumption. Diversion of an increasing share of higher output is much easier to achieve than taking away part of the current income for investment. In a static situation, investment could not be increased unless consumption was reduced, and that is what most people call ''tightening the belt''. In a dynamic situation, on the other hand, the growth of output is dependent upon growth of investments, and therefore the higher the investment the higher the growth of output. What matters most for economic growth is thus the utilization of excess capacity in the earlier phase, and raising capital investment in the second phase.

Mustafa: I found it reassuring to listen to Dr. Patel, who presents this rather glorious picture for the Africa of the future, but I doubt very much whether I would go with him all the way. It seems to me that sufficient attention has not been paid to one or two practical considerations in the treatment of this particular subject.

Some of the factors which encouraged the growth of industry in Europe in the last 100 years no longer exist. A 100 years ago only a few countries in Europe were industrialized to any appreciable extent; the rest of the world constituted a huge market which was capable of absorbing all that could be produced. I am not so confident that this is the case now. The number of industrialized countries has increased tremendously and the world market for industrial produce has been greatly reduced. African countries will also be facing a fierce challenge from countries which have preceded them by over a century in this field. One facet of this challenge is that the cost of producing goods locally is often much higher than the cost of imported goods; for example, we are producing sugar in the Sudan at three times the cost of imported Cuban sugar. We are starting textile industries and the cost is more than twice what we pay for imported Japanese or Chinese material. We are marketing dairy produce, the cost of which is again more than that of imported New Zealand or Australian produce. For this reason I think that the pace at which industry could develop in Africa is certainly going to be much slower, because the incentive will not be there. Also, in Europe and America there were countries which already existed as sound economic units, whereas in Africa today this is not so.

Patel: It may be useful to review here how industrial growth took place in western Europe. The classical economists assured us that free trade was good for everybody. The British industrialists suggested that what was good for England was good for the world. But hardly any major industry in Europe or the United States developed without some degree of protection. Except for England, which was industrialized before other countries, no other country really practised free trade. Most new industries in the developing countries are bound to have high production costs initially. Take the example of the steel industry in Italy. In the early stages, steel output was much more costly per ton in Italy than in England, Germany and France. But after 15 years the differences in costs are now very narrow. Moreover, steel has helped in the establishment of a whole range of subsidiary industries in the engineering and chemical fields.

The second point, and I think perhaps a much more significant one for Africa, is that we are trying to work towards sub-regional co-operation in the continent. The pace of development would be rapid if arrangements were made, for example, for the Sudan to specialize in textiles, Uganda to specialize in sugar, Congo and Zambia in copper industries, and so on. But under the present national division of African labour, there is a serious danger that in fact the pace of growth of these less developed countries could well turn out to be lower than what in fact was the experience of the last 150 years in the industrial countries.

Bourgeois-Pichat: I am not really convinced, and I think you are a little too pessimistic about Europe. During the past century in Europe the rate of increase in the population has never been more than 1 per cent. If the population is increasing at 1 per cent per year, and if capital investment is, let us say, 15 per cent of the national income every year, and a return of 1 out of 5 is adopted, this means that the gross national product will rise at 3 per cent per year. If you allow for 1 per cent of growth of population, that gives you a 2 per cent increase in income per head. But if you want to do that with the population growing at 3 per cent, you need for the gross national product an annual rate of growth of 5 per cent instead of 3 per cent, and this means that you must invest five times this percentage of the gross national product, i.e. 25 per cent instead of 15. And if, in addition, you want the same evolution in 50 years instead of 100 years you have to invest 40 per cent of the national income each year, which is almost impossible. When I am told the story, from the economist Keynes, that £40,000 at 3¼ per cent interest will after a very short time reach the whole national income of the whole British Empire, I am of course convinced of the powerful effect of compound interest, but I also have the feeling that our ideas about compound interest are not sound ideas, because if the length of the calculation is extended a little more, this will go far beyond the national income of the whole world, which is obviously impossible.

319

I once made the calculation that if the French in France had been as fertile as the French people who left France for Canada around the middle of the 18th century (and who had the same fertility rate then), the population of France would now have reached two thousand million people, which has no meaning.

So I do not think that the way in which Europe developed in the last 100 years can be used as an example or even as a guide for the development of a continent like Africa or Asia. It is something different; they have to go the same way, it is true—they have to pass from an income of 100 dollars per head to one of 1,000 dollars; but it is a little like two cars travelling the same road, with one (the car representing the developing country) needing to have a speed twice as high as the other (the car representing the industrialized country).

Patel: I would fully agree that growth at compound rates cannot be continued indefinitely. If anything grows at 10 per cent, it will increase 14,000 times in 100 years, and in 200 years it would run into millions. This is quite true. But I am not suggesting an indefinite time perspective or a growth rate which is outrageously high in comparison with the past.

The attainment of a 5 to 6 per cent growth rate of output per head can no longer be dismissed as a crazy idea. Many countries in the second half of the 19th century have attained such growth rates. Much is known about their actual experience. This can serve as a general guide to the developing countries. The task of the planners in each country is to work out the concrete details of policy necessary for realizing high growth rate under the given conditions.

Last: I admire your vision of African economic development, Dr. Patel, and I hesitate to say anything which might dim this vision, but someone has said that underdeveloped areas are underdeveloped for the simple reason that it is very difficult to get the things done which would develop them. E.C.A. reports or World Bank reports on the countries in Africa often stress the absence of a body of local entrepreneurs with experience who will take practical steps to create or extend economic activity. I think it is true to say that in Europe before 1850 we had a considerable body of experience of this kind. In Africa we have to start more less from scratch in this respect.

Another thing that makes the initial step very difficult to achieve is this question of skill, not only training but the whole cultural outlook on things technical. This involves the whole population. Those of us who have something to do with education in Africa very often overestimate the background experience of our pupils. We are faced with more than just the institution of a number of training courses for specific purposes; what is wanted is a whole cultural revolution. In this connexion there are some interesting comments in Felix Greene's book on China, "The Wall has Two Sides"[7]. In dealing with the multiplication of so-called backyard furnaces which took place two or three years ago in China, Greene says that the whole purpose of this operation was not to extend the industrial capacity of China, but to give the maximum number of people the maximum amount of experience with the elements of technology. So people dabbled with smelting iron and produced simple articles in the villages, and this achieved—again according to Greene—something of a cultural and technological revolution in a very short space of time. Maybe we should do things like that in Africa. In their absence this ominous gap will persist.

These are two of the background items in the existing economic state of Africa which may delay things a little bit more than you think.

Apeadu: Anything Dr. Patel has said should be regarded as having a prophetic value, but he gave a warning that attainment of these goals will depend upon one or two assumptions being made good: the assumption concerning the cultural revolution which has just been referred to, and the assumption concerning the willingness of states to work together. Three or four years ago hardly anyone thought that we would have such a body as the Organization of African Unity, and now it is here. A similar surprise in the field of economic co-operation no doubt awaits the sceptics, though one cannot deny that their doubts are sometimes founded on facts. Thus, while we have the Economic Commission for Africa busily preaching the gospel of teamwork on a sub-regional basis on the continent so that we shall operate our plants at maximum capacity and not waste the investment resources, many African countries are equally busy setting up separate factories within their own borders—a process that can only slow the pace of economic growth.

Take also the question of efficient management of enterprises. It is now the popular thing for governments to go into business— in agriculture, industry and all kinds of business. The results in some countries are so discouraging that they will certainly impose a drag on economic and social advancement. The demands of the African family system sometimes make it difficult for ministers and other responsible persons in government to appoint the best men to positions of managerial control, even if they are available. It is unfortunately also true that many governments go into comparatively uneconomic business ventures, put up imposing public buildings, construct highways, railways, harbours, etc., where they probably won't be adequately used for very many years.

I am trying to say that all these factors constitute so many limitations on the theory of fast economic growth that has been put forward for the African situation. So we need to bear in mind that we are making a large number of assumptions, some of them exceedingly difficult, when we accept Dr. Patel's thesis.

Patel: I agree that there are a number of assumptions in such an exercise. But to bring the problem within the realm of probability in itself helps to generate forces which have a propensity to overcome obstacles. This may be made clear by comparing it with the demand for political independence, say in India in 1930. The very fact that this demand was raised created the forces which finally overcame the obstacles in the path of its realization. What I have in mind is that by putting higher goals before the people, the possibility will be created of unleashing the forces to realize them.

Monod: The problem is, I think, a two-fold one. On the technical side some writers are not sure that such a rapid growth of industrialization is possible in Africa. The second aspect is the human one. A few years ago Professor Crocker from Australia wrote a paper[8] on the price to be paid for industrialization in Africa from the human point of view. For instance, what benefits would camel breeders from the western Sahara obtain from working in iron mines? We would give them wages, of course, then we would take part of these wages back in selling them various gadgets, some of which may be of dubious utility. The question remains, will the men be happier? Perhaps, but perhaps not, nobody knows. It is a big question, this human side of the problem. That is where the social worker, the anthropologists, the people who are interested in the complexities of organization and so on will have something to say.

Bourgeois-Pichat: Dr. Patel told us that an annual rate of growth of 6 per cent in output is not uncommon in the present world economy. This is true, but this rate of growth has only been observed recently in developed countries, and not in underdeveloped countries. It is true that the underdeveloped country has *only* to do the same as the developed country, i.e. to raise output 6 per cent per year, but the problem is precisely the word *only*. How can we do this? Let me give you another example of the powerful effect of compound interest. An American demographer, Ansley J. Coale, calculated a few years ago that if the world population continues to increase at the same rate as today (1·9 per cent a year), then in 6,000 years from now mankind will consist of a sphere of living matter expanding with the velocity of light.

Patel: Let us take the net rate of growth of output per head of population in different countries at the time they were developing. The growth rates per head which operated in England and

France were 1·2 and 1·4 per cent. In the next group of countries, Germany, United States and Canada, the growth rate was 1·6 to 1·8, then in Norway, Sweden and Japan it was 2·1 to 2·8 per cent, and in the Soviet Union it was 4 per cent or higher, depending upon the estimator. There has been a tendency for the rate of growth of output to rise as industrialization spread from its original centre to other areas.

I am suggesting that a growth rate of 5 or 6 per cent has even been exceeded in a number of countries which have just begun to develop.

Sutton: I don't quite understand the reasoning behind the higher rates in the earlier periods in most of your projections, as against the increase in gross national product. Gross national product trebles in 20 years between 1960 and 1980, but things like energy consumption go up four times, electricity six times, steel eight times, and education up six times, and then fall off.

Patel: Again I wouldn't be able to show this in great detail; but there is no doubt that different sections of the economy grow at different rates. This is what brings about a structural transformation. Agriculture loses in relative importance and industry gains; and within industry, light industry loses ground to heavy industry.

Goody: I think your general idea is perfectly sound, Dr. Patel, but your comparison starts with the wrong take-off point. Africa in 1950 showed greater unevenness of development than Europe in 1850. Technologically it is much more backward. For example, Europe had a metal plough, whereas until the colonial period Ethiopia was the only part of Africa which had even the Mediterranean plough. In large parts of Africa farming is by hoe and water control is limited. Again, literacy was minimal. This means that Africa has a lot further to go in training people for more technical skills.

A third point is social organization. In 1850 in Europe there was already a relatively small nucleated family. The large-scale family units of Africa today no longer existed. We know that achievement in the economic field will reduce the extent of kinship ties. Very rapid economic change will produce very rapid changes in family structure, much more so than occurred in Europe, and this is bound to bring social costs of the kind Professor Lambo has spoken about, which will in turn affect the rate of economic growth. This means that a much larger investment in the social services and various non-economic types of planning is needed than has been anticipated.

We have to consider yet further certain social costs of economic growth in a realistic way. In Europe over the last 100 years economic growth was not unrelated, perhaps as cause, perhaps as effect, to a whole series of wars, two world conflicts, and various colonial wars. It may be possible to avoid war, but it must be remembered that increased growth is going to mean magnified competition for scarce resources. So another cost of economic growth should be investment in forms of organization that will help to control the inevitable friction.

Finally, one must always bear in mind that the tropical environment is in many ways very favourable to man; we do not need to make the same investment in clothing, housing or heating as is required in northern Europe. Indeed, when you think of the conditions of life of an industrial worker in a northern slum compared with those of an African peasant, it makes one want to look carefully and closely at the meaning, in social terms, of economic growth. There are great dangers in taking recent European history as our model for development, in economics as in the rest of social life.

Gille: To reach the level of industrialization mentioned by Dr. Patel there is no doubt that in African countries a lot of research in all kinds of fields, particularly in natural resources, must be done.

The question of the availability of sufficient numbers of adequately trained personnel and the question of financing of research and its economics were studied in detail by the International Conference on the Organization of Research and Training in Africa in relation to the Study, Conservation and Utilization of Natural Resources, held in Lagos in 1964, to which I referred earlier. From statements made by the delegates from the 28 participating countries, it appears that most African countries (over 85 per cent) have no research council or its equivalent, nor are their national research funds sufficient to permit the co-ordinated and planned financing of scientific activities.

The Conference therefore considered it appropriate to indicate an order of magnitude for such expenditure to serve as a guiding target; this was tentatively set at 0·5 per cent of the gross national product, or 6 per cent of the investment budget, to be set aside for the research sector, subject to periodic review and pending closer analysis of the cost: benefit ratio in research. It was estimated that the minimum target for the number of scientists should be set at 200 per million population. This includes senior officers of Ph.D. level, graduate scientists in all sectors and all university science teachers. The projected population being 277,882,000 for 1970, 312,333,000 for 1975, and 353,243,000 for 1980, the aggregate number of scientists should therefore be, respectively, 55,600, 62,400 and 70,600. The gross national product at the same dates having been estimated, in millions of U.S. dollars, as 39,696, 49,895 and 65,238, the total expenditure for research should therefore be (in millions of U.S. dollars) 198·5 (i.e. 39·7 for fundamental research and 158·8 for other research), 249·5 (i.e. 49·9 for fundamental research and 199·6 for other research) and 326·2 (i.e. 65·3 for fundamental research and 260·9 for other research).

These figures primarily give an overall picture of the needs of Africa for scientists and research resources. They are targets in the sense that each country will have to make national plans in both areas in the light of the criteria established by the Conference and the country's own political aims and economic resources. It should also be noted that these tentative targets are relatively low by international standards.

Brown: If expansion in Africa is to go on at anywhere near the rate which Dr. Patel envisages, a mass direction of labour seems to me to be an inevitable concomitant. I wonder whether such a programme on the scale that would be necessary is really likely to be feasible, apart from any question of desirability or otherwise.

Africa has mostly a tropical climate and the disease pattern here is very different from that in the northern European countries. This is particularly true of the communicable disease field, and I would like to take this opportunity to clarify a point I mentioned earlier (p. 166), when I pointed out that there is a part of the health programme, and probably of other social programmes too, which is a part of the input and output of the economic programme. Now health is also, what very few factors are, an end in itself. My plea is that there should be a full recognition of the imperative need for adequate treatment of the health factor in economic planning. In fact this is probably an essential if these countries are to progress in the first phase. Probably in the second phase and afterwards life will be easier for everybody and many health problems will be taken care of in the natural course of events. For instance, one of the greatest problems we have had in African countries is to get young doctors to devote themselves to public health, which contributes directly to economic development. In Ethiopia there are some 30 Ethiopian doctors, but as far as I know not a single one is working in this field. At the Ministry of Health all the senior medical staff are foreigners, and we cannot get the young doctors to come into this field. There are many reasons for this, and the only way to make them come in would be to direct them in. I suspect that this is true of other sectors too. A programme of this magnitude would have to be worked out in very great detail.

Patel: I fully agree that such a plan has to be worked out in detail. It is very important. I can only say that the degree of direction required also needs to be worked out in detail. If the plan is a good plan and if there is enthusiastic co-operation by the people, the degree of direction of labour, with a harmful connotation, will be lower.

Goody: Could you say something about the effect the rapidly increasing defence expenditure in Africa will have on the projections you have made?

Patel: Defence expenditure will obviously divert resources away from more productive uses and will to that extent be responsible for a slower pace of development.

Gayer: Many of the problems that have been discussed during the past few days will be solved with industrial development, whether this is at 6 per cent or 4 per cent. The rest of the world might help by improved organization produced by industries coming in and setting up plants and helping to train people for industry. This would help to take care of the needs of the country, and would help to eliminate some of the problems which otherwise might make the growth rate less than 6 per cent. I have heard people agree that lectures on this topic are not nearly as effective as some good concrete examples.

The vital question on which I am not quite clear concerns training in management. That must come, but how can it be organized? In addition, there must be co-operation between countries so that their development policies are compatible with one another. This is where the concept of African unity has a great rôle to play, in giving an overall direction to African economic development.

Patel: One of the interesting aspects of the world we live in is that some of the things that could not be done earlier could be done now. Take, for example, the need for a more equitable distribution of world income. This may sound like a crazy idea, but only 20 years ago most of the industrial countries hardly used taxation as a conscious instrument for a more equitable distribution of income. Perhaps in 10, 20 or 30 years we may succeed in constructing a system of international taxation which would promote a more even distribution of income throughout the world.

15

INVESTMENT PLANNING AND DEVELOPMENT IN AFRICA

G. MANCINI

INVESTMENT planning nowadays is recognized as one of the major tools whereby economic planners aim at certain pre-determined targets for the purpose of developing given economies or economic sectors.

In formulating investment planning for a given economy, these main problems or stages may be recognized:

(1) the choice of the total investment volume (both public and private) for the economy as a whole;

(2) the distribution of the total investment volume between industrial sectors; and

(3) the distribution of the total investment between "regions" of the economy.

The size of the investment largely determines the rate of growth, while its composition reflects the strategy of develop-ment. Both aspects of the investment planning are conditioned by the limited resources available over a certain period of time, the corresponding technological knowledge and the political and social environment prevailing at that particular time. Further-more, they are subject to a process of adjustment due to the changing of the original conditions which, in turn, is brought about by the dynamic nature of the development itself.

The decisions in each of the three stages mentioned above have to be based on a formulation of the aims of the economic policy and have to consider the many interdependencies that exist between the economic phenomena in the given economy.

Africa has only recently emerged and the aims of an African economic policy may therefore be described as still being in a "formative" stage. These aims are emerging while governments keep themselves busy in framing development plans and policies as well as experimenting with various tools and techniques. And it may be added that a great deal will depend on social and political developments in the different countries before economic aims may be clearly defined in a truly African context. All that can be reasonably said at the moment is that Africa is aware of the need to change its economic structure from the production of mainly agricultural and primary goods to industrial and more diversified production, and that in doing so it plans to rely primarily on public action.

The end result of any development process is recognized by the growth of national product per head. Overall targets of income increase are therefore established and the total investment requirement then derived. This is checked against the availability of financial resources, domestic as well as external and, if required, readjustments are made in relation to the available means.

According to data at present available, an overall annual target rate of growth of the national product of the order of 5 to 6 per cent has been set as an average for all Africa for a period of between 5 and 7 years. Incremental net capital/output ratio for the same period averages up to 3 per cent; the annual component rate of population growth for the same period averages 2·5 per cent. Thus an investment requirement for a target of 5 per cent increase in income would be of the order of 15 per cent of the national product.

The immediate subsequent problem in investment planning is the consideration of public versus private investments.

No matter how important the private sector might be, and regardless of its scope, the programme of public investment in almost all national development plans in Africa appears to be the most important and decisive part of the entire investment programme. It may be estimated that public investment accounts for 60 per cent of the total. The investment programmes of the public sector are the direct responsibility of the government and reflect actual investment decisions that have to be taken by the operating agencies for implementation. The programme of investment for the private sector, however, is essentially an estimate of the performance which can be expected from this sector under certain conditions.

Among investments in the field of economic development, a major division exists between investment in "physical infrastructure" or "overhead capital for the economy as a whole", such as transport, power, etc., and investment in directly productive activities, such as agriculture, manufacturing industry, etc. The proportion of investment in these two broad fields in the public investment programme of the different African countries is usually appraised in the light of the corresponding proportion in the private sector. In countries where the private sector is relatively large, government investment in "directly productive activities" is bound to be proportionally less than in countries where the private sector is relatively small. Nevertheless, it might be said that the most recent tendency of most African governments is that of rather massive investment (at least in the form of participation) in "directly productive activities". Government investment in physical infrastructure, especially transport and power, appears to be less flexible.

The existing national development plans show that the emphasis on the development of transport systems is common and, particularly in the least developed countries, transport ranks as first priority. This suggests that transport is the major need for the development of Africa and that its improvement is certainly a prerequisite for any degree of growth. An inadequate transport system is the main obstacle to the development of internal markets and the integration of the indigenous inhabitants into the market economy.

The argument concerning external economies which lies

behind the strategy of heavy investment in basic economic facilities presupposes that development in directly productive activities, especially in the manufacturing industry, has been hampered by the lack of transport facilities or power supply. While this appears to be true in some African countries which enjoy private enterprise, an adequate market organization and sufficient final demand, the same might not be true in areas where these elements of ability to invest are lacking. Under the latter conditions, excessive investment in physical infrastructure may result in extensive idle capacity for at least some time before "the ability to invest" grows sufficiently. It may happen, for instance, that a highway is built before it is justified by the volume of traffic, so that it is little used and, therefore, left without adequate maintenance. Such idle capacity is clearly a waste of resources which could be devoted more productively to agriculture or industry.

On the other hand, this "pressure" approach also has its disadvantages. Physical infrastructure projects, such as roads, railways and hydroelectric power stations are generally large projects characterized by bulkiness. Their construction requires rather a long time. If it is necessary to wait until demand for their services has accumulated to the extent of exercising pressure, time may be lost and the time required to extend other needed assistance to directly productive fields prolonged.

Thus, balanced investment between physical infrastructure and directly productive fields appears to be essential. The actual implementation of this general principle, however, greatly depends on the continuous and accurate assessment of growth in both sectors and on timely adjustments in the planning and implementation of the individual projects concerned. At present it seems that about 25 per cent of the total investment is devoted to infrastructure, mainly transport and hydroelectric facilities.

The observations made above reflect a more general consideration that infrastructure investments and basic facilities, although a necessity in Africa, do not necessarily generate or bring about an inducement for additional economic activities. African economies begin their development process through other factors; and the mere existence of an infrastructure will hardly induce growth. In particular, education, training, technical and administrative skill and experienced personnel to utilize these factors, and what is known as the "human factor", must be largely available before an African development process can be expected to start, especially in the more directly productive sectors of the economy. It is therefore of some interest to know whether African governments make entries for investment in "human factor" in their planning, and if so to what extent.

Public expenditure on social development in the development plans only supplements or complements the total national effort in this field. First, activities in the fields of education, health, housing and social welfare have always been carried on by households, non-profit-making institutions and private enterprises. Secondly, in some African countries, part of the government expenditure on social services is included in the current accounts of the budget, but not in the development expenditures under the plan. Indeed it is difficult to determine what social expenditure is current and what is developmental in nature. At any rate it may be said that investment in education, research and training accounts for about 15 to 18 per cent (as average) of total government expenditure per year, and the social sector, which in addition to education would also include health and housing, accounts for 15 to 20 per cent or thereabouts of the total investment of the countries concerned.

Public intervention in the industrial sector is to a certain extent conditioned not only by the existing development of the economy, but also by the political philosophy of the government concerned. Generally speaking, however, it might be said that government intervention in developing the industrial sector is becoming one of the major preoccupations in Africa. The Ivory Coast and Cameroon, whose first national development plans showed no public capital expenditure on industry, have more recently made provisions to this end. The majority of African governments feel that a positive effort on the part of the public authorities is required to stimulate a more rapid rate of growth. Whether this is premature, leading to subsidized industry or capital loss or both, or whether the governments concerned will succeed in simultaneously removing all remaining obstacles to growth, only time and experience, or a more thorough analysis than the one offered here, will show.

Agriculture is the remaining factor to which all governments give at least some attention in their programmes—either (1) by limiting their intervention to research with a view to improving yields and quality of production for export as well as for the domestic market, or (2) getting more involved in the problem of concentrating on production techniques and the production structure of traditional agriculture and going so far as to provide for agrarian reforms, or (3) (and the Ivory Coast may be a case in point) concentrating on increasing and improving export crops. At this stage, however, it might be useful to recall that unless planned efforts are concentrated on increasing and diversifying export crops, in which case success depends on foreign markets, agricultural development need only follow, *pari passu*, development in other domestic sectors—provided that any existing deficiencies have been covered. As is well known, it is the other sectors that have to lead the way to rapid growth, permitting a shift of economically active population away from agriculture, creating domestic demand for agricultural produce and increasing productivity and income per head in the agricultural sector, and thus creating markets for their own products. However, the agricultural sector obviously must develop simultaneously with the rest of the economy in order to avoid the obstruction of rapid growth by the lack of agricultural development. Some governments therefore rightly devote special attention to the necessary changes in rural life, particularly as some of them take a long time and may almost be classified as elements of the required social infrastructure.

At this point it may be interesting to note that, on average, investment in the agricultural sector ranges between 18 and 25 per cent of the total investment, while the industrial sector ranges between 35 and 40 per cent of the total. This shows that despite the great interest in industrialization, African governments devote great attention to the agricultural problem.

To summarize, it seems that the total planned investment in Africa for the next ten years shows the following distribution among sectors:

Agriculture	21 per cent
Industry	35 per cent
Social services	18 per cent
Infrastructure and public administration	25 per cent
Other	1 per cent

The formulation of an investment plan implies the distribution of the total investment between industries and, whenever applicable, between regions. However, the investment plan has to be filled up with concrete investment projects. At this stage the problem of the economy of scale starts to play its deterrent rôle. Most of the African countries cannot offer internal markets sufficiently large to sustain industrial development on an economic modern scale and their total economic activity in some instances does not justify certain capital intensive infrastructure projects.

A different attitude is therefore required: co-operation in the economic field with a view to making the different economies complement each other better. This implies at the same time the introduction of multi-national or sub-regional development plans or provision in national plans for supernational projects, or even the adoption of complementary evaluating criteria which could shape national development within the context of a more comprehensive sub-regional development.

African countries appear to be favourably disposed towards such an approach. The sessions of the Economic Commission for

Africa and of the various specialized committees have repeatedly emphasized the need and desirability of concerted action in the development of African countries as well as of certain economic sectors. Practical arrangements have already been made to study the possibility and advisability of developing certain industrial sectors on a sub-regional basis.

The aims of the newly-established African Development Bank may perhaps express in the most eloquent way the determination of African governments to set up machinery to help them to formulate investment and development criteria on a larger basis than their own political boundaries. In fact, the Agreement establishing the African Development Bank clearly indicates that the Bank shall devote its financial resources primarily to those "projects and programmes which by their nature or scope concern several members", and to "projects or programmes designed to make the economies of its members increasingly complementary and bring about an orderly expansion of their foreign trade".

In conclusion, there have been cases in the last five years which have proved that such a high rate of growth as the 5 to 6 per cent already mentioned can be achieved in Africa. However, if African governments co-operate among themselves and co-ordinate their efforts, and if the developed world continues and perhaps increases its financial and technical assistance, then Africa may enjoy a speedy growth of development and perhaps overcome its backwardness in a relatively short time.

DISCUSSION

Lambo: I am very much aware of the urgent economic needs of the young people of the African populations, but a social scientist cannot help having some misgivings. Dr. Patel gave us earlier a brilliant review of his thesis, and now Mr. Mancini has told us about the thoughtful, highly organized plans of economists for investment, and yet when I listen to my economist colleagues talking, I feel that the human element is really lacking.

African peoples as a whole very much value their cultures, their social heritage, and their traditions, and it would be a pity if, in this dramatic race to catch up with the prosperity of the western world, they lose their heritage, ending up with material wealth but without social and cultural values. A note of warning should be given to our national leaders who are trying to shape our destiny: in this race there should be a balanced kind of planning, taking into account what Mr. Mancini himself called the human factor.

Mr. Mancini mentioned the study which is being undertaken to locate the sources of foreign capital and to determine the conditions under which people would invest in the African countries. The very small countries, by the very nature of their size and their meagre economic basis, can hardly hope to attract foreign investment and foreign capital. Is there any institution or any organization working through E.C.A. which can protect and then build up these small countries? This does not apply to those countries which have already attracted foreign capital—they will always be able to attract more if they develop properly. As far as foreign investment is concerned, the major factor is to put money in a sound economy, either potential or actual, and the small countries are at a disadvantage in this respect.

Mancini: I am grateful for your comments, particularly those concerning the human factor, i.e. putting more emphasis on the development of skills, personal knowledge, imaginative activities, and the development of enterprises which will help human beings in Africa towards their freedom.

On the second question, perhaps I didn't make myself clear. I said that E.C.A. is trying to make a survey of all the financial resources that exist in the world which have relevance for African countries. It is equally important to make a survey of the potentialities of the investment projects that exist in Africa and are open to non-African investors. A study has already been done by the United Nations on investment possibilities in Africa. A report was produced, I believe, in 1958–59, and it was revised, I think, in 1961.

The machinery for developing small countries in Africa may be recognized in the purpose and functions of the African Development Bank, which will consider the development of small countries not only in the perspective of their individual sizes and resources but also by projecting them into larger markets by combining the markets of two or three countries together. For example, because the country is too small a shoe factory in Togo may not be an economical proposition, but a shoe factory in Togo could produce shoes for Ghana also, if Ghana agrees to buy the shoes from Togo, and if the factory is not considered as a Toganese undertaking but as a joint venture of the two countries concerned, financed by the Bank. The interests of the two countries can then be combined and they can share in the integrated development. However, the two countries must also accept the other consequences of such a joint project, such as the free movement of merchandise, the movement of workers, arrangements for payments, etc. This machinery of a financial institution will help small countries to expand their economic boundaries—to become part of a region rather than a separate national entity.

Lambo: The example which you have just quoted is a rather ominous one; problems between other countries are involved here, not only between Togo and Ghana.

You mentioned projects being financed from international sources. It does not follow that the development in which we would be interested in Nigeria is necessarily the same as that in which our colleagues in America or in Great Britain would be interested, and this may make bilateral or joint programmes very difficult. In Africa in practically every large town I have visited there are breweries, and I am sure Africa does not need as many breweries as all that. Certainly the foreign investors want to sell their beer, and the national governments have no choice if they want to interest the electorate who need work.

I don't know what E.C.A. or any of us can do to make the choice of projects more appropriate and more in tune with the needs of the country.

Patel: Mr. Ewing had to miss most of this symposium because he was going to a conference in West Africa which was to decide on the location of one or two steel plants which will supply most of the West African sub-region.

Howard-Goldsmith: In Algeria, Tunisia and Morocco, motor assembly plants have been planned so that certain types will be produced in one country and certain others in another country. This is mainly due to one firm—Renault.

Mancini: I think the choice of what kind of sector is going to be developed, and what kind of industry is to be started within a sector, are matters that only governments can decide. When finance is needed, an appeal can be made to financial institutions, either domestic or external, private or public, regional or international. This is where the summary of financial resources which is to be published by E.C.A. will be useful.

Dekker: You have spoken about foreign capital and foreign sources of finance. Could you comment on the possibility of internal revenue, income tax, and so on, as a source of funds for investment?

Mancini: It very much depends on the non-banking financial institutions that exist, and on the confidence in the government among the non-African sector of the population. The response among Africans to date has been very limited. Funds can be raised in the urban areas, but unfortunately it seems that the agricultural sector is capable of saving even less than the industrial sector. There is not yet sufficient organization to reach the small savings. However, several African countries have succeeded in issuing bonds, but they have relied mainly on the foreign banks operating in their own countries, and on insurance companies, pension funds, etc.

Acock: Professor Lambo gave me the impression that he had a kind of nostalgia for the old ways of doing things, and even resentment against this monster of economic growth, as he called it, being rammed down people's throats. He seems to resent wide streets and good houses. I wondered why the human touch should necessarily be associated with bad housing? He quoted beer as a bad thing; I think beer often tends to promote human happiness.

Economic growth is not something that economists love to ram down people's throats—it is necessary in view of the rapid population growth. Resources are simply not enough even to maintain the old ways, and, with the desire of people everywhere for progress, it is absolutely essential to have changes as rapidly as possible. That, I think, is the attitude of the economists. They are not trying to reduce human happiness, but to promote it.

Lambo: I don't think anybody is against a high rate of growth and rapid economic development. All I was trying to emphasize was that we must not lose sight of the essential basic need of humanity for happiness. I am basing my judgment entirely on facts from some of the affluent countries which have become so obsessed with great material prosperity. I do not wish to retain the old tribal ways; certainly, on the other hand, I do not think it would be wise to turn the African continent in another generation into another artificial society—an affluent society with no spiritual or basic human values left in it at all. I am only trying to sound a note of warning. We can still go on with our massive development and widen our streets and have multi-storey buildings all over the place, provided we don't lose sight of the essential basic needs of the African peoples.

Apeadu: Professor Lambo raises a point which I think is very relevant to our discussion: he asks how we can be sure that governments will select projects that are beneficial for the people and not make costly mistakes. He wanted to know what E.C.A. could do and I think Mr. Mancini gave the right answer when

he said that in the last analysis the choice must rest with governments. However, I believe something could be done to advise
governments about what facilities exist and to make sure that
they have all the facts before they make a decision. Governments
do not always have the patience to wait for the results of studies
which may last a long time in some cases.

Although the policy-makers naturally want to have rapid
results, because they have invariably promised so much during
their election campaign and the fight for independence, there is
still the necessity to wait for the results of experiments, trials
and pilot schemes. It is, of course, possible to go ahead and
obtain loans for establishing a factory in a matter of a few
months, but it should be borne in mind at all times that the
enterprise has to last for generations, and serve the people of
the country long after members of the existing government are
dead and gone.

Another point is that risks are inherent in some of the
agreements which African governments contract for setting up
industries and other development projects. It is a pity that these
governments cannot always get the help they need from multilateral sources. One does not wish to decry bilateral sources of
assistance, but the unhappy experience of some African countries
with these sources is something that everyone should bear in
mind, and new governments in particular might be able to
avoid some of the pitfalls if they knew better what they were.

There was, for instance, a case where a developed country,
by all its actions, indicated that it was more keen to sell machinery
than to aid the undeveloped country, that is to say, the attitude
was more one of economic gain than one of economic co-
operation between the two parties.

In this case, since the motive was wrong and the selling
country was only interested in doing business, it was not particular whether the size of the machinery was adequate for the
country, whether satisfactory pre-investment preparations had
been made, and whether, as in this case, another factory already

existed nearby for producing the same commodities, and which was not fully employed. Another difficulty here was that since the selling country was not particularly interested in the fortunes of the factory after the sale of its machinery, it would not enter into any discussion about terms of payment beyond those that suited the lender, though these looked from the start to be unduly onerous for the borrower. The borrower's difficulties were compounded by the fact that a good manager and maintenance engineer could not be obtained. Thus, poor management and bad plant maintenance from the start, with bad conception and bad planning, have made this factory a constant national liability. Unfortunately the African industrial landscape today has far too many factories of this kind.

Sometimes political gain or political advantage is one of the motives. Recently we heard of one African government where the Prime Minister got into trouble with his Cabinet because a country wanted to trade political advantage for the economic assistance it was promising. It should be remembered that credit is not so difficult to get these days. There are so many countries wishing to sell machinery, and there are so many countries wishing to make friends with the budding African governments, that it is not necessary to rush headlong into any agreement, because in the last analysis for a good project you can often get good credit terms if you go about the business with circumspection.

Mancini: One can get credit but one may not get good terms. This is why we want to draw the attention of governments to the terms and conditions that are made available by the various sources. All the disadvantages of bilateral arrangements may be just as you say, but I don't think we can do much at this stage. It is obvious that if country A aids country B, it is not done on a charitable basis. Several African countries do not wish to give up the idea of bilateral arrangements. However, additional efforts are being made to try to regulate bilateral arrangements, both in technical and financial forms. I would repeat that the African

Development Bank may guide and help African governments in this way, but it will take some time.

Last: I agree that governments can borrow funds for their development projects, but even when they borrow from the international organizations which lend large sums of money, very often the conditions under which this aid is granted seem to be disadvantageous to the development of the economy of the country. There is a natural tendency to inflate the foreign cost element in loan financing (since this is more acceptable to the loan organization) and to reduce the proportion of local costs (which are unlikely to be covered by external aid). This does not encourage the development of local industry.

Mustafa: I am alarmed by the extent to which African countries are relying on foreign investment. As a layman, I think that this is a very unhealthy sign. Some African countries go to the extent of basing their development plans on foreign aid or foreign investment. I don't know what the result of this will be, but how far do you think the African Development Bank can help in solving this rather unhealthy habit—if you agree that it is unhealthy?

Mancini: When I said that the amount of investment which has been planned in Africa for the next seven to ten years shows that a great deal of the financial resources must come from outside Africa, I did not mean foreign investment in the sense of funds invested by foreign business organizations. I meant that African governments must borrow funds for a certain period of time outside Africa, but the investments made by governments should be national investments. If a country borrows money from the African Development Bank, it is just the same kind of operation as when you arrange an overdraft for three or four hundred dollars from your own bank for your own purposes and pay monthly interest at a certain rate on the overdraft: you are the owner of the money and you can do whatever you want with it.

*   *   *

Mustafa: I hope I will be forgiven if I say that law has only been represented by accident at this symposium. That accident was a very happy one for me, but I respectfully submit that law is indeed a very relevant and very important subject for this symposium. All my colleagues who have given papers here I am sure were talking about an Africa in which there was law and order, where everything was working within a regulated framework. It is perhaps not necessary to emphasize here the importance of law in the regulation of human behaviour and conduct in general, but there is one specific point I should refer to. In Africa today nearly all the states have different constitutional structures, and this must have an effect on the unified Africa of the future. How are we going to overcome this problem? These states all have different legal systems: some have the French system based mainly on Roman law, others have Roman-Dutch law, and so on. Again, how much of a challenge is this, and how are we going to overcome it?

These states also contain thousands of tribes, governed by different tribal codes in matters pertaining to personal status. How far can we go in unifying these customs? And how far is it necessary to unify them?

One aspect which has been mentioned concerns international rivers, which present special legal problems. Africa has border disputes too, which present many further problems. Is the answer an African international court, or a court of arbitration, or something else? All these problems would have warranted the representation of law in its own right in this learned symposium.

16

COMPREHENSIVE ENVIRONMENTAL DEVELOPMENT AS APPLIED TO AFRICA*

E. A. A. ROWSE

THIS contribution represents an attempt to put in perspective and in a coherent form an experiment now being conducted by a department of the Imperial Ethiopian Government which is charged with the implementation, in physical form, of a plan for the economic expansion of this developing country. The ideas expressed have a background of some 37 years of pragmatic approach to the way man may make the fullest use of both his own and his colleagues' brains to control more effectively the environment in which he has evolved: these ideas have been adopted in the hope that they will yield practical results after the stage of empirical testing has been passed.

Methods by which the intellectual functions leading to decision-making and executive outlets may be expanded are at present being studied in various cultural contexts. The human brain, the organic expression of intelligence, which apparently has rigidly finite limits, does not appear to fit into such an ambitious programme. To meet the demands of "planning" as a function of the contemporary brain, two alternatives appear possible at present:

(1) The continuation of specialization in selected fields, adopted since the nineteenth century by the majority of

---

* This paper was not presented at the meeting but was requested after the members of the symposium had visited the Technical Agency, Addis Ababa, at the kind invitation of Ato Habte-Ab Bairou, and seen the impressive work being carried out there.

345

western universities. The resulting narrowness of outlook and the difficulties encountered in communication between the subdivisions of knowledge are too evident to be disregarded.

(2) The adoption of a more generalized approach, now being experimentally tested. This attempts to introduce the individual brain to a broader context, to provide an answer to the complexity of the environment in which it must work out a common destiny for mankind.

Since no proven basis for an approach to "planning" appears to exist, developing countries are faced with a dilemma which they may not be able to solve. It is with diffidence, therefore, that so difficult a problem is approached.

The theoretical intention of the "composite mind" is to organize the continuum of knowledge and experience in a structure composed of individual, related brains, each specialized in one or more fields, to achieve as an ultimate objective optimum mastery over the environment, in the service of the survival and further evolution of mankind.

Ideally, these brains should have undergone an educational experience extending from infancy, which would enable them to create the climate of behaviour of the "meek" or gentle—"who shall inherit the earth"—in which the ideal planner can work. Without such preparation, bitter experience has shown that the uncertain control of the amygdala, and its proximity to the rationalizing areas in the frontal lobes of the brain, result in the repeated breakdown of collaborative associations, for the maintenance of which rational behaviour is essential. It is improbable that so patient and long-term an experience can be available before the closing decade of this century. Therefore, despite all discouragements, it is imperative that the most searching criticism should be brought to bear on all existing theories and practices of education among eastern and, with particular severity, among western cultures.

Tentatively, in practical form, at least one of many articulated structures of the "composite mind" has been worked out over the past 30 years and tested under physical and psychological conditions of environment as far apart and widely divergent as Indonesia and North America. The form of multi-disciplinary association adopted for *ad hoc* application is given in the attached appendix. It dates from laboratory tests conducted at the School of Planning and Research for National Development in London between 1934 and 1952. Further experience will show what modifications are necessary.

THE METHODOLOGY OF ENVIRONMENTAL DEVELOPMENT: THE ORGANIC UNITS OF PLANNING

The chronic tendency to fissiparous tribal-national fragments runs counter to the ideal aim of a planetary society. There are, however, encouraging signs that the continent is emerging as an attainable entity, forming an intermediate step towards a world society. Within the confines of a continent, sub-continental regional units can also be defined with considerable exactitude.

Geographers offer varying suggestions as to the divisions into which Africa would naturally fall. Six to seven have been proposed. Considerations of ecology indicate that the great river basins are formative factors of the first order, while the Sahara exerts a negative influence which offers as great a challenge as do the Arctic conditions of north Asia. Preliminary steps taken in connexion with the harnessing of the hydrological and hydraulic potentials of the Nile, Niger, Congo and Zambezi groupings offer a promise of unifying trends, nullifying the disruptive effects of pseudo-national frontiers left as a legacy by foreign domination. The work already undertaken in this direction by the Economic Commission for Africa encourages a guarded optimism in those who believe that Africa can offer opportunities for the organization of environmental development on a continental scale, which may eventually provide lessons from which the whole world may profit.

The regional approach can give valuable openings for educational training of cadres of planners, who some day, not too far in the future, may exercise their knowledge on the grand design of a continental component of a world society. This is no idle dream. In spite of all evidence to the contrary, men of good sense and goodwill are already thinking of a Nile-Horn combination, which will parallel a similar movement to unity in the Niger Basin.

It has been evident for nearly 50 years that the formulation and execution of a development plan on a continental scale is possible. The equivalent in terms of population has already been so organized in the Soviet Union, China and India. For 17 years an embryonic plan for Africa has been in existence. Its application might have been possible in 1948, had the colonial powers been capable of collaboration on such a task. In spite of the tragic frustrations consequent on this failure of leadership, Africa and also Latin America, with their immense latent productive potential, could become sources of strength and stability to the rest of the world during the coming half-century.

A NATIONAL PLANNING ORGANIZATION

For the present, the political unit forms the basis from which models for testing may emerge. The national planning authority, of whatever form, may be regarded as the nursery in which the methodology and techniques appropriate for larger-scale units may be worked out while the conflicts of interests and the pressures to preserve sovereignty are resolved between the nations. It has not yet been found possible to create an operative organization as comprehensive and complex as that suggested in the appendix to this paper.

Although the authority of a national organization is limited to its prescribed political frontiers, very early in the "planning" process overlapping social and economic interests compel the extension of solutions offered for national problems into contiguous areas and among neighbouring peoples often of the same cultural background. Thus the "national" plan becomes blurred very early in the process of its creation.

It has been found necessary to organize the national planning authority in hierarchic form, usually falling into a three-tier structure, responsible for policy, formulation and implementation. The interrelationship, ideally, should ensure gradation from the national government to the individual citizen, in such form that the creative dynamic of the latter is willingly released in active co-operation in the execution of projects.

First tier: the Planning Commission

This is the ultimate authority responsible for laying down policy and for making final decisions on all matters of conflict. The chairmanship of this body most frequently remains in the hands of the First Minister or his direct delegate. In Ethiopia the highest function is performed by the Planning Board under the chairmanship of His Imperial Majesty, the Emperor.

Second tier:

(*a*) *The Planning Bureau or Office.* The ordering of policy decisions into a coherent body of statistically supported project-proposals, in broad form, is often conducted by a separate office, controlled by a junior minister under the direction of the First Minister. Within the structure of the Imperial Ethiopian Government, the executive arm of the Planning Board is the Planning Board Committee composed of senior ministers under the chairmanship of the Prime Minister. The Planning Board Office under an assistant minister acts as the secretariat of the Planning Board Committee.

(*b*) *The Development Authority.* To ensure executive implementation to a firm timetable, this form of the organization takes over.

The counterpart of the Authority in Ethiopia is the Technical Agency, which is responsible for the implementation and run-in of the Plan, under an assistant minister.

In the Ethiopian model both the Planning Office and the Technical Agency are under the control of the Prime Minister.

349

Third tier: the Regional Planning Office

Here the Plan is taken down to the level of local studies and projects, best handled in close contact with the people. Constant reference and feed-back of information and criticism to the central agency is imperative, in order that the free expression of informed public opinion is safeguarded.

As is suggested in the appendix to this paper, a consultative body incorporating the broader and most expert advisory sources available should, where possible, stand behind all three levels of planning, for reference when necessary.

THE TECHNIQUE OF ENVIRONMENTAL DEVELOPMENT

At all levels of environmental development, or "planning", the procedure adopted is broadly the same. The stages or phasing of the work are:

(1) *Research and survey*. Although in developing countries an attempt is made to conduct such work on lines that are as comprehensive as possible, lack of statistical material, within and without the national limits, makes attainment of the desired standard temporarily impossible. The build-up, over successive plans, of a reservoir of data processed by an adequately trained staff under expert editorial control, will in due course remedy the defects and shortcomings inherent in any organization during its creation.

(2) *Analysis*. The complex of problems involved is broken down into its constituent elements and cross-relationships are established as a basis for collaborative association. The objectives and means for their attainment are suggested.

(3) *Formulation of solutions*. When time allows, alternatives in tentative form are presented in a flexible technique, capable of rapid adjustment to meet creative criticism.

(4) *Evaluation of solutions*. This stage is necessary in the decision-forming process and in the allocation of priorities.

(5) *The feed-back*. The provision of a clear channel is imperative,

to ensure that reactions at the "grass roots" are conveyed to the centre and responsive modifications are made to the plan in good time. The people who will be affected must have an opportunity to test the value of proposals made for development, against their personal interests and those of the society of which they are members. Since the central purpose of most national plans is the doubling of the *per caput* income in a period of 15 to 20 years, success or failure is of the greatest importance to the individual citizen, and every effort must be made to secure his understanding co-operation. Yet "counter-planning" is perhaps the most neglected aspect of the whole procedure.

(6) *Decision making.* On the basis of the staff work done in presenting relevant, digested and evaluated statistics and proposals, a Council of Ministers or Planning Commission can send down the final decisions and directives for formulation in:

(a) *The policy programme:* giving the main objectives and the outline of the means to achieve them.

(b) *The physical realization:* passing through the stages of documentation and building procedure from the Frame Plan to the handing over of packaged projects in running order.

(7) *Documentation.*

(a) *The policy plans:* maps at a scale of from 1 : 4 million to 1 : 12 million, giving in outline the supporting visual presentation of the programme. Initially these maps give only the broadest indication of decisions taken. As stage (b) progresses it becomes possible to go into greater detail with more assurance.

(b) *The National Frame Plans:* these are intended to give the setting, within the politico-geographical unit, of the inter-related problems of national development and their solution in progressive stages. (See Figs. 1 and 2.)

Figs. 1 and 2. Examples of Frame Plans at the Technical Agency, Addis Ababa. The originals measure approximately 6 ft × 8 ft; coloured symbols are used to distinguish the various features.

Each series of maps, in their international context, is worked out under the control of panels of expert and informed collaborators, as suggested in the appendix.

[Many examples of Frame Plans of Ethiopia, covering physical features, water, cultivation, epidemiology, health services, schools, communications, population densities, etc., were inspected at the Technical Agency in Addis Ababa by members of the symposium, who were immensely impressed by the wealth of information—and the ease of keeping it up to date—presented to the same scale and with striking clarity.—EDS.]

(c) *The regional study:* this should bring the plan to the people. It should, therefore, be developed in forms readily understood by the layman. It can then function as a feed-back mechanism and bring the planners down to reality. The scale for national studies is most conveniently kept between 1 : 500,000 and 1 : 1,000,000. That for districts forming constituents of a political unit lies most frequently between 1 : 100,000 and 1 : 250,000.

(d) *The National Development Atlas:* the economic perspective plan, which forms an integral part of the policy programme, requires capital input rates of between 6 per cent and 27 per cent of the national income annually. The range over which the rise in investment is achieved is three to four plans. The sources are the public sector (governmental) and the private sector (entrepreneural). Both require feasibility studies to be prepared to establish the viability of all project proposals.

The Atlas should form a compendium of all information incorporated in the Frame Plans, after it has been tested by criticism directed on it from knowledgeable persons. Thus the investor should be able to consult the Atlas with the assurance that he is being provided with sound factual information on which he can base his decision to proceed.

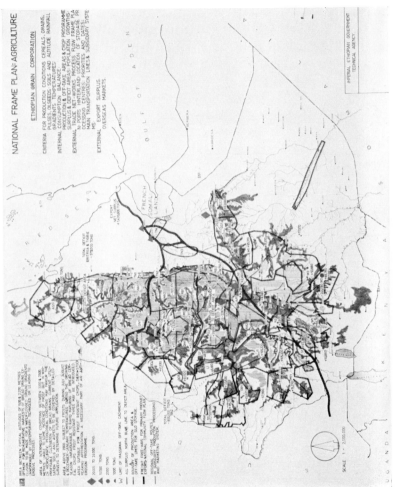

Fig. 1

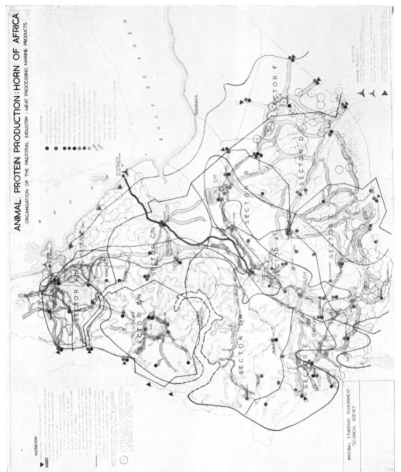

Fig. 2

Equally, government departments and ministries should have the same confidence in it.

(8) *Implementation.* The physical realization of the greater part of the plan forms the most important step in the development of an economy. Delays, while inevitable under actual conditions of uncertainty in developing countries, soon become cumulative, so that the backlog extends into and cripples the subsequent plan. The available reserve of technical assistance is in such short supply, the world over, that all means to fill the gaps in personnel available to developing countries must be employed.

Designs for urban and neighbourhood planning and for building elements are both an engineering and architectural responsibility.

Preparatory procedures call for concentration on micro-locational factors, cost-price analysis, plant process-flow, and market research in specific areas, all carried out by economic engineers.

Contract documents are circulated and tenders called for and evaluated as local conditions direct. The award of the contract, after costing checks, must be conducted in accordance with legal procedures laid down to prevent malpractice.

Supervision of works can be carried out by the government agency, or may be shared with the consultants responsible for the preparation of the preliminary studies and contract documents.

The winding-up of the contract and the running-in process, until management is firmly installed, remains the responsibility of the agency implementing the plan. This helps to ensure smooth integration between the hoped-for output from the capital input and the rise in national and *per caput* incomes, which the economic perspective plan is intended to achieve. With success at this point, the plan passes into history, forming the environmental foundation on which the succeeding sectors of the policy programme can be implemented.

THE AGRICULTURAL BASIS OF ECONOMIC EXPANSION IN
DEVELOPING COUNTRIES

As an example of the tasks the Ethiopian Technical Agency is now tackling, the complex problem of food production will now be considered in its world and temporal contexts.

World population is currently estimated at 3,283 million. The annual natural increase is given as 65 million. No foreseeable probability exists that birth limitation will check the acceleration of the rise in time to prevent an explosive crisis in the conflict of interests always existent among the peoples of the world. It is almost inevitable that by the turn of the century world population will be of the order of seven milliard, an increase of about 3,700 million over the present total. Of this seven milliard, Africa will not be supporting more than 600 to 700 million. If its territory were utilized at the pressure dictated by the world demographic situation, the population-supporting capacity of the continent would need to be of the order of 1,700 million. One milliard of daily rations of the essentials of life, to be exported or consumed within the continent, can be considered the minimum which the African continental economy must meet before the year 2,000.

As subsistence farming is abandoned and the labour force needed for agricultural production shrinks, and as mechanization and automation become widespread in application, so the flight from the countryside to the towns in search of employment gathers momentum. The town or city dweller is parasitic as far as the production of food is concerned. The trend of the balance between rural and urban populations is towards a ratio of 25:75 overall. In urbanized countries, such as the United Kingdom, the proportion of town dwellers may be as high as 94 per cent. It seems inevitable that almost all the increase in population will enter the towns over the next two decades in all the countries of Asia, Africa and Latin America. The magnitude of such a shift of emphasis and the strain it throws on resources of all kinds, human and material, is self-evident.

The anticipated rapid rise in the demand for food will dictate the fullest use of the latent productive potential of the fertile areas of the land and water surfaces of the planet, supported by a programme of rehabilitation of arid areas on an unprecedented scale. In Africa the Imperial Ethiopian Government has realized the urgency of the situation and is giving top priority to the attainment of optimum efficiency in the agricultural and pastoral sectors. To illustrate the form proposals now under consideration in Ethiopia may take, a small selection from the total of about 84 Frame Plans ultimately required for the implementation of environmental development is described here. These maps illustrate some aspects of the problems in agricultural and pastoral production outlined above. They have been prepared by the Technical Agency of the Imperial Ethiopian Government for the purpose of visualizing the proposals in the Second Five-Year Plan.

ENVIRONMENTAL DEVELOPMENT FRAME PLANS AT NATIONAL LEVEL IN ETHIOPIA

(1) *Agriculture*

All African crop yields are at present low. The harsh conditions prevailing over much of the continent make this inevitable, until countermeasures to remedy them are matured and applied. The cost of haulage over great distances is high. As a consequence, competitive capability is only maintained at present when the farmer is prepared to accept a return for his labour which is insufficient to maintain an acceptable rise in his standard of living.

The Ethiopian proposal here presented has as its central target the doubling of cereal yields from the present average of nearly 6 quintals per hectare to 12, or if possible more. On this basis an export capacity of one and a half million tons is proposed for achievement during the Fourth and Fifth Plans.

The provision of modern storage facilities is gradually being extended over the country through the agency of the Ethiopian Grain Corporation. This takes the form of silos with a capacity of between 10,000 tons and the 100,000 tons of a port handling installation, plus on-the-farm bin stores, amounting in all to a final target of 900,000 tons.

(2) *Soil fertility*

Fertilizers, organic and inorganic, are at present used in very small amounts in Africa. As a result, the collapse of soil structure, due to a lack of humus content, leads to widespread and severe erosion. The cyclic return of by-products of animal and plant origin (dung, compost from the farm, and blood and bone meals from the meat-processing industry) to cropped and pasture lands must therefore be more generally practised to counter the loss of fertile topsoil.

This plan shows the relationship of the sources of fertilizers to the mechanized agro-industrial units of the Ethiopian plateau and to the irrigated plantations of the lower river valleys which are to be created during the Second, Third, and part of the Fourth Plans.

An initial production target for inorganic fertilizers of between 20,000 and 50,000 tons per annum has been proposed. This should form the first phase of a programme for the production of phosphatic fertilizers, to be followed by one utilizing the excess energy potential of the run-off from the Ethiopian massif for, amongst other applications, nitrogen fixation.

(3) *Processing of animal products*

The national herd has been variously estimated at up to 25 million head of cattle and up to 38 million sheep and goats. The off-take from the former should provide 400,000 carcases by 1967 and 800,000 to 1,000,000 by 1980. The consequent addition to the Gross National Product would be of the value of U.S. $40 to 60 million. Powerful financial and technically expert interests are already committed to the attainment of these targets, with the support of U.S.A.I.D.

The range of technology extends through the application of the latest methods of handling stock in transit to the operation of canning and freezing plants, several of which have been located and opened in these first phases. Exports are now flowing to the ports at the rate of several thousand tons of meat per year.

(4) *Underground water reserves*

Ethiopia extends over approximately 1,000,000 square kilometres and about 50 per cent of the country has a rainfall of between 200 and 450 mm., used almost exclusively for pastoral lands, with the exception of agricultural settlements on the flood terraces of the rivers. The uneven distribution of water in the volcanic and sedimentary rocks, at depths accessible to the primitive well-digging methods of the nomads, results in the under-grazing of wide areas because of a lack of watering points within 20 kilometres of each other.

The range country and semi-deserts surrounding the Ethiopian massif are being opened up by the introduction of bore-wells and stock-ponds in the deficit areas and along the stock routes which facilitate the movement of cattle to market and the meat-processing plants. In the Southern Steppe, as a second phase in a programme of development, a further 150 deep bore-wells and subsidiary stock-ponds are currently being provided.

Range management techniques are being applied at strategically placed points throughout the cattle country. The programme is concentrated at present on the development of a series of ranches, each of 20,000 hectares, as holding areas for slaughter stock.

(5) *Veterinary services*

Formerly some 50 per cent of the annual calf crop was lost because it was impossible to apply timely prophylactic treatment. The country is now organized into six to seven off-take areas, each supporting a basic herd of proportions adequate to supply one or more slaughter and processing plants. The animal husbandry and veterinary services in each off-take area are based on a regional and quarantine centre, usually located close to the main processing plant.

There is at present a shortage of trained personnel in all departments of the pastoral and meat-processing industries. A current annual entry of 27 qualified veterinarians into these industries will go far to alleviate this situation within the next five years.

(6) *Transportation*

In the process of opening up the latent potential of under-developed areas, the various categories of transport (rail, road, air, inland water transport, and marine) are of the highest importance. Coupled with a spinal network of freightways, feeder-roads constructed by local initiative have proved a most potent agent of economic expansion. Past and current programmes of road construction and rehabilitation bring the total to some 8,000 kilometres of first and second category roads, and 1,500 kilometres of feeder-roads.

The schemes just mentioned include those necessary to integrate the national road system with that of a possible continental network of high-speed freeways. This has been considered at successive international conferences, but does not yet exist as a plan in fully coherent form. Our suggestions are intended to help clarify the form the main transportation system of the Horn of Africa might take.

Other aspects of the environmental development currently under consideration range over: geophysical and geothermal manifestations, climatology, epidemiology, health and hygiene, demography, parasitology, education, erosion, mineral resources, internal migration, and tourism.

We are trying in Ethiopia to develop one of the harshest environments in the tropical belt, the volcano-dominated deserts of the eastern littoral, through the southern part of which runs the Awash River, currently being developed by the Awash Valley

Authority under an assistant minister. It is our hope that here we may work out some of the lessons on the reclamation of deserts which may help in solving problems of a similar nature in the even more daunting Sahara.

When the full sequence of about 84 study plans is complete, and Ethiopian experience compared with that of other bodies carrying out similar work in various parts of the world, it will be possible to lay down a firmer structure for the theory and practice of environmental development on national and continental levels.

CONCLUSION

An attempt has been made in this contribution to give in outline the theory, methodology and practice of environmental development in Africa, as experienced in one developing country, Ethiopia. The ideas advanced and suggestions made are intended to stimulate creative criticism, which would be welcomed as a means of correcting errors and modifying what of necessity are thoughts that only experience can bring to full maturity.

Appendix

THE STRUCTURE OF THE COMPOSITE MIND

It is hoped that eventually what may be termed multi-brain intellection will be recognized as an important field in psychology. It may evolve from an interlocking system of individuals each having specialized knowledge and experience in the fields suggested below, but collaborating in panels over sufficiently lengthy periods to engender cerebral intercommunication of a high order.

The structure here outlined results from a pragmatic approach to the problem of the extension of the potential of the human brain beyond the limits of its present capacity, to meet the challenge of the multi-disciplinary problems to be solved in environmental development in a rapidly changing world.

The articulated structure might take the following lines:

Panel I: Physical Sector

Group (1)   Field: (*a*) Astronomy
             (*b*) Physics
             (*c*) Chemistry

(2)   (*a*) Geophysics
             (*b*) Seismology

(3)   (*a*) Geology
             (*b*) Mineralogy
             (*c*) Pedology

(4)   (*a*) Climatology
             (*b*) Oceanology
             (*c*) Hydrology

Panel II: Biological Sector

Group (5)   Field: Zoology

             (*a*) Mammalogy
             (*b*) Ornithology
             (*c*) Ichthyology
             (*d*) Herpetology
             (*e*) Entomology
             (*f*) Micrology

(6)   Botany

             (*a*) Morphology
             (*b*) Physiology

             Ecology

             (*a*) Vegetable
             (*b*) Animal

Panel III: Sociological Sector

Group   (8)   Field: (*a*) Anthropology
                     (*b*) Ethnology

        (9)   (*a*) Religion and Ideology
                     (*b*) Philosophy
                     (*c*) Aesthetics

      (10)   (*a*) History
                     (*b*) Philology
                     (*c*) Education
                     (*d*) Social Psychology
                     (*e*) Social Structure and Organization

Panel IV: Health Sector

Group (11)   Field: (*a*) Medicine (clinical)
                     (*b*) Dietetics
                     (*c*) Epidemiology
                     (*d*) Pharmacology

      (12)   (*a*) Mass Psychiatry
                     (*b*) Criminology

      (13)   (*a*) Public Hygiene
                     (*b*) Medicine (preventive)
                     (*c*) Human Genetics

Panel V: Food Production Sector

Group (14)   Field: (*a*) Agricultural Technology
                     (*b*) Agricultural Engineering

      (15)   (*a*) Agro-biology
                     (*b*) Biochemistry

      (16)   (*a*) Genetics (animal and plant)
                     (*b*) Veterinary

      (17)   (*a*) Silviculture
                     (*b*) Pisciculture

Panel VI: Economic Sector

Group (18)   Field: (*a*) Political Economy
(*b*) Demography (statistical)
(*c*) Demography (dynamic)
(*d*) Statistics (general)

(19)   (*a*) Resources (location and utilization)
(*b*) Industrial Chemistry
(*c*) Technology (applied)
(*d*) Metallurgy

(20)   (*a*) Industrial Organization
(*b*) National Trade and Commerce
(*c*) National Banking
(*d*) National Finance

Panel VII: Dynamic Resources Sector

Group (21)   Field: (*a*) Engineering (Civil)
(*b*) Engineering (Mechanical)
(*c*) Engineering (Aeronautical)
(*d*) Engineering (Marine and Naval)

(22)   (*a*) Geography and Land Use Survey
(*b*) Building, City Planning and Landscape
(*c*) Development Cost Estimating

(23)   (*a*) Utility Organization
(*b*) Regional Physical Organization

Panel VIII: Legal and Security Sector

Group (24)   Field: (*a*) Constitutional Codes (National)
(*b*) Law Systems (National and International)

(25)   (*a*) Internal Security
(*b*) Police Administration

Panel IX: Political and Administrative Sector

Group (26)   Field: (*a*) Political Science
                    (*b*) National Political Organization
       (27)   (*a*) Supra-national and International
                         Administration
                    (*b*) National Administration

       (28)   (*a*) Mass Psychology Media
                    (*b*) Propaganda and Information Tech-
                         niques

Panel X: Strategic Sector

Group (29)   Field: (*a*) World Strategic Appreciation
                    (*b*) National Defence Organization

Note: The proposed structure of multi-brain associations was submitted as a part of a course of lectures, delivered at the School of Social Sciences, The Hague, in 1957.

Epilogue

G. E. W. WOLSTENHOLME

The one subject on which all other members were agreed, at this point during the conference in Addis Ababa, was that since no one wished to summarize any part of the proceedings, this task should be given to its organizer, myself, to fulfil later at my 'leisure'. Until they read this part of the book, the members will not know what I am writing, so that the views which I shall now express are peculiarly my own.

According to the Oxford Illustrated Dictionary an epilogue is ''a speech, a short poem, by one of the actors, to end play''. This is neither a speech nor, sadly, poetry, nor is it the ending of play —this game, if so non-serious a word is permissible, is just beginning, and every reader of this book is a player.

In all these papers and discussions what are the abiding impressions? Perhaps we could run through what has been said in a much-shortened, selective way and then try to draw a few conclusions:

''Man has come from bewilderment through knowledge to truculence and the brink of self-destruction. To survive, he must add understanding of himself to knowledge of his environment.'' (Last, p. 22)

''. . . in spite of his mechanical achievements, man has not yet emerged from prehistory, and is still wavering on the brink of humanization . . .'' (Monod, p. 274)

''The boundaries which divide African states are so nonsensical that without our sense of unity they would be a cause of friction.'' (President Nyerere, quoted by Last, p. 18)

''The regional approach can give valuable openings for educational training of cadres of planners, who some day, not too far

364

in the future, may exercise their knowledge on the grand design of a continental component of a world society.'' (Rowse, p. 348)

"It is not so much the traditional division of language, race and culture, but rather . . . the premium placed on small political units by present international organizations (Togo has the same voting strength as India in the United Nations), which gives rise to the deepest problem for the creation of larger entities . . .'' (Goody, p. 105)

". . . evolution can occur only at some cost. Necessarily in the process something that exists must give way to something that is for greater good . . .'' (Young, p. 4)

"In all spheres of activity the arduous task of weaving up a country of tribes into the larger unit of a nation demands that certain sacrifices should be made by one tribe or other within the national unit . . .'' (Antubam, quoted by Goody, p. 101)

". . . the loss of language and culture means that the social personality of the individuals involved can no longer be reproduced. A part of one's immortality is wrested away.'' (Goody, p. 102)

". . . two languages can be taught together not only with no loss, but with real gain.'' (Sutton, p. 116)

". . . the value and use of superior teachers can be multiplied by using television, but this does not mean that teachers can be eliminated.'' (Sutton, p. 189)

"The egalitarian spirit that now pervades Africa makes criticism of the rigours and selectivity of the old (educational) system easy; it does not clearly encourage substitutes for them.'' (Sutton, p. 206)

"It is not easy for young university graduates to regard their talents humbly or to appreciate that they may not yet be of much use to society.'' (Sutton, p. 205)

"Those of us who have knowledge to impart must learn how to teach, and those of us who seek this knowledge must learn how to learn.'' (Gayer, p. 185)

"There is a dilemma between the radical socialist spirit of modern Africa and the doctrine of costly education for the few at the expense of equal opportunities for the many." (Sutton, p. 197)

". . . it is a wise country that knows its own limitations . . . and joins with its neighbours in providing educational and training centres at sub-regional level for its professional health staff (e.g. doctors, nurses and sanitary engineers) . . ." (Russell, p. 157)

". . . the number of female nurses in a country provides an indication of the degree of that country's development." (Russell, p. 154)

". . . the average tribal African lives in thralldom to sickness. For him sickness is the norm; it starts at birth, or even before, and continues until death. And he is a very lucky African who is not sick of more than one thing . . ." (Kimble, quoted by Last, p. 17)

". . . a man laden with parasites and training is better off than a man laden with parasites only." (Acock, p. 249)

". . . the traditional cultures of Africa are endowed with a diverse range of built-in adaptive mechanisms . . ." (Lambo, p. 134)

"Education for most Africans cannot, in the short run, be a preparation for employment. It will either be a preparation for unemployment or for some form of self-employment, mostly agricultural." (Sutton, p. 200)

"Each farm family supports itself and less than one non-farm family, whereas in the wealthy industrialized countries each farm family supports 10, 15 or more non-farm families . . ." (Acock, p. 241)

"Africa applies about 2 per cent of the world's chemical fertilizer production to 17 per cent of the world's arable land; and most of that is used in the U.A.R. and South Africa." (Acock, p. 245)

"Africa is, on the whole, a thirsty continent . . ." (Monod, p. 262)

". . . during the Roman and Byzantine times, North Africa did not enjoy better climatic conditions than today. The deterioration of the water resources of this area and the devastation of what was once cultivable land are therefore not due to changes of climate but to human actions." (Dekker, p. 39)

". . . it might be advantageous for a country to have its storage reservoirs outside its borders in the headwater area of the river, i.e. in a neighbouring country. This calls for deep and mutual trust between neighbours." (Dekker, p. 55)

"'Will the development of African resources be able to keep pace with the growth of her populations?' seems to be over-shadowed by the larger question: 'How can the resources of Africa contribute to the growing imbalance of world population and food production?'" (Last, p. 18)

"Decreasing mortality is one of the major events which has occurred so far in the evolution of the human species." (Bourgeois-Pichat, p. 82)

". . . birth rates are high everywhere in Africa, but particularly in the north of the sub-Saharan region where values are close to the maximum ever recorded for the human species." (Bourgeois-Pichat, p. 73)

". . . in the short run, compulsory education, compulsorily paid for, would bring a change (in population growth) more quickly than anything else." (Goody, p. 79)

". . . Africa, which may be truly described as a treasure house of mineral resources." (Howard-Goldsmith, p. 282)

"The continent could produce on its own the equivalent of all the power already produced in the world." (Last, p. 15)

"The processing and transformation of mineral production in its country of origin should be based as a rule on economical and technical reasoning and not on political expediency. There is no more stigma attached to the export of copper metal from Zambia or phosphate rock from Morocco than to the sales of wheat, rather than flour or biscuits, by the United States and Canada.'' (Howard-Goldsmith, p. 283)

''. . . transport is the major need for the development of Africa and . . . its improvement is certainly a prerequisite for any degree of growth.'' (Mancini, p. 331)

''. . . balanced investment between physical infrastructure and directly productive fields appears to be essential.'' (Mancini, p. 332)

''. . . the industrial transformation of Africa by the end of the century . . . depends for its realization on the vision, wisdom and vigour with which the countries in the continent apply themselves to the task of accomplishing in half a century what took nearly a hundred years in the industrial countries.'' (Ewing and Patel, p. 315)

''. . . in using exclusively the word 'resources', are we not arbitrarily and perhaps dangerously limiting to their practical uses the wealth of riches nature can—and does—offer to man?'' (Monod, p. 259)

''When will the extermination of a living species be deemed as heinous a crime as murder, or the destruction of some priceless work of art?'' (Monod, p. 263)

''. . . our ultimate aim is to increase the sum total of human happiness and contentment. To increase the gross national product is not an aim in itself; . . .'' (Brown, p. 161)

The selection was mine, and I chose the order in which to present these quotations. Other readers might well emphasize entirely different points, but however the choice is made they seem to add up, in the words of John Gayer, to: ''a story to fire the imagination of any thinking person''.

Why was this meeting held, and what, to me, are the main lessons to be drawn from it? The symposium would not have taken place if I had not been convinced that the peoples of Africa are supremely capable of exercising the huge responsibilities which most of them have now acquired. In the Herculean tasks which each new nation faces, however, there is a risk that the progress which must be made, no matter what the available and appropriate resources in manpower and material, will be partly at the expense rather than in support of each other. Neighbourly, sub-regional, regional, and as far as possible, continental planning is vital to the rapid and effective development of Africa.

So far, much of the early promise of African unity is negatively based. Inevitable and desirable opposition to the surviving relics of white supremacy seems not to provide the best of reasons for united effort. It is rather like electric shock therapy given by a doctor to remove a state of confusion: it promotes health, but if carried to excess, or replaced by military surgery, then there is a real risk of enfeeblement of the whole body of Africa for a generation to come.

Immodestly, therefore, I thought it worth while to bring together a group of experts, and subsequently to publish their discussions, in order to stress the positive aspects of unity and development in Africa. Especially I wished to emphasize the benefits of co-operation between any two, and preferably many more, national groups in achieving the fabulous growth which is required in the interests of both Africa and the world at large.

This may well appear to be a strange and disproportionate challenge to be taken up by a very small international centre for medical research, British in law and character and Swiss in inception, but the more fundamental research with which the Ciba Foundation is normally concerned will not be of much value if the framework of human society within which it can be used does not achieve a more stable, sane and peaceful equilibrium.

This conference and book can constitute only one tiny cell, which will depend on the readers for nourishment, elaboration, organization, growth and development.

Why Man *and* Africa ? Most of what has been said and written here has been concerned with Man *in* Africa. How can African man become healthy and stable, bring up his family in security, give education to all, foster the brilliant few, re-animate rural society, raise agricultural production and power potential by

369

200-fold and industrial enterprise 50-fold and at the same time strengthen his family unit and preserve all that is best in his history, traditions and culture?

This might well be enough, but not for me and indeed not for anyone else. There are perhaps 20 years left in which the world as a whole must find the answers to the problem of all problems in man's history: the sudden, dramatic effects of modern medicine's first modest steps towards keeping more people alive, to produce in their turn more surviving children, so that the global population has doubled in a lifetime and can hardly do anything less than double again by the time today's babies become parents. The task of raising the standards of life to the meanest tolerable level in much the greater part of the world for the existing population is so stupendous that only those with the stoutest hearts dare tackle it; yet every day and every week and every month the greatest efforts are not enough even to keep up with the problem.

I think it is Africa, where man probably began, which can give men hope of a new life. By an immense, combined effort Africa can save itself and give time, a vital breathing space, to the rest of the world. Man everywhere needs Africa.

Even more, I believe Africa, so near to a fresh start, can set an enviable example to the older world of composite, humane planning and co-operation carried out in such a manner that individuality, decency, tolerance and neighbourliness, even humour, will be preserved under the most intense pressure of development.

Who can say what will count most—intelligence, diligence, humility, energy, compassion, faith? I hope also trust. Older non-Africans, such as my middle-aged self, may be irretrievably contaminated by earlier exploitation, superiority, paternalism, and ugly failure to provide opportunity. The world, nevertheless, throngs with younger people careless of the past, concerned for the future, and impatient of frontiers of nation, race, colour and creed. If Africa gratefully accepts their help it will not only bring its own struggle within sight of success, but will make a unique contribution towards the essential, evolving concept of a world society.

Can 270 million people, 8 per cent of the world's population, occupying 25 per cent of the world's surface—and that a treasury waiting to be unlocked by the energies of unselfish men—give themselves and their neighbours a chance, possibly a final chance, of sanity and survival?

Bibliography

I. THE GEOGRAPHICAL IMPLICATIONS OF MAN AND HIS FUTURE IN
AFRICA

1. Henseler, M. C. de (1963). *Azimuthal Equidistant Projection centred on Addis Ababa*. Addis Ababa: Economic Commission for Africa (provisional edition).
2. Church, R. J. Harrison (1964). *Africa and the Islands*, p. 32. London: Longmans.
3a. Clark, C. G. (1963). Agricultural productivity in relation to population. In *Man and His Future*, p. 23, ed. Wolstenholme, G. London: Churchill.
3b. Food and Agriculture Organization (1962). Report on the possibilities of African rural development in relation to economic and social growth. In *Africa Survey*. Rome: F.A.O.
3c. Food and Agriculture Organization (1964). The food and agricultural situation in Africa. A five-year review. In *Agricultural Economics Bulletin for Africa*, No. 5. Addis Ababa: U.N.E.C.A./F.A.O.
4. Economic Commission for Africa (1963). *The Situation, Trends and Prospects of Electric Power Supply in Africa*. Addis Ababa: U.N.E.C.A., E/CN/14/EP/3.
5. Economic Commission for Africa (1962). *Industrial Growth in Africa. A Survey and Outlook*. Addis Ababa: U.N.E.C.A., E/CN/14/INR/1.
6. Davidson, B. (1964). Which way Africa? In *The Search for a New Society*, p. 39. London: Penguin African Library.
7. Stamp, L. D. (1964). *The Geography of Life and Death*, ch. 6. London: Collins Fontana Library.
8. Kimble, G. H. T. (1960). *Tropical Africa*, Vol. 2, p. 33. New York: The Twentieth Century Fund.
9. Economic Commission for Africa (1964). *Economic Bulletin for Africa*, Vol. 4, No. 1, Part B. Special Articles, pp. 82–83. Addis Ababa: U.N.E.C.A.

10. Nyerere, J. (1963). A United States of Africa. In *Journal of Modern African Studies*, 1, 2.

11. Church, R. J. Harrison (1956). African Boundaries. In *The Changing World*, ed. East, W. G., and Moodie, A. E. London: Harrap.

12. See Reference 4, Part 3, p. 10.

13. See Reference 8, p. 432.

14. Economic Commission for Africa (1963). Report to E.C.O.S.O.C. Quoted by Sewell, J. P. Africa's Economic Parliament. In *Africa Report*, July, 1963. Washington, D.C.: The African-American Institute.

15. See Reference 6, p. 35.

16. Hance, W. A. (1958). *African Economic Development*, p. 285. New York: Harper.

17. Worthington, E. B. (1964). A definition of natural resources. In *Conference on the Organization of Research and Training in Africa in relation to the Study, Conservation and Utilization of Natural Resources*. Paris: U.N.E.S.C.O./C.O.R.P.S.A./4.A.

18. Hoagland, H. (1963). Potentialities in the control of behaviour. In *Man and His Future*, p. 305, ed. Wolstenholme, G. London: Churchill.

19. Chisholm, G. B. (1963). Future of the mind. In *Man and His Future*, p. 319, ed. Wolstenholme, G. London: Churchill.

2. CLIMATE AND WATER RESOURCES IN AFRICA

1. Meigs, P. (1952). Arid and semi-arid climatic types of the world. In *Proceedings of Seventeenth International Geographic Congress*, Washington, D.C.

2. Yule, U. G., and Kendall, M. G. (1950). *An Introduction to the Theory of Statistics*. London: Hafner.

3. Biel, E. R. (1943). *Introduction to Weather and Climate*, 2nd edn., ed. Trewartha, G. T. New York: McGraw-Hill.

4. Hurst, H. E. (1951). The Nile. London: Constable; New York: Macmillan.

5. Hawes, C. G. (1951). *Report on the Possibilities of Development on the Kafua River and the Organization of the Water Development and Irrigation Department*. Lusaka: Government Printer.

6. NEDECO. (1958). *Niger and Benue River Studies*. The Hague.

7. ORSTOM. (1962). *Monographie du Niger Supérieur*. Paris: ORSTOM.

8. Hofmeyr, W. L., and Schulze, B. R. (1963). Temperature and rainfall trends in South Africa during the period of meteorological records. In *Symposium on Changes of Climate*. Paris: U.N.E.S.C.O. NS. 62. III.25.AF.

9. Alimen, H. (1955). *Préhistoire de l'Afrique*. Paris: Boubée.

10. Butzer, K. W. (1961). Climate and its modifications in arid regions since the Pliocene. In *A History of Land Use in Arid Regions*, ed. L. Dudley Stamp. Paris: U.N.E.S.C.O. NS. 60. III.21.A.

11. Dubief, J. (1963). Contributions au problème des changements de climat survenus au cours de la période couverte par les observations météorologiques faites dans le Nord de l'Afrique. In *Symposium on Changes of Climate*. Paris: U.N.E.S.C.O. NS. 62. III.25.AF.

12. Di Maria, P. (1954). Capacités des réservoirs pour la régularisation des débits des cours d'eau du point de vue industriel. I.A.S.H., Assemblée Générale de Rome. Gentbrugge: A.I.H. publ. no. 38.

13. Vita-Finzi, C., and Vorhis, R. C. (1961). Man-made changes in the water resources of Tripolitania, Libya. I.A.S.H. Symposium, Athens. Gentbrugge: A.I.H. publ. nos. 56, 57.

14. Archambault, J. (1962). *Les eaux souterrains de l'Afrique Occidentale*. Paris: C.I.E.H.

15. Martin, H. (1961). Hydrology and water balance of some regions covered by Kalahari sands in South-West Africa. In *Inter-African Conference on Hydrology*. Nairobi: C.C.T.A. publ. No. 66.

16. Cornet, A., and Rognon, P. (1961). Estimation de la valeur des débits circulant dans la nappe du continent intercalaire au Sahara Sud Algérien. I.A.S.H. Symposium, Athens. Gentbrugge: A.I.H. publ. nos. 56, 57.

17. Griffith, J. F. (1962). The Climate of East Africa. In *The Natural Resources of East Africa*, ed. Russell, E. W. Nairobi: Hawkins.

18. Fournier, F. (1962). Carte du danger d'érosion en Afrique au Sud du Sahara (10:1,000,000), et notice explicative. C.E.E. and C.C.T.A.

19. Jackson, S. P. (1961). Climatological Atlas for Africa. Lagos-Nairobi: C.C.T.A./C.S.A.

20. International Union for the Conservation of Nature (1964). Proceedings of the General Assembly of I.U.C.N., Nairobi, 1963 (on the ecology of man in a tropical environment). Morges, Switzerland: I.U.C.N.

3. PROBLEMS OF POPULATION SIZE, GROWTH AND DISTRIBUTION IN AFRICA

1. United Nations (1955). *Demographic Yearbook.* New York: United Nations. Sales No. 55. XIII.6.

2. United Nations (1963). *Demographic Yearbook.* New York: United Nations. Sales No. 64. XIII.1.

3. United Nations (1963). *Population and Vital Statistics Report,* Series A, vol. XV, Nos. 1 & 2. New York: United Nations.

4. Gallais, J. (1964). Quelques particularités démographiques de l'Afrique noire. In *Bulletin de la Faculté des Lettres de Strasbourg,* March, pp. 325–361.

5. Mudd, S. *et al.* (ed.) (1964). *The Population Crisis and the Use of World Resources.* World Academy of Art and Science, 2. The Hague: Junk; Bloomington, Indiana: Indiana University Press.

6. United Nations (1964). *Provisional Report on World Population Prospects as assessed in 1963.* New York: United Nations. Document No. ST/SOA/Ser. R7. (Not yet on sale.)

7. Dorjahn, V. R. (1958). Fertility, polygyny and their interrelations in Temne society. In *American Anthropologist,* **60,** 838–860.

4. TRIBAL, RACIAL, RELIGIOUS AND LANGUAGE PROBLEMS IN AFRICA

1. Childe, V. G. *What Happened in History.* London: Penguin Books.

2. Greenberg, J. H. (1963). The Languages of Africa. In *International Journal of American Linguistics,* Vol. 29, part II, No. 1.

3. Antubam, K. (1963). *Ghana's Heritage of Culture*. Leipzig: Koehler & Amelang.

5. SOCIOECONOMIC CHANGES IN AFRICA AND THEIR IMPLICATIONS FOR MENTAL HEALTH

1. Esquirol, J. E. D. (1838). *Des Maladies mentales considerées sous les Rapports médical, hygiènique et médico-légal*. Paris: Baillière.

2. Maudsley, H. (1880). *The Pathology of Mind* (3rd edn. of *The Pathology and Physiology of Mind*, Part II). New York: Appleton.

3. Hecker, J. F. C. (1832). *Die Tanzwuth, eine Volkskrankheit im Mittelalter*. Berlin: Enslin.

4. Sigerist, H. E. (1945). Disease and Music. In *Civilization and Disease*. Ithaca: Cornell University Press.

5. Herskovits, M. J. (1961). Economic Change and Cultural Dynamics. In *Tradition, Values and Socio-Economic Development*, ed. Braibanti, R., and Spengler, J. J. Durham, N.C.: Duke University Press.

6. Raymaekers, P. (1960). Conjonctures socio-économiques à Léopoldville, 3ᵉ Bulletin. In *Notes et Documents de l'Institut de Recherches Economiques et Sociales de l'Université de Léopoldville*, No. 6.

7. Raymaekers, P., and Lavry, J. (1961). Conjonctures socio-économiques à Léopoldville, 4ᵉ Bulletin. In *Notes et Documents de l'Institut de Recherches Economiques et Sociales de l'Université de Léopoldville*, No. 16.

8. Raymaekers, P. (1963). *L'Organisation des Zones de Squatting*. De l'Université Lovanium de Léopoldville.

9. Collomb, H., and Ayats, H. (1963). *Cahiers d'études Africaines*, No. 9.

10. Lambo, T. A. (1960). Survey of displaced and detribalized people in Yoruba country. Unpublished material.

11. Ødegaard, O. (1932). *Acta psychiatrica et neurologica*, Suppl. 4.

12. Ødegaard, O. (1945). *Acta psychiatrica et neurologica*, **20**, 247.

13. Ødegaard, O. (1954). *Acta psychiatrica et neurologica scandinavica*, **29**, 333–353.

14. Ødegaard, O. (1961). In *Proceedings of the First Pan-African Psychiatric Conference*, ed. Lambo, T. A. Ibadan: Government Printer.

15. Jaco, E. G. (1957). Social factors in mental disorders in Texas. *Social Problems*, **4**, 322.

16. Faris, R. E. L., and Dunham, H. W. (1939). *Mental Disorders in Urban Areas: An Ecological Study of Schizophrenia and other Psychoses*. Chicago: University of Chicago Press.

17. Vickers, G. (1964). *Human Relations in Industry and Mental Health*. London: World Federation for Mental Health, AM.17/33/6/64/241.

18. Lambo, T. A. (1961). Mental Health in Africa. *Medical World (London)*, **95**, 198.

19. Asuni, T. (1961). Suicide Trends in Western Nigeria. In *Proceedings of the First Pan-African Psychiatric Conference*, ed. Lambo, T. A. Ibadan: Government Printer.

20. Hoselitz, B. F. (1961). In *Tradition, Values and Socio-Economic Development*, ed. Braibanti, R., and Spengler, J. J. Durham, N.C.: Duke University Press.

21. Rankin, A. M., and Philip, P. J. (1963). An Epidemic of Laughing in the Bukoba District of Tanganyika. Special report to the Ministry of Tanganyika (unpublished).

22. Kagwa, B. H. (1964). The Problem of Mass Hysteria in East Africa: paper presented at 1964 Annual Conference of the Association of Physicians of East Africa (unpublished).

23. Leighton, A. H., Lambo, T. A., Leighton, D. C., Hughes, C. H., Hughes, J., and Macklin, D. (1963). *Psychiatric Disorder among the Yorubas*. New York: Cornell University Press.

24. Shaw, D. J. (1964). Labour problems in the Gezira scheme. *Agricultural Economics Bulletin for Africa*, No. 5, pp. 1–41. Addis Ababa: U.N.E.C.A.

6. EPIDEMIOLOGY AND THE PROVISION OF HEALTH SERVICES IN AFRICA

1. Cullumbine, H. (1950). An analysis of the vital statistics of Ceylon. *Ceylon Journal of Medical Science*, **7**, parts III & IV, pp. 91–272.

2. World Health Organization (1963). *Second Report on the World Health Situation*, 1957–1960. Geneva: W.H.O., No. 122.

3. Orihuela, L. A. (1963). *The Community Water Supply Programme in the African Region*. Geneva: W.H.O.

7. LAND AND AIR TRANSPORT WITHIN THE CONTINENT OF AFRICA

1. Economic Commission for Africa (1963). *Intra-African Trade.* Addis Ababa: U.N.E.C.A., E/CM.14/STC/20/ADdl.

9. AFRICA'S EDUCATIONAL NEEDS AND OPPORTUNITIES

1. *Rapport sur les Problèmes Posés par la Scolarisation dans la République de la Haute-Volta* (1960). Société d'Etudes pour le Développement Economique et Social and Institut Pédagogique National.

2. Fortes, M. (1946). The Ashanti Survey: a preliminary report. In *Rhodes-Livingstone Journal*, No. 6, pp. 1–37.

3. Fortes, M., Steel, R. W., and Ady, P. (1947). Ashanti Survey 1945–46: an experiment in social research. *Geographical Journal*, **60**, pp. 149–179.

4. Ashby, Sir Eric (1960). Investment in Education—the Report of the Commission on Post-School Certificate and Higher Education in Nigeria. Lagos: Government Printer.

5. Barber, William (1961). *The Economy of British Central Africa.* Stanford, Calif.: Stanford University Press.

6. *Education in Northern Rhodesia* (1964). A report and recommendation prepared by the U.N.E.S.C.O. Planning Mission, 28th September to 2nd December, 1963, p. 12. Lusaka: Government Printer.

7. *Uganda Statistical Abstract*, p. 92 (1963).

8. Central Statistics Bureau (1963). *Employment and Earning in Tanganyika*, p. 2. Dar es Salaam: Central Statistics Bureau.

9. *Kenya Statistical Abstract*, p. 98 (1963).

10. Newman, P. (1964). *East African Journal*, 1, 16.

11. Harroy, J.-P. (1944). *Afrique, terre qui meurt.* Brussels: Hayez.

12. Dumont, R. (1962). *L'Afrique Noire est Mal Partie.* Paris: Editions du Seuil.

13. U.N.E.S.C.O./E.C.A. (1962). Final Report of Conference of African States on the Development of Education in Africa. Paris: U.N.E.S.C.O./ED/181.

11. AGRICULTURAL POTENTIALITIES IN AFRICA

1. Food and Agriculture Organization (1963). *Production Year-book, 1962.* Rome: F.A.O.
2. Food and Agriculture Organization (1964). *Report of the E.C.A.-F.A.O. Expert Meeting on Government Measures to promote the Transition from Subsistence to Market Agriculture.* Rome: F.A.O.
3. Food and Agriculture Organization (1963). *Report of the Fourth Inter-African Conference on Food and Nutrition.* Rome: F.A.O.
4. Food and Agriculture Organization (1964). *Report of the First F.A.O. African Regional Meeting on Animal Production and Health.* Rome: F.A.O.
5. Economic Commission for Africa (1964). *African Timber Trends and Prospects.* Addis Ababa: E.C.A., E/CN.14/272.
6. Food and Agriculture Organization (1962). *Africa Survey.* Rome: F.A.O.
7. Food and Agriculture Organization (1962). *Agriculture in the World Economy.* Rome: F.A.O.

12. CONSERVATION OF NATURAL RESOURCES IN AFRICA

1. Worthington, E. B. (1964). Une définition des ressources naturelles. In *Conférence sur l'organisation de la recherche et la formation du personnel en Afrique, en ce qui concerne l'étude, la conservation et l'utilisation des ressources naturelles,* pp. 10–12. Paris: U.N.E.S.C.O./C.O.R.P.S.A./4.A.
2. Huxley, J. (1961). Introduction to *The Humanist Frame,* pp. 13–48. London: Allen & Unwin.
3. Huxley, J. (1961). *The Conservation of Wild Life and Natural Habitats in Central and East Africa,* pp. 21–22. Paris: U.N.E.S.C.O.
4. Farnes, S. S. (1964). Better living through conservation planning. In *The Population Crisis and the Use of World Resources,* ed. Mudd, S. *et al.* World Academy of Art and Science, 2. The Hague: Junk; Bloomington, Indiana: Indiana University Press.
5. Bates, M. (1961). *The Forest and the Sea.* New York: Mentor Books.

379

6. Elton, C. (1958). Quoted by Marston Bates, Ref. 5, p. 202.

7. Huxley, E. (1963). *Beasts and Men*. London: The World Wildlife Fund, reprinted from *Punch*.

8. Harroy, J.-P. (1962). Surpopulation en Afrique centrale. In *Bulletin des séances. Académie royale des sciences coloniales (d'outre mer)*, **8**, 524–527.

9. Brasseur, G. (1961). Pression démographique et équilibres naturels. *Notes africaines*, Nos. 91–92, pp. 119–127.

10. Fournier, F. (1962). Carte du danger d'érosion en Afrique au Sud du Sahara (10 : 1,000,000), et notice explicative. C.E.E. and C.C.T.A.

11. Darling, F. Fraser (1963–64). The Unity of Ecology. *Advancement of Science*, **20**, 9.

12a. Kimble, G. H. T. (1953). The Way of the World. New York: Grady Press.

12b. Portères, R. (1950). La recherche agronomique dans les pays chauds. *Revue internationale de botanique appliquée et d'agriculture tropicale*, No. 231–2, pp. 241–263.

13. Harroy, J.-P. (1944). *Afrique, terre qui meurt*. Brussels: Hayez.

14. Dekeyser, P. L. (1962). Une réalité de tous temps: la nature Africaine. *Impact of Science on Society*, **12**, 267–290.

15. Harroy, J.-P. (1963). La protection de la Nature dans les pays en voie de développement. In *Bulletin des séances. Académie royale des sciences coloniales (d'outre mer)*, **9**, 557–565.

14. PERSPECTIVES FOR INDUSTRIALIZATION IN AFRICA

1. United Nations (1963). *Industrial Growth in Africa*. New York: United Nations. Sales No. 63.II.K.3.

2. Patel, S. J. (1964). Economic distance between nations: its origin, measurement and outlook. In *The Economic Journal*, **74**, 119.

3. Ewing, A. F. (1964). Industrialization and the United Nations Economic Commission for Africa. In *Journal of Modern African Studies*, **2**, 351.

4. United Nations (1962; 1963). *Yearbook of National Accounts Statistics*, 1961; 1962. Sales Nos. 62. XVII.2; 63. XVII.2.

5. United Nations (1959). *Patterns of Industrial Growth, 1938–1958.* (Tables 9 and 10.) New York: United Nations. Sales No. 59. XVII.6.

6. Economic Commission for Europe (1960). *Long-term Trends and Problems of the European Steel Industry.* New York: United Nations. Sales No. 60. II.E.3.

7. Greene, F. (1962). The Wall has Two Sides. London: Cape.

8. Crocker, W. R. (1950). Faut-il accélérer ou freiner l'industrialisation de l'Afrique ? In *Présence Africaine*, No. 8–9 (ed. Th. Monod), of *Le monde noir*, pp. 409–423.

Members of the Symposium

Members who took part in or contributed to the symposium on Man and Africa, held in Addis Ababa, 1st to 6th October 1964

A. M. ACOCK
Liaison Officer with World Food Programme, F.A.O. Headquarters, Rome, since June 1964.

Postgraduate research at Cambridge, Yale and University of California; Research Officer, Waite Agricultural Research Institute, S. Australia, 1940–42; Served R.A.A.F., 1942–44; Chief Officer, Economic Secretariat, Australian Food Control Organization, 1944–46; F.A.O.: Production Economist, 1946–50; Technical Assistant Economist, 1950–56; Chief, Near East and Africa Section, 1956–59; Chief, F.A.O.–E.C.A. Joint Agriculture Division, Addis Ababa, 1959–64.

K. K. APEADU
Director of Research Division, United Nations Economic Commission for Africa, Addis Ababa, since 1964.

Educated Ghana and Oxford University (Philosophy, Politics and Economics, 1949 and 1959); Ghana Civil Service, 1949–64; Responsible for national co-operative development, national industrial development, etc.; Permanent Secretary to a number of Ministries, 1959–64.

J. BOURGEOIS-PICHAT
Director, Institut National d'Etudes Démographiques, Paris, since 1962.

Graduate of Ecole Polytechnique, Paris; Officer in French Army, 1935–43; Staff member: Fondation Française pour l'Etude des Problèmes Humains, 1943–48; and Institut National d'Etudes Démographiques, 1946–53; Senior officer, Population Branch of the Bureau of Social Affairs, United Nations Headquarters New York, 1953–62. Member: International Statistical Institute; and International Union for the Scientific Study of Population. Publications include: numerous articles on demographic problems.

A. E. BROWN
Office of the World Health Organization Representative, Addis Ababa.

Medical Officer to U.N.R.W.A. Mission, Hungary, 1946–47; W.H.O. Representative, Hungary, 1947–48; Medical Officer, Port of London Health

Authority, 1948–49; Research Officer, Medical Research Council, 1949–50; Medical Officer of Health, Norfolk County Council, U.K., 1951–53; Public Health Adviser, Cambodia, 1953–54, Vietnam, 1954–55; W.H.O. Representative, Cambodia, Laos and Vietnam, 1956–62; Deputy Chief, W.H.O. Mission, Congo, 1962–64.

G. DEKKER

Adviser, Water Resources Development, United Nations Economic Commission for Africa, Addis Ababa, since 1962.

Graduate of Delft University; on staff of Bureau of River Studies, Public Works Department of Netherlands Government; engaged on river survey and hydrological studies in Africa; for some years Principal Hydrological Engineer, Department of Inland Waterways of Federal Republic of Nigeria.

A. F. EWING

Director, Economic Development Division, United Nations Economic Commission for Africa, Addis Ababa, since 1961.

Graduate of Oxford University; entered Administrative Class of U.K. Civil Service, 1939; Principal Private Secretary to successive Ministers of Works, 1942–46; Assistant Secretary in charge of Building Materials Branch, Ministry of Works, 1946–49; joined Secretariat of U.N. as Deputy Director, Industry and Materials Division of E.C.E., 1949; subsequently Director, Steel, Engineering and Housing Division, E.C.E.

J. H. GAYER

Member, International Frequency Registration Board (I.F.R.B.) of the International Telecommunication Union, Geneva, since 1953 (Vice-Chairman, 1955 and 1962, Chairman, 1956 and 1963).

Graduate of University of Nebraska in Electrical Engineering; Advanced Electronics Study at Massachusetts Institute of Technology; Advanced Communication Study and Communications Instructor at Harvard University, 1942–43; Management and Economic Studies, U.C.L.A. and George Washington University; Director, Harrisburg Radio and Electronics School, Harrisburg, Pennsylvania, 1945–46; Electronic Design Engineer, Douglas Aircraft Co., Santa Monica, Calif., 1946–47; Communications Consultant-Adviser and Chief of Communications Branch, U.S. Military Government in Germany, 1948–51; Partner/Associate and Professional Consulting Engineer, Washington, D.C., 1951–53. Professional Societies: Secretary/Treasurer, Geneva Section of the Institute of Electrical and Electronics Engineers, 1961–63, Vice-Chairman, 1964; Secretary/Treasurer, Region 8 I.E.E.E.

(Greater Europe); Organizer and President, International Amateur Radio Club, Geneva; First Chairman, International Television Symposium, Montreux, 1961, Hon. Chairman, 1962 and 1963.

A. GILLE

Science Officer for Africa, Department of Natural Sciences, United Nations Educational Scientific and Cultural Organization, Paris, since 1959.

Graduated in agriculture (Ingénieur Agronome), Institut National Agronomique, Paris; Postgraduate research, Univ. of Montreal, Canada; Postgraduate work at Cornell University, U.S.A.; Consultant to U.N.E.S.C.O. for the U.N. Scientific Conference on the Conservation and Utilization of Resources, 1949; Officer responsible for conservation matters, and teaching and diffusion of science in the Department of Natural Sciences, U.N.E.S.C.O., 1950–59. Member of: Société de Biogéographie; Société Nationale de Protection de la Nature et d'Acclimatation de France; Association des Ecrivains Scientifiques de France.

Publications include: *Enseignement et conservation; Education for Conservation and More Efficient Use of Natural Resources; Teaching People about Nature and Natural Resources; Our African Heritage;* A Review of the Natural Resources of the African Continent (editor), published by U.N.E.S.C.O.; and various papers in symposia and scientific journals.

J. R. GOODY

Department of Anthropology, University of Cambridge.

Fellow of St. John's College, Cambridge, since 1960; currently visiting Professor, Institute of African Studies, Legon, Ghana.

Graduate and post-graduate work, University of Cambridge; Education Officer, 1947–49; Balliol College, Oxford, 1949–50; Sociological Research Officer, Ghana, 1950–52; Lecturer in Comparative Sociology, Cambridge, since 1954; Fieldwork in Ghana, 1956–57; Fellow, Center for Advanced Studies in the Behavioral Sciences, Stanford, 1959–60.

Publications include: *The Social Organization of the Lowiili; Death, Property and the Ancestors; The Development Cycle in Domestic Groups* (editor); and various papers in sociological, anthropological, historical and linguistic journals.

HABTE-AB BAIROU

General Manager (Assistant Minister) of the Technical Agency, Addis Ababa, since 1963. (This Institution is responsible for the implementation of the second five-year development plan.)

Studied Economics and Economic History, London School of Economics, 1952–55; Ministry of Education and Election Board (member of the staff

which organized the first election in Ethiopian history on universal suffrage), 1956–57; Director General of Commerce Department and Research, Ministry of Commerce and Industry, 1958–62; Governor of Kaffa Province, 1962–63.
One of the founders and editor of *Ye Tebeb Zena* (Culture); established and first editor of *Ethiopian Economic Review*.

*J. B. S. HALDANE
Genetics and Biometry Laboratory, Government of Orissa, Bhubaneswar, Orissa, India, 1962–64.

Reader in Biochemistry, University of Cambridge, 1922–32; Fullerian Professor of Physiology, Royal Institution, 1930–32; Prof. of Genetics, London University, 1933–37; Prof. of Biometry, London University, 1937–57; Research Prof., Indian Statistical Institute, 1957–61. Darwin Medal, Royal Society, 1953; Darwin-Wallace Medal, Linnaean Society, 1958; Kimber Medal, National Academy of Sciences, Washington, 1961; Feltrinelli Prize, Accademia dei Lincei, 1961. Foreign or corresponding member of: Soviet Akademia Nauk; National Institute of Sciences of India; Humboldt Academy, Berlin; Royal Danish Academy of Sciences, Leopoldina, Halle; National Academy of Sciences, Washington.
Publications include: 300 papers in scientific journals, and 25 books, among them—*Daedalus; Possible Worlds; The Inequality of Man; Enzymes; The Causes of Evolution; New Paths in Genetics; The Biochemistry of Genetics*.

Deceased.

* A. M. HEGAZY
Professor, Faculty of Commerce, Cairo University, Cairo, United Arab Republic.

Director, General Organization for Maritime Transport; Consultant and Auditor for General Organizations of Ministry of Transport (Railways, Inland Waterways, Post Office and Telecommunication). Member of Committee for Co-ordination of Internal Transport; Member of Technical Committee for Local Government.

R. C. HOWARD-GOLDSMITH
Technical Adviser, Resources and Transport Division, United Nations, New York.

Graduated at Lausanne, and Royal School of Mines, London University; Field service in British Army, 1939–44; Tin exploration and production in Nigeria, 1944–48; worked in South American base metal mines and later became superintendent of copper and coal properties in Peru; associated with the development of iron ore deposits in Central and South America; United Nations adviser to the Niger Republic, 1961–63; Regional Adviser on mineral resources development, U.N. Economic Commission for Africa, Addis Ababa, 1963–64. Member of the Institution of Mining and Metallurgy, London, and the A.I.M.E., New York.

His EXCELLENCY LIDJ KASSA WOLDE MARIAM
President, Haile Sellassie I University, Addis Ababa, since 1962.

Graduated 1956, Seattle Pacific College, Seattle, Washington; University of Washington, 1956–58; Assistant to His Imperial Majesty's Private Secretary, 1958; Assistant Minister in the Ministry of the Pen and Private Secretary to His Imperial Majesty, 1960; Vice-Minister of the Pen, 1962.

T. A. LAMBO
Professor of Psychiatry and Head of Department of Psychiatry, Neurology and Neurosurgery, University of Ibadan, Nigeria, since 1963.

Graduated at Birmingham University, 1948; General Hospital and Midland Nerve Hospital, Birmingham, 1948–50; Medical Officer, Nigerian Medical Services, 1950–54; Specialist, Western Region Ministry of Health, Neuro-Psychiatric Centre, Aro, 1957, Senior Specialist, 1960; Consultant Psychiatrist, University College Hospital, Ibadan; Member of Expert Advisory Panel on Mental Health, W.H.O., Geneva; Member, Scientific Council for Africa, 1960, Vice-Chairman, 1964. Awarded the O.B.E. 1962.
Publications include: Neuro-psychiatric Observations in the Western Region of Nigeria (*Br. med. J.*, 1956); The Concept and Practice of Mental Health in African Cultures (*E. Afr. med. J.*, 1960); Further Neuro-psychiatric Problems in Nigeria (*Br. med. J.*, 1960).

G. C. LAST
Adviser for Social Studies in the Department of Curriculum and Research, Ministry of Education and Fine Arts, Addis Ababa, since 1963. Also concerned with physical planning for educational development programmes.

Graduate of the London School of Economics, University of London, 1948, and the Institute of Education, University of London, 1949; Taught geography and economics in London and Addis Ababa, 1949–57; Headmaster, Medhane Alem School, Addis Ababa, 1957–63.
Publications include: *A Regional Survey of Africa; A Geography of Ethiopia; Social Studies Atlas for Ethiopia;* and a number of school texts for elementary and secondary schools.

G. MANCINI

Chief, Monetary Section, Economic Commission for Africa, Addis Ababa.

Graduate of Bari University, Italy; postgraduate work at Harvard and Chicago Universities; Lecturer in Economics at University of Bari, Italy, 1952–54; Market Research Adviser, Italian Embassy, Washington, D.C., responsible for Italy's dollar drive in U.S.A., 1955–58; joined U.N. secretariat as Associate Economic Officer in the Fiscal and Financial Branch, 1958–60; joined the U.N. Civilian Operation in the Congo as Adviser to the Congolese Government on foreign exchange control, 1960–61; Regional Fiscal and Financial Adviser, Economic Commission for Africa, 1962.

MESFIN WOLDE MARIAM

Assistant professor and Head of the Department of Geography, University College, Haile Sellassie I University, Addis Ababa.

Graduate of the University of Panjab; Postgraduate at Clark University; Associate Director of Mapping and Geography Institute, 1957–59; In the Faculty of Arts of the University College since 1959.
Publications include: An Estimate of Population of Ethiopia (*Ethiopia Observer*, 1961); *A Preliminary Atlas of Ethiopia*, 1962; The Awash River Basin (*Ethiopian Geographical Journal*); The Background of the Ethio-Somalia Dispute (*Journal of Modern African Studies*).

A. R. MICHAELIS

Science Correspondent, *Daily Telegraph*, London.

Chemistry graduate and Ph.D., London 1941, Editor of B.I.O.S. Overall Reports, 1945, and various appointments in British chemical industry; at Sydney University, Australia, lectured on scientific cinematography and made numerous research films, 1950–54; later specialized in communication of science by television, radio, books, journals and daily newspapers; Holder of Foreign Leader Grant from State Department, Washington; Editor of *Discovery*, 1955–62.
Publications include: *Research Films;* chapter on History of Cinematography, in *History of Technology*; *From Semaphore to Satellite* (the official centenary history of the I.T.U.); many articles in scientific journals and newspapers.

TH. MONOD

Professor at Muséum National d'Histoire Naturelle, Paris.

Sec.-General, 1938, Director, 1938–65, Institut Français d'Afrique Noire, Dakar; Professor, University of Dakar, 1957–59; Dean, Science Faculty, Dakar, 1957–58.
Member, Institut de France (Académie des Sciences), and of Académie des Sciences d'Outre-Mer; Gold Medallist: Royal Geographical Society, 1960; American Geographical Society. Officier de la Légion d'Honneur, 1958; Commander, Ordre du Christ.
Publications include: *L'Hippopotame et le Philosophe; Bathyfolages;* and many scientific papers in learned journals.

MULUGETA WODAJO

Dean, Faculty of Education, Haile Sellassie I University, Addis Ababa.

Graduated University College, Addis Ababa, 1956; Postgraduate work in Education and Sociology, Harvard University, 1957; Graduate Fellow, Columbia University, 1958–60; Assistant Professor of Sociology, State University of New York (conducted seminars on African education), 1960–63; Assistant Professor of Education, Syracuse University, 1963.
Publications include: articles on Ethiopian education in American professional journals.

ZAKI MUSTAFA

Dean, Faculty of Law, and Head of Department of Commercial Law, University of Khartoum, Sudan.

Graduated from Faculty of Law, University of Khartoum, 1959; LL.M., London School of Economics, 1961; Head of Department of Commercial Law, University of Khartoum, 1962–63; Associate Secretary, Sudan Law Project since 1962; General Editor, Sudan Law Reports (Civil).

S. J. PATEL

Officer-in-Charge, Economic Development Branch, United Nations Economic Commission for Asia and the Far East, Bangkok, Thailand.

Doctorate in economics, University of Pennsylvania, 1949; taught economics at Bombay University; United Nations Department of Economic Affairs in New York, 1950–55; U.N. Economic Commission for Europe, Geneva, 1955–62; Chief, Planning and Policies Section, U.N. Economic Commission for Africa, Addis Ababa, 1963–64.
Publications include: *Agricultural Labourers in Modern India and Pakistan*

388

(1952); *Essays on Economic Transition* (1964); and a number of papers on problems of economic development in leading economic journals.

*E. A. A. ROWSE

Co-ordinator and Planner, Technical Agency, Imperial Ethiopian Government, Addis Ababa.

Senior Lecturer in Town Planning and Architecture, College of Art, Edinburgh, 1929–33; Principal of the Architectural Association School of Architecture, London, 1934–37; Principal of the School of Planning and Research for National Development, London, 1934–40 and 1947–52; Private practice in development planning in various parts of the world since 1927.

*H. B. L. RUSSELL

World Health Organization Liaison Officer with the Economic Commission for Africa, Addis Ababa, since July 1964.

Surg. Lieut. R.N.V.R., 1941–46; served in various capacities in Ghana, including Senior Medical Officer, Overseas Civil Service, 1947–55; on behalf of W.H.O. led a rural health team through the remoter parts of Ethiopia to ascertain health needs and advise on the development of suitable health services, 1956–58; W.H.O. Regional Adviser in Public Health, Eastern Mediterranean Region, 1958–60; W.H.O. Regional Adviser in Rural Health and Community Development, South East Asia Region, 1960–63; combined the two posts of World Health Organization Representative to Imperial Ethiopian Government and Liaison Officer with the Economic Commission, from January 1963–June 1964, when the two posts were separated.

F. X. SUTTON

Resident Representative for East and Central Africa, Ford Foundation, Nairobi; and official of the Ford Foundation, New York, since 1954.

Graduated at Harvard, 1950; taught at Harvard, 1949–54. Visiting Professor, Columbia, Massachusetts Institute of Technology, University of California, Los Angeles, and Salzburg Seminar in American Studies.
Publications include: *The American Business Creed; The Behavioral Sciences at Harvard;* and numerous articles on educational, sociological and African topics.

G. E. W. WOLSTENHOLME

Director, Ciba Foundation, London, since its opening in 1949.

Educated University of Cambridge and Middlesex Hospital, London; Adviser in Transfusion and Resuscitation, Central Mediterranean, 1943–45; Organizer 1963 and Adviser 1963–64, Haile Selassie I Prize Trust, Addis Ababa.

Vice President, Zoological Society of London; Hon. Secretary, Royal Society of Medicine; Member of Council, Westfield College, University of London; Fellow, Royal College of Physicians; Fellow, Institute of Biology; O.B.E. (mil.); Chevalier, Légion d'Honneur; Gold medal, Italian Ministry of Education.

Chief editor, Ciba Foundation symposia, colloquia and study groups since 1950; Editor, *Royal College of Physicians of London: Portraits*, 1964.

F. G. YOUNG

Sir William Dunn Professor of Biochemistry, University of Cambridge, since 1949. Master of Darwin College, Cambridge.

Educated at University College, London, and the Universities of Aberdeen and Toronto; formerly Member of the Scientific Staff, Medical Research Council, and Professor of Biochemistry, University of London.

Has served on many medical, scientific and other official bodies, including the Medical Research Council, Council of the Royal Society, the Medical Sub-Committee of the University Grants Committee, Commission on Higher Education for Africans in Central Africa, Commission on the Establishment for the new Chinese University in Hong Kong, Inter-University Council for Higher Education Overseas, International Expert Committee on the Irradiation of Food, Executive Council of the Ciba Foundation. Has visited nearly fifty foreign countries including Ghana, Kenya, Nigeria, Northern Rhodesia, Nyasaland, Southern Rhodesia and Tanganyika, and lectured on his research in most of them. Is an honorary or corresponding member of many foreign, scientific and medical bodies. Fellow of the Royal Society, London, since 1949. Fellow of Trinity Hall, Cambridge, and of University College London. Publications include: over 200 papers in the *Biochemical Journal*, and other scientific and medical journals, mostly on hormones and metabolic control.

* Author not present at the meeting.

INDEX OF AUTHORS*

*Numbers in bold type indicate a contribution in the form of a paper;
numbers in plain type refer to contributions to the discussions.*

* Author and Subject Indexes compiled by Mr William Hill.

INDEX OF SUBJECTS